RE

MW00612654

"I think that this book is a tribut[e]
— MICHAEL "DO~ ~.~~~~, 1/~1u. Airborne Association

"I just can't stop reading WALL OF BLOOD! I actually feel I am with you in fighting every battle, walking every mile, and crying over every friend lost."
— BRAIN MOEBS, U.S. Marine

"In poetry and prose you breathe life into the (American Civil War) movement and (Confederate General John Hunt) Morgan lives again."
— JAMES A. RAMAGE, Prof. of History, Northern Kentucky University

"This book should be of great healing value to other veterans suffering from PTSD as well as helping the non-afflicted to better understand the trauma and pain associated with such an affliction."
— COL. HAROLD A. FRITZ, Recipient, Congressional Medal of Honor

"Like the Vietnam Veterans Memorial Wall (in Washington, D.C.), the book is a heart breaker.
— TIM PAGE, former Vietnam War photographer

"This book teaches us lessons of war and the more we know, the better our chances are of stopping the next useless war."
— LOUISE STONE, wife of CBS photographer Dana Stone who was captured in 1970 and still listed as missing

"Couldn't put it down. Sent a copy to my good friend CNN News correspondent PETER ARNETT.
— HORST FAAS, Pulitzer Prize winner, former Saigon AP Bureau Chief

"WALL OF BLOOD is in itself a reminder that freedom comes with a price. I wish there were more veterans willing to tell others about their experiences.
— TOM LUBERDA, President Lansing Veterans Memorial

"He has the sheer innate ability to bring across the times and places of an era in such an uncompromising fashion. I cried from cover to cover.
— ROXANNA NGERNTONGDEE, former Vietnam War journalist

". . .powerful combat vignettes and outstanding poems. . . ."
— LARRY R. JOHANNESSEN, Assistant Professor of English

What a book. You really captured the heart of the war."
— DAVID KENNERLY, Pulitzer Prize winner, TIME photographer

Wall of Blood

Greg,

To A Defeat

For Teach

Grand Rdon
Allong
1998

Books by Fred Leo Brown

NON-FICTION

CALL ME NO NAME (1973)

WALL OF BLOOD (1992)
SECOND EDITION (1997)

VIETNAM WAR DIARY (2000)

FICTION

LESSONS OF WAR (1999)

VIETNAM WAR SAGA (2001)
    Book 1: GUNFIGHTERS
    Book 2: LAST STAND
    Book 3: GRIM BUSINESS

PLAY

LESSONS OF WAR (1993)

Wall of Blood

STORY OF A VIETNAM WAR VETERAN

FRED LEO BROWN

COMBAT READY PUBLISHING

Publishing

Printed and manufactured in the United States of America.

FIRST PRINTING 1992
SECOND EDITION 1997

Brown, Fred Leo
   Wall Of Blood
      Includes preface, appendices, glossary, illustrations, photographs.

ISBN 0-942551-07-9

Library of Congress Catalog Card Number
LC 97-94706
      1. Vietnam history. 2. Vietnam personal.
      3. Vietnam poetry. 4. Vietnam literature.
      5. Vietnam illustration and photography.

ATTENTION: SCHOOLS & CORPORATIONS
This book is available at quantity discounts with bulk purchase for educational, business, or sales promotional use. For information please write Combat Ready Publishing, P.O. Box 39, Palos Heights Illinois, 60463

DEDICATION

To my daughter Cara,
my first true love

Cara, thought I'd tell you in this little
poem on your 11th birthday because
I thought you'd like to know.
Your smile is like a beautiful
rose in b l o o m, your
voice carries l i k e
a dove, t o hold
you is to know
I live, and
to watch
you
grow
i s   t o
u n d erstand
love. I've been
through the jungle but
thinking of you puts it
all to rest. And as I toil
through the day I'll thank God
for bringing us together. "Good night,
Cara. Love you." "I love you too, Daddy."

Contents

Illustrations

Preface

How best to say this: In the early 1980's my childhood friend/business partner along with my father conspired to strip me of my livelihood.

Not long after the collaboration to bankrupt me, my x-best friend died from a massive heart attack at the age of thirty. My pathetic father went to his early grave a few years later by putting a bullet through his head. Let the devil have Its due. Greedy, dishonest, ego driven people will never grasp the *true* meaning of life.

In need of relief, I turned my energies to writing. As the years rolled on so did words upon the page. And the more I wrote about the lives of the soldiers and people from the Vietnam War era, the more I reaffirm the importance of my own existence.

Through numerous conversations, I found out that my Advanced Infantry Training class at Fort Gordon, Georgia, destined to become Alpha Company, Second Battalion 173rd Airborne Infantry, took an unprecedented 100% casualties while fighting in the Vietnam War. I was one of the five men who after AIT went straight to Vietnam. I became part of the 1/ 6 198th Light Infantry Battalion, Americal Division. While in-country my elite unit took over one-thousand casualties (WIA) with over one-hundred more killed in action (KIA).

"I will live for them," became by personal battle cry. My journey through my mid-life crisis became crystal clear.

Continuing to empower myself, I began realizing the importance of the small things in life. The importance of just sitting quietly to watch a sunrise or a sunset. The importance of taking time to ride a bicycle through the woods. The importance of standing long enough to contemplate the birds, deer, squirrels and bugs. The importance of taking time to refill ones soul.

Early on, I realized there was no place in my writing for embellishment and out and out lies. As a trial lawyer explained, "Fred, one lie on the stand by *them* is worth ten of our best witnesses." When you look hard into the mirror and it looks back—God knows a lot of tears and courage are associated with raw truth.

In 1969, after my combat tour of duty and a seven month stay in an army hospital for rehabilitation, I returned to active duty at Fort Hood, Texas. On a weekend pass I hot-rodded my green 1969 Plymouth *Road Runner* over to Waco, Texas. After parking across the street from the local USO, I decided to explore the town. With the sun shining and time on my side, I sat on a curb and pulled out a pen and a piece of crumpled paper. While contemplating, my eyes wandered to an inscription cut in stone: HOME OF DOCTOR PEPPER, ESTABLISHED 1885. I looked from the building to the piece of paper where I penned the title of my first poem, *Yamane,* in remembrance of my squad leader who died in my arms on March 16, 1968.

Going back in time: In 1973 I published my first book *Call Me No Name,* which was a collection of my letters home. After its publication I turned mostly to writing poetry. But on July 3, 1981, the first birthday of my second daughter Kathryn, I decided it was time to write another book. The first words of the book were:

"Fasten your seat belts. We are ready for takeoff." It is November 26, 1967; the aircraft, a Boeing 707, departing from Travis Airport, California. Destination, Vietnam.

Those words sent me headlong into this project—an undertaking that, with the 1992 publication of *Wall Of Blood,* took twelve years to complete. Which coincidently is the same number of miles from Chicago to Vietnam. My second edition, published in 1997, took another five years to write and has added an additional one-hundred pages.

With the passage of time, I found it easier to reflect on the past. That's when I realize how exceptionally brutal the fighting and living conditions were for the infantryman in Vietnam. On a regular basis the Vietnam infantryman was subjected to more types of fragmentation devices that could maim or kill than any time in modern warfare. The fighting often became face-to-face, hand-to-hand and savagely brutal. It became clear that a Vietnam infantryman's life could be best compared to that of an American Civil War soldier. And like the Civil War counterpart after living through that savagery, the Vietnam grunt had trouble melding back into society.

As a final note, the reader will not be spared the hardships of the Vietnam War. They will trudge through the swollen, snake infested river during a monsoon. They will cross flooded rice fields with mud and water up to their neck, and will hump triple canopy jungle mountain trails with heat hoovering around one-hundred degrees. When they pass through the villages the reader will learn how the common Vietnamese suffers and endures. They will walk alongside Brown and realize that while he is searching for someone to kill, that same someone is waiting to kill him. They will soon know him intimately as radio telephone operator, rifleman, blood strip sergeant and Gunfighter the pointman. And they will feel the terror when he is left behind marked for death.

Acknowledgments

How could I appreciate a mother more? Thank you, Mom, for helping me live through the war and helping me make it back through this manuscript.

To my dearest sister, Roxanna (Brown) Ngerntongdee, who because she was a freelance journalist from 1968-1975 in Vietnam, provided indispensable counsel.

To Louise (Smiser) Stone, who helped me reach a new dimension of thought. And who willed me her husband's, Dana Stone's, collection of Vietnam War combat photographs.

To Laura Jane Thornberry who means more to me than a few words.

To Edna, Clyde, Connie and Karen of the Cobb family, and to Elizabeth and Clifford White, for taking a chance with a crazy vet.

To James Ted Smith, my fellow combatant and dear friend who still calls me on Veterans Day.

To my lovely wife Barbara of twenty-five-years and my precious beyond words college bound daughters, Cara and Kathryn.

To Jean Altepter who through her passion gave me brilliant illustration and the title of my book, *Wall of Blood*. Who in 1992 met a tragic death.

Author photography by Al Buschauer (Designer Photography), Barrington, Ill.

Illustrations by:
John Tylk, Art Rydell, Jean Altepter, Curt Chiarelli, Frank Schaffer

Wall of Blood

Section One

PTSD

An eagle soars, its wings lifted by the same warm breeze that nudges a quiet army of clouds over the choppy waters of Lake Michigan. As Sunday evening approaches, the grey-blue clouds spread and stretch into ghostly forms that swirl and thread themselves around, through and in between Chicago's granite, steel, and glass city-scape, chilling the thousands of spectators.

It was June 15, 1986, two days after Chicago's historic Vietnam Veterans Welcome Home parade. More than eleven years after the Fall Of Saigon and the climax of an ill fated sixteen year Vietnam War effort. The longest war in United States history and considered its first major defeat.

The shadow of a cloud-body swoops low, licking sweat off a Vietnam veteran wearing a frayed Marine soft cap who stands alone on the city sidewalk. Across the nape of his neck is an olive drab colored army towel that drapes over a fragmentation jacket both hugging his body like tired old friends. Around his waist is a captured North Vietnamese Army (NVA) pistol belt complete with a canteen and on his wrist is a brass Montagnard bracelet. From a vantage point some one-hundred yards away, the lone veteran scrutinizes each of the one-hundred and forty black panels that stretch two-hundred and fifty feet across a city park lawn.

"A parade and a nice *big* monument," he said bobbing his head in disdain. "I am so impressed. But a little after the fact don't ya think guys? So what's the big deal?" he hums. "Trying to make people care about what happened? Fat chance. Just another example of a promise that can't be delivered?" he mumbles spitefully. "And promises not kept are what got me into this mess in the first place. Same crap, different packaging." He gazes with un-checked scorn over the park lawn. "Nothin' new here. Same old, shit."

And what about the *first* promised parade? he thinks. Other long-ago Victory At War homecomings play through his mind, a flickering newsreel in black and white. It was a hero's return then. Ticker tape and confetti spill out the windows of towering buildings to mix with whistles, shrieks, claps and cheers. And the women. Oh, yea*hhhh*. The ones with boobs out-to-here who reach out and with breathiness say, "I'm a sucker for a man in a uniform. Kiss me." Gladly darlin'. Then let me dip you back and plant another wet one on your succulent warm neck. Red lips that form the words, "I love you."

"Only in my dreams," the vet snorts shaking his head. No, not *our* parade. Not by a long shot. No, our belated "Welcome Home" parade along Michigan Avenue consisted of a mob of fuckups who graduated from the University of South Vietnam. A parade loaded with a bunch of deranged, cynical-minded thugs. To America, they'd become a nothing but a bunch of cripples, loners, dropouts, homeless derelicts and losers. In a word *parasite* on the landscape.

Plate 2   Welcome Home Parade *(Illustration by John Tylk)*

And, can you believe it? "Body Count" General Westmoreland as grand marshal. Was someone outta lunch? What the hell? I mean were the organizers trying to fill Westy's dance card? Geee-zzz, man. I mean really, *Westmoreland?* Mister "Light at the End of the Tunnel." "Grab 'em by the balls and their hearts and minds will follow." The pompous West Point *asshole* himself, right up front. The newspaper photos and evening news made him appear more like a court jester than the former *almighty* Commanding General of the most powerful military force on earth.

Hey, folks, wake up and look in the mirror. For chrissakes! That's the guy who set up the necktie party. Him and the rest of his Second World War and Korean War cronies. A bunch of buffoons with the mentality of: "Your job is not to question why but to do and die. Now *charge* that hill!" "Yes, sir." "Well, why are you still standing here?" "My weapon is jammed, sir." "Well then grab some rocks." "Right away, sir."

The veteran remembers times during the Vietnam War when his superior officer actually dared to venture into the field and talk to the soldiers.

"So how are ya doin' there soldier?" the superior officer would ask, dressed in a clean spiffy uniform complete with crease and offset by spit shined boots.

"Fine, sir," I would say. *I mean what else could I say? "Begging your pardon, sir, but I'm sick and tired of all this fuckin' shit. And I want go home."*

"Where're ya from there soldier?" the superior officer would ask in a starched voice.

"Chicagoland, sir." *Actually I just came from hell. But I don't wanna really talk about that right now. But what I do want to talk about is where the fuck you're sending me next and what're my chances of survival. Especially since my rifle keeps fuckin' jammin'.*

"You've been gettin' three squares a day?"

"Yes, sir." *That's if you call that fat caked shit-in-a-can I shovel into my mouth on a plastic spoon food. Fact is all the accommodations suck big time.*

"Carry on there soldier and make sure you write the folks back home."

"Thank you, sir." *Hey, just because I'm an infantryman doesn't mean I'm an animal or some kind of a moron. Of course I write home. Every chance I get. Hell, they're the only ones who might give a damn whether I live or die over here.*

The vet, a former Vietnam War combat infantryman, tilts the brim of his old Marine soft cap to cut the sun's glare. Crossing his arms, he settles back on his heels and gazes scornfully upon the wreckage of a generation, a herd of broken, run-down lost souls.

"I don't need this shit," the vet spits. "I'm outta here." While continuing the inner discussion, he unconsciously places a finger on his forehead. At that exact moment, he spots something jetting through his peripheral vision. He quickly swings but whatever it was, is gone. "Hum*mmm*." That's strange, he thinks. Had it simply vanished or was it ever really there?

With thumbs hooked onto his blue-jean pockets, he stands rigid and keen as a rifle bayonet. On second thought, he figures he might just stick around for a while and wait for a possible reappearance of. . . . *Whatever?* And although he doesn't consciously admit it, his illusions do sometimes turn into reality. Thanks to Posttraumatic Stress Disorder, PTSD.

While continuing to stand at the edge of the sidewalk, he begins snaring bits of conversation from curious pedestrians. They slow their pace to ponder the temporary outdoor memorial that after a week will be disassembled and moved throughout the year from site to site across the country.

"Jack," a man said, elbowing his partner who bites into a hot dog, mustard and ketchup gushing onto his hands, "take a look." He points as they walk on the sidewalk parallel to the memorial. "See what they got there in the park. I think that's what I've been reading about in the *Chicago Tribune*. It's like a wall with all the names of the guys who died in the Vietnam War."

They pause and stare reverently as if in prayer at a grave site.

"Shit, that's a lot of names," the one named Jack said breaking the silence. Both men continue walking, their eyes drifting across the panorama and toward the lone veteran, who shift his stance pretending to be oblivious to their presence.

Another set of onlookers near. "Say, how did that old protest yell go?" one asks his walking partner. "Oh, yeah, I remember. 'Heah, L.B.J. how many kids did you kill today.' And of course," he began to roller coaster his voice, "my all time favorite, ' Hell no, we won't go. *Hellllll*, no . . . we won't go.'"

"If you ask me, the whole fuckin' thing was stupid," the first man said. "And I'll tell you something else. It's even stupider the way they keep wasting money commemorating it."

"Talking about wastin' lots of time and money. How about that POW/MIA issue thing? They actually think there's still some prisoners over there."

"I've heard they spend some two-million dollars for each set of MIA bones they dig up."

"Ever find one alive?"

"Nope. Not from what I've been hearing," he said shaking his head.

"Fuckin' nuts is what it is. Just fuckin' nuts."

"Give me all *that* money and hell, I'll show 'em what to do with it."

"Bahama momma here we come. A big old yacht and . . ."

". . . chicks in string bikinis suntanning on deck."

" Oh-*hhh* yeah. Say honey, it looks like you need a little coconut oil along those *un*-tan lines of yours."

"Cause really, man, you know what it all comes down to?" the walking partner asks.

"What's that?"

"Only morons go off and fight in wars. And for what?"

"Well, you know how the old saying goes, 'Dorks die young.'" They guffaw and slap each other on the back while tears of laughter moisten their eyes.

Black hatred rises into the veteran's face and his fingers curl into white-knuckle fists. Who you callin' dorks, huh? I've killed dozens and don't mind adding two dorks to the notches on my guns, the veteran's ego screams inside his head. Again, his hand rises to his forehead, but this time, instead of merely touching, his finger begins to dig.

He mumbles under his breath, "You shit-for-brains cocksuckers don't have the slightest idea what the hell that war was all about. Youuu miserable. . . ." He remembers that during the American Civil War they called PTSD, Nostalgia or Brave Heart.

"Problem, Gunfighter?" a tough, rawhide voice rings out.

The lone veteran freezes in position. Has he been talking out loud? Oh God, I'm losing it. He braces himself for the onslaught of syrupy remarks from some well-meaning pantywaist who has no idea, no clue, not a fuckin' hint. A man who can probably talk-the-talk but can he walk-the-walk? Doubt it.

He turns, ready to shout, "Yeah, I got a real big problem. You and all the other assholes like you!" But there is no one remotely near. He twists his head around and around. That can't be. The voice had been clear as a bell and whoever spoke couldn't have been more than a few feet away.

The name *Gunfighter* echos through his mind and it dawns on him, that yes, in years long past his nickname in Vietnam had been Gunfighter. But spoken with a southern drawl? That left only the intuitive voice of his third-eye/second brain, that all knowing internal voice.

So how did *it* get out? He remembers the day well, October 27, 1968, the day he was wounded just west of Hill 69, near Chu Lai, South Vietnam. That day he closed the *book* on a gruesome chapter of his life. He tossed it through the entrance and slammed the door on his Third-eye and a sea of blood, sweat, and tears. He had locked the door tight, nailed up cross-boards, installed a

Plate 3   Keep Out! *(Illustration by John Tylk)*

padlock, wedged a chair under the doorknob and flung the keys into the Forgotten Sea. For good measure, he even splashed across the door:

KEEP OUT!!!

"Granted," he begins an interior conversation, "somehow you figured out how to work your way back into my consciousness, but like before you are an illusion—not real. I made you up. I created you because at the time I needed someone/something but that was a long time ago." The veteran sneers, waving his hand as if clearing away a cloud of bothersome smoke. "So go away. Evaporate. Zap you're gone."

"I am real, Gunfighter. And like your disorder, I don't just evaporate."

"Bullshit! I can handle this alone. And since I created you— I can just as easily *un*-create you." He snaps his fingers. "See, you're gone."

"Have it your way, Gunfighter. But did you really think that by locking me up along with your past, you could be rid of it?" the voice of the Third-eye probes. "I mean, you actually thought you could just up and walk away, scot-free? Leave all the blood and guts, atrocities, terror, and fear behind?" the Third-eye scoffs. "Haven't you learned anything, Gunfighter? The more you restrain your past, the more powerful it becomes. The more it will eat you up from the inside out."

As the Third-eye talks, the veteran peers around trying to find the source of the voice.

"Quit your twistin' and turnin'. You'll only draw attention and make a fool out of yourself. You can't see me. Now, listen up! There isn't much time."

"Much time?" the veteran questions. "What are you talking about?"

"You only locked one door. Another passageway exists," the Third-eye explains in a thick voice. "And the door is now settin'

Plate 4   Demons and Phantoms *(Illustration by John Tylk)*

wide open. It's only a matter of time before the demons and phantoms find their way out. And when they do, they'll be coming for *you.*"

The veteran's mind swims in confusion and beads of sweat begin to pop out on his forehead. His black leather combat boots suddenly feel like they are anchored in concrete. A dark dread begins to pour into his body filling him from the bottom on up.

"Demons and phantoms." His bloodshot eyes fill with pain.

"That's right," the Third-eye continues. "Now, you'll need all the strength you can muster, so quit wasting it complaining about what strangers say while they walk down the street. That will only dislocate your already *bad* back. Besides, it's downright stupid to spend time on things you can't change or do anything about."

"I know," the veteran apologizes meekly. "I mean, I'm not trying to. . . ."

"To what, Gunfighter?" the Third-eye screams. "Just stop bein' a complete fool. All right? Pull the reins in on that ego of yours and quit acting like a drunk shooting up the town and howling at the moon."

"Okay-*okkkkkay.*" The veteran raising his arms in resignation. No, he did not want to dislocate his spine and go through a month of neck and back pains. "But you hear me out, Mr. Illusion. I've had it, man! I mean, I've had it with uppity human trash. I've had it with those mindless, sneering, snotnosed, better-than-thou assholes who *never* had to fight in a war and know they *never* will. Bleeding hearts, who don't give a flying fuck about anything or anybody but their precious, righteous selves. When it comes right down to it, they'd step on the bodies of their own countrymen while waving the American flag in a mad dash for the almighty buck. Bunch of smart ass, over educated hypocrites is what they are."

The veteran angrily scuffs the sidewalk with the toe of his combat boot. He remembered that during World War I they called PTSD, "Shell Shock."

Wait just one minute, he said to himself. I don't have to justify. . . . He searches his senses, but the presence has vanished. This is insane. I'm actually standing here carrying on a conversation with my own imagination. He shakes off the notion. A breeze brushes his face and helps cool his seething temper. Closing his eyes, he takes a deep cleansing breath, then lets out a resounding sigh. Because way down deep inside, he knows it isn't just his imagination. A bitter taste plays on his tongue.

"I'm out of here," he mumbles. "Before I start talking to myself again." He reaches for the train schedule then for his money. "Can't trust anybody in this crowd," he sneers, looking over his shoulder. Patting the wallet in his back pocket, he felt the edge of his driver's license. It held all the particulars. Fred Leo Brown, height: 5'10". Weight: too skinny for my own good at 148. Hair: what's left of it—dark brown going silver gray. Eyes: once full-of-life brown, now stormy green.

Another cloud-body sweeps past as he steps off the sidewalk in the direction of the monument. Halting abruptly, he cocks his head. Could have sworn he heard a sound? Like the fragment of a name. With the back of his fingernails, he brushes the side of his head realizing there was something awfully familiar about that sound. He shrugs off the notion. Probably just the noise of a big city echoing through the park lawn. He looks at *The Wall* . . . maybe that, too.

Brown weaves past a cluster of veterans. Noticing with disapproval, their female companions have bodies either too skinny, too fat, out of shape, pear shaped, or just simply bowed. The things in common were breasts that look heavily fondled and jeans that fit tight as girdles.

"No eye candy around here."

He grimaces further as he overhears the grating comments that squawk from the mouths of these barnyard hens.

One clucks to her veteran, "Now honey, don't go boring everyone with your crazy war stories. I think we've all heard enough about it."

Plate 5   Barn yard hens *(Illustration by John Tylk)*

Another accusing voice, "You've been sneaking around talking with your bizarre friends again, haven't you?"

Yet another complainer, "You must have a screw loose inside your head or something to be talkin' like that."

And still another supreme bitch, "I've put up with enough of this crap!"

Then he hears one more hen cluck-cluck-cluck to another scratch-and-peck, "And how has it been, living with *your* vet all these years? I think I've just about had it, too."

Oh you too, huh? You bunch of whining rags are really behind your fighting men, aren't ya, Brown swears bitterly. From the sounds of it, I bet you nag your war veteran each and every day, all day long about his shortcomings. Oh*hhhh* yes, of course, with the best of intentions. You know what? You're probably just pissed off because you can't eat or shop your way around this one. You bunch of criticizing fat-asses.

First, and let me make this perfectly clear, no matter what you think, you could never—even—begin to understand or imagine what happened to us in Vietnam. That said, we don't need your tears, sympathy or pity. And we're not asking you to be part of our fan club either but whadoya think, we wanted it to end up like this?

Come on, man. Shi*tttt!* I'm tired of it, too. Tired of the nights when my shouts go no farther than the middle of my throat. Tired of the nights when I wake to my wife's screams and find my hands wrapped around her throat. Tired of hearing her plea, "Wake up. Wake up. Damn you—wake up! You're dreaming again." And then, "You scare the hell outta me when you do that."

Oh, yeah, you bet. I'm tired to death of it, too. And I don't like shoutin' back, "I'm not dreaming—it's real. I know it's not to you, but it's *real* to me. Very, very real. So why don't you just knock it off. Stop it right there." Then after the shouting match, he storms upstairs to spend the rest of the night on the floor behind the sofa.

Brown reminded himself that in World War II, PTSD was called "battle fatigue."

Plate 6   Battle fatigue *(Illustration by John Tylk)*

He remembers that during World War II they called PTSD, "Battle Fatigue" or "Bloodless Wound."

During this internal tete-a-tete, a veteran approaches with a compliment of medals and patches adorning his army soft cap and fatigue shirt. "Welcome home, there, buddy," the slouching veteran greets Brown, raising his hand to shake.

Brown doesn't understand why, but he lets his hand go limp when they clasp. Then he stares hard-eye into a face with hollow cheeks and deeply set lines. The man appears to be about his age, height and build but with a beer-belly paunch that rolls over a tarnished brass military belt buckle.

"Americal Division, huh?" the veteran said, nodding with approval toward the division pin Brown wears on his soft cap.

"Yep. The Southern Cross."

"Say, I could use a smoke. You got a spare?"

"Don't smoke. Anyway, like they says, CIGARETTES MAY BE HAZARDOUS TO YOUR HEALTH." Brown almost laughs at his brashness. He feels like adding, I wish I had a coffin nail though, so you could get lung cancer, choke and die. Then you'd leave me alone. Now wouldn't that be peachy.

The veteran is seized by a hacking cough. He leans over and spits out a huge amount of phlegm. "I think I got Agent Orange," he said thumping his chest. "You know they kept spraying that shit all around the perimeters to keep the vegetation from growing inside our mine fields. And I-Corps, where we were, they had the highest concentration of defoliant in the country. We all got it."

"Think so?"

"Know so. It was everywhere. We drank it. Showered in it. Ate it. Ever paint a room without getting speckles all over the place?"

"Humm," Brown mutters and notes the veterans blotchy skin and strangely yellow facial color.

"We'll probably all end up dying from it. So what the hell," the vet said with lame bravado. "Party-hardy while we got the chance." Searching his pockets he finds a broken cigarette. "Did I ask if you had a cigarette?"

"Yep but like I said, I don't smoke." Brown motions toward some veterans smothering themselves and others in a cloud of cancerous tar and nicotine. "Why don't you ask them."

"What year were you in the 'Nam, man?" the veteran asks, ignoring the brush-off.

"Nineteen-sixty-seven, sixty-eight," Brown answers, deliberately short, still not certain why he doesn't hold up his end of the conversation. Under normal circumstances, being openly rude isn't part of his nature but something was irritating about this veteran, like a fly that buzzes around your head, then lands and spits on your food. You swat at the pest but you keep missing and no matter what, you can't get the little bastard to leave it alone.

"Ain't that something. I was there myself in sixty-eight. That Tet Offensive was some badass mother, huh?" the veteran said boastfully. "We lost a whole lot of good men when. . . ."

God, not another long-winded war story, Brown thinks in dismay. He turns off the veteran's buzzing voice and just stares absently at this pesky fly of a man. Wait a minute. The guy isn't looking back. Brown's eyes glint past a raised eyebrow. He half grins. Only a faker with a lot of phoney war stories wouldn't stare back. Just another Dog and Pony show, ain't that right, Flyman?

"I was with Bravo Company, first of the sixth, 198th Light Infantry," Flyman continues. "Got myself a Purple Heart and a Bronze Star for valor."

"Don't say. Small world, ain't it?" Brown said not caring to disguise his sarcasm. "I was assigned to Reconnaissance in that same battalion. So, during the 1968 Tet Offensive you must've been at the battle of Lo Giang just outside of Da Nang. Right?"

Flyman nods with reassuring scrunched lips.

"So tell me," Brown swallows ready to savor the moment, "what happened when you guys got cut off during the battle?"

Plate 7

Flyman *(Illustration by John Tylk)*

"Well, I, uuuuh," Flyman coughs as he fumbles for words, "I wasn't actually in the fighting myself. You know, I mean, uuuuh. . . ."

SPAT! The fly swatter comes smashing down. *Gotchaaaaaa.* What is it with these guys? Does stretching the truth and an out and out lie give them a rush? I know who gave you those filthy medals for phony valor—the Candy Man. The officers and high ranking NCOs passed them out like lollipops to all the suck-ups. Wait. What did we call suck-asses like this in the rear with the gear? It only takes a second for Brown to recall. Oh *yeahhhhhh*, REMF, short for Rear Echelon Motherfucker.

"So, how did you like walking over those land mines on those long, scorching hot road sweeps outside of LZ Baldy?" he said cutting off Fyman's buzz. "I'll tell ya what, those mines were big enough to blow you to hell and back . . . easy. And how could anyone forget Sniper's Alley, Rocket Pocket, LZ Center, AK Valley. God, remember all them? And how about the badest of the bad Que Son, the Valley of Living Death?

"Yeah though I walk through the Valley of The Shadow Of Death," Brown said as he clicks his heels together and comes to the position of attention. "I fear no evil for I am the badest mother here," he said finishing a religious combat verse that he and the others would occasionally recite for strength while in a freefire zone.

Plate 8   Valley of Living Death *(Illustration by John Tylk)*

"Oh, yeah, sure. I remember the valley," Flyman said with a hand gesture. "But like I was saying, I wasn't actually in the bush that much." Flyman begins talking as if reciting lines from a piece of paper. "This one time I was on patrol and there was movement behind some thick bushes," Flyman explains. He positioned both hands as though clutching an M-16 rifle. "In a split second, I opened fire. We ran over and saw this woman holding her dead child." Then with misting doe-eyes, he dares a peek at Brown. "Shit, man, I didn't know it was a mother and child."

Oh *boo-hoo-hoo.* What a sad story. I feel like crying, Brown thinks sarcastically. "Yeah*hh*, those were the good old days when you could shoot first and ask questions later," Brown replies, intent on shocking the vet with his callousness. "Everything was so easy. Whenever you needed to blow off some steam you just went into the bush and blew someone away."

So tell me, why do these fakers always have to pick on defenseless civilians and babies? They could just as easily lie about killing NVA, North Vietnamese soldiers. But, come to think of it, that wouldn't work. Now would it? Because any hard-core combatant could push holes as big as his fist through a story like that. And if it *really* did happen—I mean if Flyman really did mistakenly kill that child, I don't think he'd go walking around broadcasting it to a perfect stranger.

Must be a virus REMFs like this catch? Yeah, that's it. The symptoms are one Purple Heart, a medal for valor and murdering at least one lily white, innocent child or civilian. Brown looks savagely at Flyman, who continues in a half-hearted buzz.

Why don't you quit stinking up the place? Stop all this bullshit and tell the fucking truth for once in your life? *Tell me what you did*, Brown challenges through a stern gaze. Tell me about that little piece of hell stuck way back inside of that pea brain of yours. Tell me about the guy running toward you. The guy with blood bubbling out of his mouth, with spaghetti nerve endings flopping in the air where his arm used to be. Tell me about the look on his twisted face that screams, "Why-the-hell you run out on me?!" The guy collapses, a bundle of blood, flesh, and raw bone near the tree and bushes you're hiding behind. He lays there, gets stiff, and starts to decay and smell right in front of your fucking blameless eyes.

You're no better than a common killer. You know why? Because you figured out how to make those soldiers on that wall over there take-the-fall. What I'd like to know is how a royal fuckup like you justifies it. I mean, what does that voice inside your head say? "A man's gotta do what a man's gotta do: Cover his own ass first." Is that how you do it? Oh, wait. I know an even better one, and the media loves it too. "I learned how to survive."

Yeah right.

The problem is your secret for survival can't stop the nightmares from eating away your guts. And it can't block out the picture of that guy you let die, laying in a body bag with his blackened skin rotting and peeling off his skull. A soldier reduced to a sweet treat for maggots that wriggle in and out of his nose, mouth and ears, and dine on his putrefied eyes.

Have you got that memory?

And perched on the corpse's forehead is one of those big uglier-than-sin spiders with fuzzy legs and round eyes that looks straight through you.

I bet you can smell the decay from here. I bet the taste it leaves in your throat makes you wanna throw up. Puke it up, baby and gobble it all back down like a fly. Day after day. Night after night. That, my friend, is how you learned how to *survive*.

It's doomsday, Flyman. No DEROS out of this nightmare. There's no time left to bellyache about how *you* got screwed. That nightmare is gonna come running out of The Wall, splatter and bury you—just like you did him.

Brown begins to laugh, a deep, diabolical laugh. A sick, twisted laugh that makes his eyes jiggle, his arms flap, and his body twist as if doing some kinda idiotic dance.

He remembers that during the Korean War they called PTSD "Operational Exhaustion."

Plate 9   Reaching out *(Illustration by John Tylk)*

"Gunfighter!" the voice of his Third-eye booms. Brown drops his arms and composes himself. "Better get a rein on that wild horse! I'm warning you. Those guys in *white* holding a straitjacket already suspect you're prime for the loony bin."

Flyman's voice returns. ". . . My buddy recognized this guy in the parade who he knows wasn't even in the 'Nam, man. Shit. The guy was never in-country, let alone the service."

"Whadoya mean?" Brown asks puzzled, pulling his mind back from the edge. An edge that sometimes he gets so close, the pull of insanity leaves him teetering. And he seriously wonders when he is going to push it too far and fall right off.

"Well, haven't you noticed?" Flyman raises fingers on both hands to stroke the air with quotation marks, "It's becoming the in-thing to say you're a Vietnam vet."

"The *in-thing*? You serious?"

"Yeah, for a fact."

"Well, that might be, but really what difference does it make who was in that parade?" Brown said not caring to hide his disdain. "The people that this whole fucking thing is about aren't really here . . . are they."

"Yeah, well, you might have a point," Flyman acknowledges a little flustered.

"Might?" Brown said acidly. Hell, you know I'm right, Flyman. So what's next? Oh yeah, I know. The show must go on and on and on. And of course most everyone will be gullible enough to believe it.

ACT ONE:

You play the part of a misunderstood soldier with a bad case of Posttraumatic Stress Disorder.

"Ready on the set! Lights, camera, action."

With a coffin nail dangling from your cracked lips, you walk ever so slowly over to The Wall, crumble to your knees, place a quivering finger on a name, then drop a few tears for the Ten O'Clock Evening News.

I fuckin' hate it.

VIETNAM VETERAN

Don't cha get it? We had
to go. And now, we don't give a
damn whether you agree, because
what's r i g h t f o r y o u sure
doesn't make i t right f o r u s.
Rationalize? Our kind of reality
doesn't need it. We've always given
our best but still things got screwed
up. It wasn't the plan to kill them.
Civilians were part of it, too. It
didn't make us feel macho! Big men!
We were just trying not to die.
You've been hurt, well, what can we
say, we're sorry? Combat is like sex,
it gets dirty when done right.
Soldiers of war doing what soldiers
do, believing only God has the right
to pass judgment. So why are we
left carrying the blame? Never
will we ever fall for those
l i e s again!

Flashback

Walking from Flyman, Brown shrugs in an effort to dislodge the vice of tension that grips his shoulders. While massaging a shoulder, he ventures a look at the monument inscribed with over 58,000 names of those killed or missing in action during the Vietnam War.

"Well, here goes nothin'." He starts making his way toward the memorial stepping around the throngs of onlookers that hover about the Chicago park lawn. Strangely enough, his face reddens and his pulse quickens with each foot drop. His stomach begins to somersault, flip-floping around. Then he finds himself becoming almost panic stricken with the need to shout *incoming!* and hitting the dirt.

He lifts the brim of his cap to wipe cold sweat off his forehead. "Christ," he mumbles and lets out a tension relieving chuckle. "I must be gettin' a little gun-shy in my old age."

Spotting a sign with an ⇨ and the word INFORMATION, he walks over to wait his turn. Reluctantly, he turns his back to the black wall. Nervously rocking on his heels, he again massages the knotted muscles along the top of his shoulders while stretching out his neck.

Feeling dizzy, like he might even pass out, a vision begins to integrate. A skull-bleaching sun radiates out of a clear blue sky blanketing the land with shimmering waves of heat. An American infantryman stands next to a mound of dirt, his body and combat fatigues literally dripping with sweat. His scab covered hand grips an M-16 rife with selector switch pointing to semiautomatic. The GI watches passively as a bullet riddled Viet Cong (VC) gets dragged out of a spider-hole and is then rolled off the mound. The blood-covered body collects brush, dirt, and sticks as it tumbles down like a hundred-pound sack of potatoes. The twisted body of the near dead VC bumps into the GI's scuffed, dust-covered boots.

Ending up flat on his back, his eyes stare blankly skyward. Noticing an elongating shadow, he looks over at the dark figure that totally eclipses the sun. A soldier swings the muzzle of an M-16 rifle to rest on the bridge of his nose. Staring indifferently at the front rifle sight, the VC slowly moves his gaze up along the steel barrel, over the plastic hand guard and momentarily pauses on the calloused finger wrapped around the trigger. Finally, the VC looks directly into the face of the American soldier. The eyes of the VC are not filled with horror, but instead in their dark depths there are the scoffing words, *"Do it."*

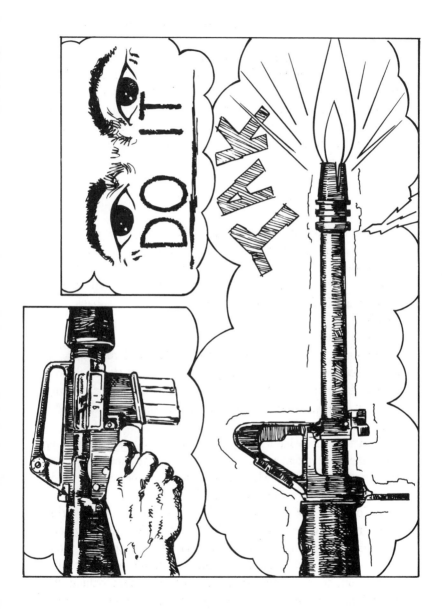

Plate 11   Do it! *(Illustration by John Tylk)*

A rifle's report breaks the silence—the vision gets shattered like glass.

Brown finds himself ducking and whirling. Three sparrows take to the air, a ghost of a breeze shuffle the leaves and scraps of paper. The drone of the crowd has remained unchanged. The smug, aloof, silent black wall has remained unchanged as well. He self-consciously straightens and, to save himself some embarrassment, pretends to signal a fellow veteran with both a wave and a nod.

"Crocodile! Crocodiiiiile, GI!"

The shriek pierces his ears. Again, he ducks and whirls. Am I the only one who heard that? The crowd continues with it's steady buzz of conversation. The Wall knows something but continues to stare smug and defiant. He shakes his head, riddled with disbelief. What's goin' on? This somekinda flashback? Or what?

"You're up."

Spinning around wide eyed and bewildered, Brown faces a ruddy-face man who sits military rigid on a short stool behind a long folding table. A former combat Marine, he surmises, noting the military insignia on the combat fatigue shirt and the USMC bulldog tattoo on the forearm.

"I don't know what's going on," Brown said hastily, knowing it was the understatement of the year. Maybe he should back out right now. Back out while he still has a chance but he finds himself asking, "So, how does all this work?"

"You give me a name and I'll try to find it," the Marine explains in an even monotone. Their eyes lock. At first glance the Marine's eyeballs appear lifeless, hardly different from those of a bloated fish washed ashore on some polluted lake. Continuing to dive, Brown detects silver flashes behind the crystalline lens. It seems as though the soldier's brain is alive with high-intensity electricity. A silver beam of light shoots from the Marine's eyes and pierces Brown's. He now finds himself on a spiral staircase that pitches and yawns downward toward the licking flames of eternal damnation.

"Hey!" The former Marine waves his hand in front of Brown's face. "Wake up. We ain't got all day." He motions to the line forming. "You got a name? Of do you need some time to think about it?"

"Huh?" Brown said, rebounding from the trance. "What was that?"

"A name? Somethin'? Anything?"

Brown probed his mind for a name, but finds none. "U-mon-ee." The phonetic name jumps from his mouth in a rusty southern voice.

"U-mon-ee?" parroted the Marine with left eyebrow rising.

Brown nods. "Sounds like a name doesn't it?"

"I guess. Can you spell it?"

"Oh, God. Ahhh." Brown's mind goes blank. "Well, ahhh, probably U-M-O-N-I? What do you think?"

"Doesn't sound like it spells much of anything."

"He was Japanese."

"Oh. Okay. Well let's start with the U's." He begins to leaf through the massive volume of KIA and MIA—soldiers killed or missing in action. When he comes to W's, he starts to rifle page by page.

Fidgeting, Brown wants to simply walk away. They'll never find the name anyhow, he rationalizes. Probably misspelled. I never could spell anything right.

"Nothin' here looks like your spelling," the Marine said his fingers gliding over the last name starting with U."

"How about Y. You know like Y-A-M. A little change of accent. I mean how do you spell a Japanese name?"

As the search continues, Brown becomes increasingly agitated. He rolls his eyes and begins to feel like a thousand eyes are drilling into him. Unnerved, he pulls off his military soft cap and runs his fingers through sweaty graying hair. Just as a precaution, he quickly glances over his shoulder. Nothing but The Wall. "It knows something," Brown mumbles continuing to stare at the black mirror surface. Then he sees a dimensional smirk rise out of the thousands of lines etched on its flat face.

"Nothin' yet," the Marine said slowly, his rough fingers continuing to skim down the columns.

Curious, Brown cocks his head trying to read the upside-down fine print.

An unexplainable dizziness again sweeps over him and his eyes lose focus. He blinks and shakes his head. His skin lets loose with a torrent of cold sweat as his eyes slowly refocus. In that split second, the entire scene has changed. He watches in horror as the pages of the book loom larger, growing thicker by the second. The table moans as it labors under the increasing weight, its legs twisting and puncturing the muddy earth to release plumes of gunpowder smoke.

The Marine now towers over the deadbook, pawing at the pages with clawed, leathery fingers. A page turns. *WHOOSH!* The wind sends Brown's hat flying and hair streaking from his forehead. Then the pages collide with a deafening *WHUMP!* that forces him to clamp palms over his ears. What the hell?

Panic rises in his throat and he chokes on a scream as *something* gruffly clamps like a vise onto his head. With head rocking back, he stares upside-down at a creature with the jaw of a camel, antlers of a deer, ears of a cow, and the neck of a snake.

Righting himself, he sees the creature's froglike belly, carp scales, feet with five long eagle-type curved talons with the soft pad of a tiger and the fishlike tail. Brown's fossil memory tells him this creature is a jade-green dragon, the kind that glides through Southeast Asian legends.

"Let me go!" he shouts hysterically, while trying to wrestle free from the dragon's claw foot that holds tightly around his waist. It lifts him to within easy touch of the yard-long deep purple whiskers that protrude from either side of the mouth. Brown dares to glance at the creature's wide, pug nose and crystal harelike eyes. He keeps pushing and tugging against the curved talons, then finally relaxes, resigning to the fact that he'd either be crushed or eaten like a sardine. Unexpectedly, a benevolent smile sweeps across the dragon's face and a sound, like jingling coins in a pouch, comes from its mouth.

Feeling the danger has momentarily passed, Brown curiously stares at the dragon and at the funny looking growth on top of its head that quivers from what appears to be air pumping from the middle of the creature's head. Brown now remembers that Asians consider the dragon to be kingly and a god, a creature that is very rough and fierce but also very wise/all-knowing.

And to prove him right, spinning in the sky next to the dragon's head, is the fable "sacred pearl." Within the translucent blue-white pearl, Brown sees the image of rolling thunder that shoots forth from the pearl's sprout appendages in sparks of red and gold. Words form inside his mind, "The pearl of truth represents the yin and yang of life. The tug and pull. The life-force."

In a whisper Brown answers, "You're telling me we can't have peace until we understand war?" He raises his head, staring unafraid and shouts, "Is that what you mean?"

The dragon acts as though it doesn't hear. Brown yells, "Are you deaf or somethin'?" Then he laughs, for of course a "lung" dragon is deaf. He spreads his arms in a manner that speaks, "Explain it to me?"

The dragon swings its head around, extends its deep red tongue, and lathers Brown's cheek with a purple, gooey saliva that surprisingly has a pleasing fragrance. With the beast's moist breath pouring over him like white South China Sea fog, Brown swoons and closes his eyes. He detects the aroma of sweet mountain air, lush jungle growth, and flowers in bloom. Opening his eyes, he finds himself standing alone at the edge of an expansive rice field with portions stretching beyond the horizon. The tranquil sea of green ripples softly in the cool breeze.

Plate 12   Lung dragon *(Illustration by John Tylk)*

Then he notices the black smoke rolling out of the distant tree lined peninsula and spots Huey gunships blasting away in the distance.

"The battlefield of Da Nang."

BATTLEFIELD OF DA NANG—He must prepare to die. Living c a n be of no importance. His mind must be altered, h i s brain must bleed. He became a man on the battlefield of Da Nang. He was brave enough t o die. He knows now, he h a d to bury the boy, burn t h e past, destroy what h e was. His brain has stopped bleeding. Now, he can Ki l l. It doesn't hurt. He revels in the gore. Limits? What limits. But if for some weird reason he returns home alive, his brain will bleed again. Because to return, he must eliminate what he has become.

"That look like him?" The Marine's finger rests upon the name YAMANE, BENJI.

Still in a daze, he stares at the page.

"There's no other name near the spelling you gave me," he explains.

"Yeah, yeah," Brown said breathlessly. "Well, then . . . I guess that's gotta be him. Right?"

The Marine casually writes

YAMANE, BENJI   **Oakland, California**
Died 16 March 1968   **Slab 45 east line 6**

on the back of a Moving Wall brochure.

Brown, far less calm, stares, transfixed. For years he had tuned out the Vietnam War experience, keeping his friend Yamane and the rest of his fellow infantrymen locked away deep inside his mind. Guys with nicknames like Okie and Ziggy, Elvis and Dig-it, Bull, Rock Bottom and Peace. And the lone-moniker warriors whose last names, like Bedford and Green and Shepard and Sloan, or first names, like Dennis and Angel and Scotty, were all that Brown could recall. But somewhere unforgettable soldiers such as sergeants "Tex" Denning, "Robin Hood" Walker, "Jelly Belly" Grauer, and "Buddy" Rogers or that fearless helicopter pilot "Peacock." Their names echoed inside Brown's mind. And what about the gambler "Doc Holliday."

But there is some consolation in knowing he hasn't made it all up. This whole Vietnam War thing isn't part of some continuing dream or book he'd read. The Marine gives him the paper with Yamane's name. Taking it, his hand begins to quake from the memory of hundreds of nights of terror in the chilling, wet field with this soldier—even after death—a close companion.

"March 16, 1968," he said thinking out loud. "Why is that date so familiar?" During the war it was near impossible to keep track of the day alone the date. So in the confusion of combat, there was no way for him to know when Yamane had actually died.

A shiver runs down his spine when he realizes the historical significance of that date. Under the same hot blue morning sky that had seen Yamane perish, a few miles south, Lieutenant William Calley and his platoon had disembarked from helicopters. They had landed in an area of high American casualties, known as the "Killing Field," bordering the hamlet of *My Lai*. The well-planned search and destroy to hunt for Viet Cong guerrillas is now listed as a War Crime and has a name all its own, *My Lai Massacre*.

Too bad, Brown thinks angrily. Too bad American's can't walk a mile in *those* combat boots. "Murderers!" "Baby killers!" Sure it was appalling. Heinous. Downright despicable. But he knows that Americans could never understand that the enemy was dressed in child and civilian clothing.

That five-year-old babies were sent out with time-detonated booby-trap baskets to set next to unsuspecting GIs. That when no one was looking, eight-year-old children would pull out the hidden rifles to shoot at soldiers. That women were master booby-trap makers and planters. That to the infantryman, it felt as if the whole civilian population was just waiting, stalking silently, praying for the chance to kill him.

To Brown, Lieutenant Calley is far from the monster depicted by the media. Brown chanced upon Lieutenant Calley and his RTO, radio telephone operator. The RTO happened to be a buddy of his from advanced infantry trained (AIT) at Fort Gordon, Georgia. His friend told him that Lieutenant Calley was a capable, brave and caring leader. His friend thought so highly of the platoon leader that he tried talking Brown into a transfer. That chance meeting took place only weeks after The My Lai Massacre, when the now-unforgettable incident was still referred to among the soldiers as a well executed battlefield victory. The brass even put Lieutenant Calley in for a Bronze Star for valor.

So what changed? Brown smirks. If *truth* is the first casualty of war—he remembers the compassion he saw in Lieutenant Calley's light brown eyes—maybe the over 200-plus

A shiver ran the length of Brown's spine when he realized the historical significance of the date: 16 March 1968. Under the same hot blue morning sky that had seen Yamane perish, Lieutenant William Calley and his platoon disembarked from helicopters outside a hamlet called My Lai 4. That particular search and destroy had a name all its own—

"The My Lai Massacre."

Brown took the piece of paper, his hand quaking with the memory of terror out in the chilly, wet field with this man, his closest companion.

Plate 13　　　　　　My Lai *(Illustration by John Tylk)*

villagers were already dead when Calley's unit arrived. Maybe—just maybe—that in all the confusion Lieutenant Calley ended up taking the credit or later the blame for the kills. That a year later, when the media trap was set, it was too late to recant.

Brown lingers on the long-ago conversation when his and Lieutenant Calley's platoons fought side by side in a grueling twenty-one-day battle in Que Son Valley, the Vietnamese so appropriately named "Valley of Living Death." His 1st Battalion, 6th Infantry Regiment, 198th Infantry Brigade, Americal Division—the 1st of the 6th for short—suffered a staggering 75 percent casualties. As far as he is concerned, only American heroes were present at that battle. Lieutenant Calley included.

As the smell of battle leaves his nostrils, Brown shakes his head and refocuses on the piece of paper that quivers in his hand.

In a gravelly voice, the Marine instructs Brown to find the year 1959—the date given as the first official Vietnam War casualty—on the six-foot and tallest mid-wall section of the monument and work to the right. Follow the numbers on the bottom of the slabs until he comes to number 45. "Then count down six lines from the top," he instructs. "Good luck."

Brown embarks on his search. The first thing he spots is a framed letter leaning against the apex of The Wall. Lowering into a dink-squat, he leans in close to read:

WALKING DEAD

On the Second of July, 1967, Alpha and Bravo Companies of the First Battalion, Ninth Marines were on patrol just a few hundred meters south of the DMZ. Bravo blundered into a well set ambush at the marketplace. Soon, Alpha, too, was into the thick of it.

The enemy consisted of a regiment of the NVA supported by artillery, heavy mortars, rockets, anti-aircraft guns and surface-to-air missiles. Companies C & D were rushed to the field in support, but the outcome had been decided. The men were overwhelmed and outnumbered. But worse than that, they were equipped with Colt M-16 rifles. Their M-14 rifles, which had proven so effective and reliable were stored in a warehouse somewhere in the rear.

The M-16's would fire once or twice—maybe more—then jam. The extractor would rip the rim off the casing. Then the only way to clear the chamber and resume firing was to lock open the bolt, run a clean rod down the barrel, and knock the casing loose. Soon, it would jam again. This was the rifle supplied to her troops by the richest nation on earth.

The enemy was not so encumbered. They carried rifles which were designed in the Soviet Union and manufactured in one of the poorest nations on earth—the so called - Peoples Republic of China. Their rifles fired. Fired every time. They ran amongst the Marines, firing at will. Sixty-four men in B company were killed that afternoon. Altogether the Battalion lost around a hundred of the nation's finest men. The next morning, we bagged them like groceries. We consigned their bodies to their families and commended their souls to God. May He be as merciful as they were courageous.

Today, people are still debating the issue: was it the fault of the ammo? The fault of the rifle? Neither. It was the fault of the politicians, contractors and generals. People in high places knew the rifle and ammo wouldn't work together. The military didn't want to buy the rifle when Armalite was manufacturing it. But when Colt was licensed as the manufacturer, they suddenly discovered it was a marvelous example of yankee ingenuity.

Sgt. Brown told them it was garbage. Colonel Hackworth told them it was garbage. And every real grunt knew it was garbage. It was unsuited for combat.

There was no Congressional investigation. No contractor was ever fined for supplying defective material. No one uncovered the bribes paid to the government officials. No one went to jail. And the mothers of the dead U.S. Marines were never told that their sons went into combat unarmed.

To all outward appearances those Marines died of gunshot and fragmentation wounds. But a close examination reveals that they were first stabbed in the back by their countrymen back home. The politicians, contractors and generals have retired to the comfortable estates now. Their ranks have been filled by their clones—greedy invertebrates every one. They should hope that God is more forgiving than I.

Brave men should never be commanded by cowards....

1st Lieutenant Harvey G. Wysong

010038

United States Marine Corps Reserve

First Battalion 9th Marine

"The Walking Dead"

"Jamin Jenny," Brown said thinking about the four different M-16 rifles he'd used during the war. "I knew her well."

Standing back a few yards he begins to methodically examine the hodgepodge of mementos and keepsakes that have accumulated at the base of each slab. An array of trinkets consisting of: a Purple Heart medal, set of dog tags, small American flags, photographs, teddy bears, beer cans—some empty, some full—music tapes, candles, crucifixes and other religious objects, jewelry, garter belts, walking sticks, flowers, both silk and real, and a myriad of other items. The meanings behind some of the offerings seemed obvious, but the relevance of others remain illusive, a secret between the living and the dead.

This traveling model, a black half-scale replica of the Vietnam Veterans Memorial in Washington, D.C., is known to the world simply as The Wall. But as Brown absorbs the mementos, the letters, the seemingly endless list of names, he gives it another more appropriate name: WALL OF BLOOD.

Plate 14   The Wall *(Illustration by John Tylk)*

WALL OF BLOOD

F l o a ting
cloud–ghosts
swoop around
the blood stream
of people w h o
glide w i t h n o
d e s i g n. Gently
placed letters and
memories strew t h e
pathway,   compelling
all to leave a token o f
honor. O n e b y o n e the
KIAs are mustered to memory,
their hollowed eyes drawing us in.
If only we could carry fresh
blood to the heart, rekindle
and replenish their spirits
through our touch. Vietnam
has formed a   legacy
of love, and we honor
the over fifty-eight
thousand who never
lived, but only died
who   heroically
await the next
caressing
finger.

Buffalo Soldier

"Yo! You guys over there," booms a baritone voice. The Chicagoland viewers turn to watch a black shaggy bearded Vietnam veteran walk in their direction, a cane gripped tightly in his right hand. Brown scrutinizes the nearly six-foot tall lanky veteran with fatigue shirt draping over broad-shoulders that belies years of hardship. "We're gonna have us a flag-raising ceremony," he points, "over there." The veteran with **STEWART** sewn on the pocket of his combat jacket pocket offers a raised palm. They clasp hands solidly. "Welcome home there buddy," his voice rings with sincerity. "We made it."

"Wow. Thanks," Brown said almost apologetically, ashamed of the previous flurry of disfunctional thoughts. "Welcome home, yourself." Noticing they both wear Montagnard bracelets but he also has a POW/MIA bracelet .

Plate 15

Stewart *(Illustration by John Tylk)*

"Yeah, yeah," he said rotating the Montagnard bracelet thoughtfully. "My dink girlfriend put it on my wrist in the 'Nam, man. Ain't been off since." His smile displays large white teeth. "It's seen everything this old Buffalo Soldier's seen."

"Buffalo Soldier?" Brown questions. "Was that a unit's name or somethin'?"

"Naw," he said good naturedly. "That's just what we black vets sometimes call ourselves."

"Why that name?"

"It's the name the Indians gave us cavalrymen back in the 1870's," he proudly announces. "As for me, my distant relatives were slaves and fought with the Union Army during the Civil War." He takes off his sunglasses and looks squarely at Brown. "My grand-daddy was at Fort Sill, Oklahoma when they brought in the Comanche Renegade Geronimo."

"No kiddin'," he said with interest peaking. "My great grandfather was on Sherman's March To The Sea during the Civil War and my grandfather must've been at Fort Sill the same time as yours." Brown is amazed by the coincidence. "Said he saw Sitting Bull, Geronimo and some other big Indian chiefs."

"Got a drawing of my grand-daddy in his get-up with a corn cobb pipe, cavalry rifle, high top boots, hat and saddle." His pride shown through dark glistening eyes.

"Wow. Mine only has my grandfather holding a saber in front of a painted back drop."

"And ya knows?" he leans in close, "this old Buffalo Soldier done his time dancing with death."

"Dancing with death," Brown repeats, savoring the words. "Man, it's been a long time since I heard that term. So you were a pointman."

"Oh-h yeah. Shit," Stewart chuckles while nodding his head. "You got that straight, and then some." The lean veteran looks around and when satisfied no one could eaves-drop, with the help of his cane, leans closer. "And you know the truth of the matter? Ain't never DEROSed. Never made it back. Still in the 'Nam, man." He squares his shoulders and shakes his legs apparently in

Plate 16   Buffalo Soldier *(Illustration by John Tylk)*

an effort to help blood circulation. "Anyway, what the hell. Got dry socks, ain't sleeping atop of no grave. And who's to say if you ain't been blown away, it ain't a *coo-ool* deal."

"I'll buy that," Brown said appreciating the candor. "But ya know, there's a catch. You'll have to remember the ones who gave you that 'cool deal.'"

Momentarily, they watch a woman place a piece of paper over a name to attempt a "wall rubbing."

"Say, I gotta get this flag-raising ceremony goin'. Take care now, ya hear?" Stewart turns to leave, but stops in mid-step. "Say," he motions toward the monument, "you watch out for The Wall. It might start doing things—might even start talking to ya."

Brown releases a gush of air in amusement, thinking the veteran has probably been spending too much time in the sun. But turns somber when he meets the dark piercing eyes. The former soldier appears dead serious.

"Thanks," Brown acknowledges with a hand gesture. "I'll watch." His ego shoots back, Watch what? This flock of worthless sheep that mill around grazin' on the past? A bunch of tired old soldiers who've already been slaughtered but are too stupid to lie down? Huh? I'm sorry buddy boy, but from the looks of it, I'd say there's a real*lll* big problem around here.

No sooner does Brown hear his ego's misgivings than a flashback sideswipes his brain. A fleck of blood splatters his vision, and his haughty Third-eye flings him back in time.

Whirling from dizziness, he drops his head and grabs his knees to wait out the *spell*.

Stretching, he now recalls a long-ago conversation at the LZ Bayonet beer hall. A drunk REMF pipes up, "Man, what's it like . . . out there?" He motions toward the rice fields and mountains beyond the minefield and barbed wire. "You know. What's it like to actually take point. To be a Gunfighter Pointman?"

The infantry grunts in the room appear to be ignoring the question. One in particular, Sergeant Bedford, takes a drink of beer and begins dancing the can on the tabletop. He stops playing with the can and turns to eye the REMF.

To be called a Gunfighter Pointman you would have been pointman at least twenty-one times. Brown and Bedford were both veteran Gunfighters. They knew the feeling of glancing over a shoulder to watch the other infantrymen saddling-up. Knew what it was like to fearlessly step onto a jungle mountain trail with air thickly quiet, every sound hanging and clamoring for attention?

"So, you wanna know what it's like to be Pointman, huh?" Sergeant Bedford said in a steely voice not caring to take his eyes off the beer. "Well, it's kinda like dancing with the devil himself."

The deep creases in a Gunfighter's forehead can reveal the price paid for the miles spent crashing through steamy terrain where each step can age him by years. Each crease in turn would speak about the endless horror, agony, and the blistering noise that cruelly forced them to watch the demons of war gash their prey clean to the bone.

The Pointman knows the path, knows how to proceed, escort, and protect when no one else can or will dare. And imprinted in the orbs is the expression of "I just watched my life get sucked through my eyeballs."

Pointman defined: *The lead soldier of a moving column of infantryman who stays approximately fifty yards in front of the other soldiers in an area commonly known as the kill zone. Considered the most dangerous position during the Vietnam War and carried a life expectancy of less than a 10th of a second.*

To Brown, Point was as close to death as a soldier could get without actually dying. And, like Stewart, the ones who got too used to it really *are* still in the 'Nam.

Plate 17   Pointman *(Illustration by Curt Chiarelli)*

POINTMAN

Sleeping   under   the   stars,
wiping off the morning dew. A lush green
jungle   surrounds,   serenades, and caresses
the grunts. Then on cue, War's reality strips them
of childish fantasies. Living in the boonies is like
embracing   a disease that   leaves you
spiritually   mutated,   with warped
emotions   and twisted   l o g i c.
T h e y   s a d d l e u p,   cautious
   to   avoid   the next pointman's
   pleading eyes, whose life expectancy
   just got scaled back to the game of
   revolver   roulette.   The   pointman
     floats   toward   the inevitable
     and curses,   "Come on!
      Come on!   I   can take it!"
     To kill, he   must   become a
     killer. The Grim Reaper smiles at his
              S   i   d   e.   L   i   k   e
       tears in the rain, memories get
          lost in time. Pray for the
           man who walks point, the
             one   who's dancing
                 with   Death.

Line Bunker

Grimly, Brown refocuses on the task of searching out slab 45 east on The Wall. He makes his way around clusters of sobbing, hugging people whom it seems relish marching into pain, sorrow, and utter despair. Stopping, he squares off with the monument to read the chiseled names.

BOBBY ROY HOLLEY ◊ RAYMOND E JOHNSON ◊
TURNER L THOMPSON Jr ◊ DAVID A DILLON ◊
BRENT I GRIGGS ◊ TERRY A DENNING ◊ GEORG

"Jesus, all the names." A dizziness sends prickly heat across his back and arms. A blink later, the names gloss over to form a smooth black finish. Appearing on the mirrored surface is the face of a smiling, innocent teenage boy with long shoulder length hair. What? His eyes dart around—no one stands even remotely near. Then how the hell?

Like at the scariest part of a horror movie, he guardedly looks back at The Wall. The image remains. However, the long shaggy hair style has been replaced by a cropped military one. Glued to the reflection, a foreboding steel helmet appears hoovering just above the teenager's head. Then ever-so-slowly it begins to settle around the boy's head, with the smile being replaced by grim reality.

Now pictured is a blood-strip sergeant who has fought with gross abandon, with little concern about the consequences of his actions. A filthy, sweat-soaked guerrilla fighter, teeth bared, angry red eyes filled with ferocity, his spirit inflamed with outrage and his body cut and scarred as a testament to the old adage that WAR IS HELL. And then comes the psychotic, slack face look of the legendary THOUSAND-YARD-STARE.

"No!" Brown screeches and tears his eyes away from what he fears, what he knows, is the image of himself when once young and a soldier.

Feeling mentally exhausted with knees weakening, he wipes a trickle of cold sweat from his brow. God, maybe I am coming down with something—a cold—the flu. My throat hurts. He coughs and stretches his neck. Maybe something I ate. He bends over and presses on his side. I think I'm gonna throw-up.

Looking up, his vision fills with cloud-ghosts that scurry about bent on pulling faint cries from the cavities of The Wall's soul, and drawing moisture from his dry, burning eyes.

"No*oooo.*"

Plate 18   Brown with Thousand-Yard-Stare *(photo by Al Buschauer)*

Caught off guard, he buckles as sadistic fear punches through his chest, its claws wrapping around his heart. He desperately tries to tear away the hand that taunts and badgers his mind.

"Stay alive, Gunfighter," his Third-eye commands. "Don't pass out on me, not yet. Open your eyes and face the fear."

Brown swings around gasping for air. The massive breathing monument stares back at him, each cold slab beckoning him to drink of its sorrows and consume its mysteries.

His eyes roll as he whiffs and tastes a familiar stench. The odor of burning, decaying flesh and blood hang heavily in the air. He starts remembering places with their sea level serving as names like, Hill 45 and Hills 350-351-352, Hill 54 and Hill 69, Hill 707 and Hill 218 and Hill 488. The unforgettable places like Sniper Valley and Anton Bridge, Suicide Valley and AK Valley, Killing Field and Rocket Pocket, Dragon Valley and Valley Of Living Death. The artillery installations commonly referred to as landing zones, or LZs. Like LZ Chippewa and LZ Center, LZ Ross and LZ East, LZ West and LZ Gator, LZ Bayonet and LZ Baldy and LZ Moore. It is all coming back along with the stench, decay and horror, especially the dusty hot days and long dark nights spent inside that tomblike line bunker at LZ Baldy.

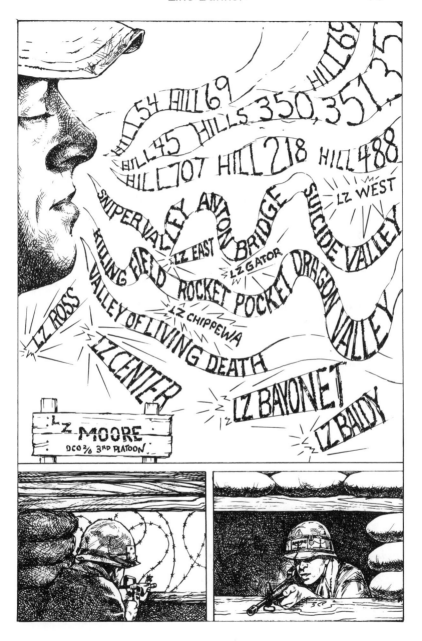

Plate 19 Names *(Illustration by John Tylk)*

LINE BUNKER - The scent of stale body odor, trampled vegetation, and nicotine swirling together stimulates and unlocks his memory. His mind peeks inside a dilapidated sandbag bunker that reeks with the stench of urine, feces, mildew, beer, vomit, and gunpowder. The dirt floor sucks in cartridges, old smokes, C-ration cans and SP packs. On bayonet-scarred benches, ignoring rodents and roaches, sit hard-sweating whisker-stubbed grunts in rotting jungle fatigues, joints dangling from their cracked lips. With deadpan eyes they inspect their weapons, ammunition, grenades, and claymore mine detonators. Through the front rifle slit they scan the minefield, over the razor-edge concertina wire and beyond to the free fire zone. The dog-tired men grumble about food, Coke and beer rations, festering cuts, the weather, fighting conditions and the lousy leadership. The bug juice can stave off the malaria borne mosquitoes that swarm about them like Vampire disciples, but it can do nothing for their depression that deepens with the clawing fingers of dusk. Raw pungent smells always bring him back, back to that war-torn bunker, back to that fear-sweat and cold reality, back to the misery of that widow-making war.

Baby Killer

Something like an earthquake or rather a rhythmic collision begins to shake the ground. Not the sort of collision you would expect in modern day Chicago, but more like back in prehistoric times when a thirty-ton carnivorous Tyrannosaurus Rex is stomping around in search of something to devour.

The ground shudders, The Wall moans. An eerie light begins to glow from behind the monument making it appear as though a volcanic fissure is opening. "God, it feels like the hark of The Armageddon . . . if I believed." But he doesn't. He prides himself on being grounded and *realistic*.

Then it appears—it can't be—but it does: an arched doorway begins to rise from behind the monument. He clasps his hands over his eyes in hopes that it will disappear. Through spread fingers he sees it continues to rise till it floats over the monument. Then the door slowly opens and it becomes evident that the ever-increasing thuds are coming from behind the doorway.

Meanwhile, a thick brew of gray-laced fog begins boiling over the door's threshold gathering momentum as it hits the ground. It froths, bunches and rolls like a rising tide along the base of The Wall.

Brown stiffens as he sees movement from within the fog. A young girl bursts from the haze running madly toward him, her arms driving at her sides. At first, the racing girl appears colorless, ghostlike, her features yet incomplete. But the closer she gets the more defined her figure, clothes and skin color become. It's as though somebody is sketching in the final features with the Almighty pen.

I'm dreaming. Right? Please, let this be a dream, he silently prays.

Cut off frayed jeans hug powerful thighs which propel feet clad in leather sandals as she outruns the fog. Her dusty blond hair streams behind like the mane of a thoroughbred mare. A tie-dyed, color-splashed pullover hangs loosely over her chest unable to restrain her breasts which leap and dive through each stride.

The hero inside kicks in and he nearly bolts to meet the damsel in distress but abruptly stops when she slows to a whimsical pace. She smiles disarmingly as though seeing a long-lost friend.

"Me?!" he mouths and points to himself while searching for a more likely object of attention.

She persists with a seductive wink of an eye and glowing smile. "Yes, you." She draws him in with a curling index finger.

As they near, Brown notices her purposeful stride, golden tan, and a face that radiants with vitality and idealism. The electrified air carries with it the faint aroma of honey blossoms. In mid-stride, the young lady turns and anxiously gazes over her shoulder at a group of people gathering near the edge of the fog. Two of them suspend a long bright multicolored banner painted with peace symbols, flowers, and the bold letters *FLOWER POWER*.

Flower children? Hippies? Brown stares quizzically at the crowd. Some sit with heads bobbing and shoulders moving in rhythm with the music of a bongo drum player. Other wayward souls, who may or may not be tuning into the singers or instrumentalist, stroll through the area like dancing fairies. Their slow motion, extravagant arm and body movements seeming disconnected.

A gangly, rather tall man with long dark hair and burly beard stands on a milk crate. Using one hand to hold an open book and the other to orchestrate his meaning, he gently recites poetry.

"Ahh-*um-humm*. Ahh-*um-humm*," the soothing chants flows from circle of flower children sitting in meditative positions. Still another group holds onto a long pole doing a type of gliding-weaving snake dance that they apparently believe can break through the hearts of the authorities when the time comes.

Fat chance of them buttering up the authorities, he says to himself. Then Brown remembers hearing that the hippy call these events *Festivals of Life*. That the majority of the crowd consisted of sons and daughters of the affluent who had money to buy their way through life or out of a war—to be exact their ticket to freedom from service would cost five-hundred-dollars. And they would spare no amount of funds to procure the dope and drugs necessary to *enlighten* their world and keep it that way. By the looks of things, they are well on the way to finding a higher "meaning of life."

Some hippies start trotting in a wide circle, for symbolism one even carries a pink baby pig in his arms, chanting and singing, while others pumped protest signs:

Plate 20   Protest signs *(Illustration by John Tylk)*

"Come on, man . . . hurry up," she pleads, jogging over. "Let's get over to the Peace Rally."

"You mean Antiwar Protest, don't you?"

Now for the second time doubt radiated from her eyes.

"No . . . no," Brown said shaking his head. "Those aren't my kind of people. I ain't no Hawk or nothin' like that. I mean, I'd like to see the war over, too. Hell, who'd want it over more than me? My buddies are dying over there. But that group," he points shaking his head, "ain't nothin' but a bunch of rich spoiled brats. Scum as far as I'm concerned." He looks apologetically into her sweet face that glistens with beads of perspiration. "I'm sorry, you must think I'm someone else."

"Noooo, don't be silly," she said with a radiant smile, dimples showing in her rosy cheeks. She tugs on his arm.

Suddenly, Brown gets shoved back as a figure slides between them. Hostile eyes glare through wire-rimmed glasses. A red bandanna restrains the shaggy, greasy hair of a hippy. The fowl body odor of the man belies days of sleeping in the park or in the trunk or back seat of a car without any effort to wash himself or even brush his teeth. Love beads dangle from around his neck to rest upon his ripped T-shirt painted with flowers. A wide leather belt holds up bell-bottom jeans that drape over brown squaretoed boots. In his left hand, he hoists a sloppily painted sign that reads:

My God, Brown thinks, I must be stuck in some kind of time warp.

Harshly grabbing the girl's arm, the shaggy activist glowers at Brown. *"Baby killer!"* his foul breath pours past ugly lips and yellow nicotine-stained teeth.

"I ain't no baby killer," Brown swore in defense. "I was sent there to stop the killing, dammit. But if you didn't know, civilians were part of it, too. Anyway, I was just following orders."

"You pitiful piece of shit." His eyes are filled with revulsion. "Defenseless little babies. Women and children." The hippie spat a thick wad of saliva.

Brown stares at the splash of spittle on his black combat boot. Seething with anger, he slowly brings up his stare. He has killed before and. . . .

Wide eyed in disbelief, they have both vanished, leaving behind the sweet scent of honey blossom perfume. But the antiwar rally is still in full swing. The crowd suddenly produces a six-foot American flag which they hurl to the ground. Converging, the hippies focus their rage by taking turns stomping and kicking the stars-and-bars like it embodies everything wrong in the world.

Then a can of gasoline is opened and the red, white, and blue gets dowsed with high octane. Off to one side a man lights his draft card and spins around hold the flaming card high to gather everyone's attention. Then with a ceremonial flick of a wrist, he sends the burning document sailing through the air to land on the stars spangled banner which immediately bursts into flames.

The air gets filled with the drones of deuce-and-a-half National Guard trucks roll onto the scene. Screeching brakes pull the trucks to a halt, and off the back jump Guardsmen totting M-14 rifles.

Now the knuckle cracking, billy club wielding policemen arrive. They are dressed in regulation blue uniforms with handcuffs attached to their belts, but also wear white helmets, goggles, and black leather gloves. On their shoulder is the familiar patch of the Chicago Police Department.

Plate 21   Anti-war rally *(Illustration by John tylk)*

"That's right," Brown suddenly remembers the time frame, "it's the 1968 Chicago Democratic National Convention."

The ranks of authority become a mosaic of solid colors encircling psychedelic ones. Police move shoulder to shoulder and begin to menacingly slap night sticks against their palms. They appear prime for a fight and anything could set them off. The Nation Guardsmen, who stay in tight formation, move ever closer to the inevitable bloody confrontation.

After all, the job of those in authority is to keep order and stay in control "by any means deemed necessary." On the other hand the protesters view their *job* as, as much as possible, being out of control and disorderly.

Also, the protesters fully understand that to achieve their heady goal, they must provoke a brutal confrontation with a possible loss of life. In this way, they believe, they can uncover once and for all the true nature of the powers-to-be.

"Kill the pigs. Kill the pigs," shouts an activist through his battery-operated bullhorn. Another activist shimmies up a flag pole and begins to strip off the American flag. Several policemen shove their way through the belligerent crowd to arrest the man as he slides back down the flag pole with flag in hand. The act serves to rile the crowd bringing it ever closer to the impeding clash. A few bottles fly from the protesters and shatter on the concrete, its glass fragments splattering the police. The shoving and shouting of obscenities begins to escalate.

"Remain calm," an activist shouts through a bullhorn as he hurries through the crowd. "That's what they want. They want us to get upset so we'll start something. But don't. Please, remain calm. Everyone, remain calm."

Protesters, some with football helmets and shoulder pads, immediately form a line between them, the police and national guard.

Appearing like the Gestapo of Germany during the Second World War, six bloodthirsty policemen push through the line and start for a man they seem to think is an instigator. Angry words pass between them. Night stick flash and the police begin to beat him into submission. The hippy's legs buckle and he drops to the ground nearly unconscious. Other protesters converged onto the scene trying to pull off the frenzied policemen.

"If blood is going to flow. It will flow all over this city," another peace-activist threatens through a bullhorn.

There are several loud "booms" that Brown knows to be from mortars firing tear gas canisters. Mushrooms of white gas begin to billow throughout the area. Screams of alarm ring as everyone begins to run for their lives. The Chicago police and Guardsmen pull on their Martian looking gas masks and converge on the scene.

The crowd rocks to the chant *"Kill the pigs! Kill the pigs!"* A hippy runs over and flings the little pig at a policeman. The officer fends off the pig that hits the ground hard, then squeals as it scurries away through the melee of trampling feet.

Sunlight glints off bottles sailing through the air. The scene explodes into a kaleidoscope of violence. Through a hail of rocks, bricks, bottles, and human feces the uniforms storm the flower children. They smack the activists with rifle butts, shoving and beating them to the ground with night sticks, shields and fists.

Activists, unlucky enough to trip and fall, would sometimes get dragged by one policeman while another would club him into submission. The police tag-teams would then jog to grab another unfortunate protester.

Some scatter but others stay together and scurry up a small rise toward the base of a bronzed general on horseback, "Black Jack" John Logan, a hero of the Civil War.

"Medic! Medic!" comes screams no different than those on the battlefields. Courteously, everyone pauses and silence envelopes the area. Two activists with white arm bands rush onto the scene and scoop up a dazed protester and hurry away.

After the wounded are cleared, the National Guardsmen begin to fire round after round of tear gas from their M-79 grenade launchers. The protesters fall to the ground and their screams and pleads for mercy fill the air.

Standing in bewilderment, Brown watches as the swirling gas eats away the sounds and images.

The menacing bank of grey-laced fog continues to roll over the scene, swallowing ever more names on The Wall.

Plate 22   Democratic convention *(Illustration by John Tylk)*

General Morgan

Balking, he unconsciously places an index finger against his forehead. At that same moment, he has an unmistakable feeling that something or someone is about to launch a personal attack. He spins with arms raised to defend himself and, with a sigh of relief, realizes it is only his elongated shadow.

"Thank God. Silly."

Then, to his astonishment, the shadow begins to lift itself off the grass—first a hand, then the head, the other hand—one part at a time, until it literally stands at full height. Within the confines of a gunpowder gray fog, he now stands face to face with a single dimensional opaque shadow.

Frozen in disbelief, he watches as the amorphous blows itself into a complete three-dimensional body. The figure then paints itself into a crusty Confederate cavalry commander from the American Civil War. The officer wears a grey campaign hat with a red feather stuck behind the right pinned up brim. Around his trim Kentucky gentleman's beard is leather-brown skin that bears the fine lines of a thousand wind-whipped, sun-beaten days. The general's grey frock coat and trouser, stained and frayed, drape the powerful torso and broad-shoulders of the six-foot frame.

Weathered buckskin cavalry gauntlets and an ivory stock engraved Colt Model 1860 Army revolver are tucked behind the maroon sash and officer's sword belt fastened with a CSA plate. The belt has attached to it another revolver in a flap holster, ammo pouch, and an officer's cavalry saber. His right-hand fingers curl around a Spencer rim fire repeater rifle, its short barrel resting against the worn-down heel of knee-high tan leather cavalry boots, silver spurs trailing behind.

The officer has an easy smile, yet the depth of his eyes belie a will of steel—he would surely be a soldier to reckon with on the field of mortal combat. The wily, sage image speaks in a rusty southern drawl, "Hi there, Gunfighter."

"We meet again," Brown said sourly. "My Third-eye, the Confederate general. That lecturing/preaching know-it-all second brain."

During the past weeks, Brown was having a series of dreams, but until *this* moment had disregarded their connection or implications. Now he begins to piece them together. In one he remembers walking along a small town's main street where he window shops at an antique mall. Inside, he goes over to a glass display case to peer at a tray of rings.

"May I help you?" a woman asks in a Kentuckian drawl.

"Yeah, sure can," Brown said without raising his head, "That ring right there," he points and nods to the dark-haired woman.

The sales clerk pulls out a wooden divider tray with an assortment of old antique jewelry. Brown picks out a gold service ring embossed with the American Eagle which has a diamond set into its breast. He slips it over his right-hand ring finger. "It fits." He raises his hand to show the clerk. "Ain't that something. Must be an omen."

"Your lucky day."

"I guess." Holding it up to the light, he admires the antique ring.

"Would you like it?"

"Why not."

On a subsequent night, the dreaming brought him to the front of an old brown stone courthouse. Erected on the front lawn was a bronze equestrian statue of a Civil War commander. Two inscriptions on either side of the granite pedestal read:

ERECTED BY THE KENTUCKY DIVISION UNITED DAUGHTERS OF THE CONFEDERACY

GENERAL JOHN HUNT MORGAN ON HIS FAMOUS HORSE BLACK BESS

He snatches a damp postcard off the moist grass. On the backside it read:

Portrait of John Hunt Morgan, Kentucky's most famous Civil War general, leader of the renowned "Morgan's Raiders."
To Southerners, he was the dashing "Thunderbolt of the Confederacy." To Northerners, he was the terrorizing "King of the Horse Thieves."

Yet another dream brought him to a park under a sunny blue sky. Accompanied by a beautiful woman, they sit on the lawn sharing a Vietnam War era camouflage poncho liner. Brown sees himself reading from a loose leaf manuscript. The woman lays contentedly on her back with knees pulled up to listen while contemplating the celestial bliss. At the sound of clomping hooves and jingling harnesses, they turn to see circling the park a white carriage. Wearing matching white top hat and tuxedo, the driver sits erect while masterfully guiding the two white stallions. Seated in the leather coach seats are loving newlyweds who wave merrily to cheering family and well-wishers.

Still, another dream brings him to an iron gate that leads to a pre-Civil War era three-story house. Alone this time, he walks up the steps and opens the massive front door with side panels of leaded glass depicting pineapples, the traditional welcome fruit. Inside, he finds a guest book. In it he writes boldly:

I have returned

The hallway leads under the platform of a spiral staircase and to a panel door that opens onto a courtyard blanketed in white haze. Moving into the thick atmosphere, he follows a brick walkway along a hedge row through a droplet-covered garden, and there *it* hovered just above the lawn. He knows it to be the exact same doorway that now floats above The Wall.

The stairway to the portal was shrouded by flourishing stems of hemp. Cautiously, he ascends the stone stairs to the arched doorway and sweeps back the plant's yellow green leaves to expose letters carved on a plaque that read:

> **When ready the
> teacher will appear**

Curiously, he reaches for the tarnished green doorknob but finds it will not turn. Rusted? Jammed? Locked? The eagle antique ring, tingles on his finger.

He looks to find the diamond releasing an intense blue light, and notices the impression in the doorknob matches that of the ring. Inserting the diamond and body of the eagle into the impression, both portal and ring take on an eerie green glow.

Plate 23   Front door *(Illustration by Curt Chiarelli)*

That ended the sequence of dreams.

Since childhood and perhaps even before, the voice of both ego and General Morgan had come to Brown. But it wasn't until joining the U.S. Army and stepping foot in Vietnam that both came to vivid life. Came into *being*. The confederate general showed up and graciously introduced himself as General John Hunt Morgan shortly after Brown's arrival in Vietnam. The ego was also in the war, but mainly as a personality trait. They had sometimes laughingly called the ego Beer Muscles, but more often Mustang. To Brown, Mustang stood for a turbo-charged muscle car where a gear shift and a push on the gas pedal could send him into a tailspin. To General Morgan, Mustang stood for a wild horse who, at a the drop of a hat, would rear-up and go charging blindly into harms way or possible death.

Brown begrudgingly learned to appreciate his third eye/second brain who served as mentor, guide, and tutor. And after all these years, the general still appears the same, hasn't aged a day. Brown, who once considered the general an old hard-case, realizes that now he, too, looks equally old and hard-case.

"So it shouldn't be of any surprise that earlier *that* was you inside my head. Now should it?"

"Nope. Not really, Gunfighter," General Morgan said gently while producing a pocketknife to trim a large cigar. "And from the tone of your voice, I'd say you're *mighty* glad to see me."

"Maybe—maybe not," Brown said a bit perplexed. "It's just that I don't buy all that crap about evil spirits coming around. Bogey-man! The sky is falling! A*ahhh!* Run for it!" he mocks. "Let's all go jump around scared and shit.

"I've had my share of flashbacks, maybe not so rampant and vivid but I've had 'em. So maybe this is just caused by somethin' I ate. Maybe the medication is wearing off. Yeah, that could be it. Anyway, I'm gonna stub my toe, trip or whatever and wake up. So . . . well . . . it'll all be over. Like I said, I ain't takin' this hook-line-and-sinker. Watch this."

Plate 24   Morgan confronts Brown *(Illustration by John Tylk)*

Brown slaps himself half-heartedly thinking that the general would fade away. Re-opening his eyes, he sees the general is still there in glorious living color.

"Okay, okay," Brown said, raising his arms in resignation. "You win. I'll admit, I'm seeing and hearing some pretty *weird* stuff. Take for instance right now. I'm actually having a conversation with my own shadow." Brown chuckles. "You know what you are?"

General Morgan raises his left eyebrow as he strikes a match and begins puffing on the cigar.

"I'll tell ya. Like years before, you're a manifestation of my mind. You're my childhood teddy bear. Angel on my shoulder. A kind of security blanket. A little GI Joe toy soldier. The Lone Ranger, cap pistol and BB Gun. But I thought I'd matured. Gotten over this."

Unaffected by the slight, the Confederate general draws on his cigar with its pungent aroma filling the air.

"Did I say you could smoke?" Brown said fanning the air.

Morgan puffs a cloud of smoke in Brown's direction.

"Cou*gh.* "

Shifting his stonewall-like stance, he swings his shrewd gaze to bear on The Wall. "Tell me, Gunfighter," General Morgan said in a cool demeanor. "I'm curious. Why did you come back?"

"Me? Look who's talkin'," Brown sneers. The general's serious expression never changes. "Come back?" his voice falters only slightly but enough to show a break in the facade. "Now why would I go and do a stupid thing like that?"

With the cigar clenched firmly between molars, Morgan calmly removes his feathered cavalry hat. He pulls out a blue bandanna from his back pocket to wipe sweat off his forehead. It is the way he gazes into the distance that catches Brown's attention. It is a patient, serene, eternal kind of gaze that seems capable of seeing and understanding things others will easily gloss over. Like the gaze of a seer from ancient times who could anticipate Autumn even before the first leaf would change color or fall to the ground.

Brown also senses that General Morgan has taken off that same worn cavalry hat a thousand times before to wipe sweat with a bandanna in that exact same manner. And while patiently drying his forehead, he gazes forlornly over a bloody battlefield, over the ragtag cavalry and infantrymen, the prisoners, the wounded, the dead and dying. That the caring commander would dismount and kneel to tend the wounded or hear the last request of a dying soldier. General Morgan replaces his dusty salt-stained hat then spits on his fingers and begins to lubricate the handlebars of this large mustache.

"You most definitely are not the sheriff in these here parts, Gunfighter," he said calmly. "And you just don't seem to get it–do you? I ask the questions," General Morgan said turning stern. "You supply the answers." He puffs on the cigar. "Shall we start? First question. Why did you open the door?"

"I didn't."

"Answer me, damn-it!"

"It just happened!" Brown shouts back. "That's all. You know things do happen. And it was in a dream for chrissakes," Brown said defensively. "I mean how do you control a dream? Huh?"

Morgan blows more cigar smoke into his face.

"Quit blowing smoke into my face!" Brown yells, waving away the cloud.

A stern look crosses Morgan's face.

"It makes me choke."

"Sorry."

"Should be."

"You were saying?"

"Okay," Brown said resigned. "I put the ring into the doorknob because I thought it was one of those science fiction kinda dreams. Didn't think it'd do any harm. So, you gonna put me over a knee and spank me?" Brown felt bitter being relegated the role of the disobedient child.

"The truth?" Brown said trying to take the offensive.

"That would be nice."

"It has to do with being fed up with gossip and rumors that blame, demean, and attack the very fabric of my soul. And if I don't find a way to get off this bloody merry-go-round of fun, I'm gonna go stark raving *mad*," he said to punctuate the last word. "Satisfied, big man?"

"You carry baggage like an overloaded pack mule," General Morgan said slowly and disdainfully. He raises his eyebrows, an expression that accentuates his crow's feet and hollows out his cheeks. "So, lemme get this straight. You're tired of hidin' behind a tree ready to bushwhack anyone who gets too near. It's your way or the highway. Everyone else is full of horse shit—but not you. Oh, of course not the God Almighty, Fred Leo Brown, who has gone through so much unfairness, prejudice and pain in his lifetime."

Brown feels his face grow red with shame.

"You want your fire and passion back?" General Morgan said his voice rising. "Huh?"

Brown lowers his head.

"Then tighten the cinch on your saddle, keep a taut rein on Mustang, and stick to the dirt road. That's *if* you have the backbone to ride this one out." General Morgan waits for a challenge. Avoiding his stare, Brown fidgets with his water canteen.

"Judging by your dress," General Morgan continues, "I'd say you ain't headed for no fancy ballroom dance."

"I'm not trying to prove anything," he barks, looking down at his fragmentation jacket, captured enemy pistol belt with canteen and combat boots. "I just wore them because it felt right. You don't have to go readin' things into it."

"None the less, it's appropriate because there's a mighty big storm brewing and it's headed your way, Gunfighter," General Morgan said his voice ringing with concern.

"Is that a weather forecast or another high-minded concept?" he said still belligerent. "I ain't stupid. Ultimately, what it comes down to is this: I gotta figure out this whole *war* thing for myself.

By myself. Either that or. . . ." Brown didn't finish the sentence. He didn't want to admit that for years he has felt as if he was crumbling piecemeal from the inside. That there were nights when he'd struggle up, escaping from sleep, a scream lodged in his throat and then spend the rest of the night afraid to close his eyes. Afraid he might end up back in *that* dream though often times didn't really remember much about it. So, never really sure what he'd just escaped.

Is not about to say out loud that there where nights when he would dream about inching his way along a triple canopy jungle mountain trail, tramps through a flooded rice field with mud up to his knees, wading through snake infested rivers or walking in a daze across sun bleached terrain. And all the while he marched, something or someone was either in hot pursuit or patiently waiting in ambush.

That in his dreams, he would collapse from exhaustion only to face off with a king cobra. The snake would rise and challenge him, its split tongue making a sizzling noise while deadly venom dribbles from its fangs. He would holler, "I'm not afraid. Damn you. I am not afraid of you." Then he'd awake to find himself still in bed swinging his fists through the air.

That far too often he'd rip off the sheets and bolt upright in bed. Only to sit there wide eyed, drenched in sweat, with the bedroom clock reading 1 A.M.. And other times, he'd wake to find himself calmly looking out the bedroom window. As though back on guard duty in Vietnam, his ears would be cocked while he scans the backyard field of fire.

How frightened he felt thinking, he might *really* be cracking up. Might really be going "mad as a hatter?" That he'd have to admit that most of his war time buddies were dead. If not, they were sick from some unknown disease, diagnoses with a variety of cancers, diabetes, MS, Agent Orange or the likes, had a stroke or heart attack. That daily life ate at him like muriatic acid. That shaving was a dreaded chore because he would have to look at the reflection of an ashen haggard face with rotting teeth and lopsided smile. That the bathroom medicine cabinet brimmed with bottles

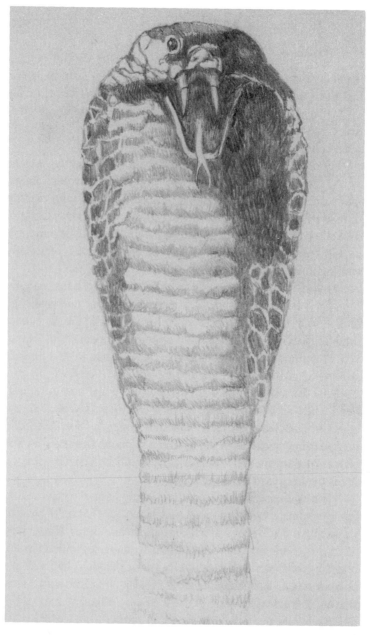

Plate 25   King cobra (Illustration by John Tylk)

and tablets of stomach remedies, cold medicines, and muscle relaxants.

"How many more Tours of Duty in Vietnam do I have to go through before it's over? Huh!?" he shouts crazed. "Answer me that."

"Don't look at me. You're the one who slammed the door!" General Morgan fires back. "And it was your choice, your choice alone, to tie me up so you could go tearing mindlessly across life on Mustang."

"Did you say *choice*?" Brown said with anger building. "You mean promises don't you? A promise of a hero's welcome home. A promise that my father would pat me on the back and say 'job well done, son,'" Brown said in a mock fatherly voice. "A promise that our fellow countryman wouldn't leave us behind as POWs or written off as MIAs. That our supreme sacrifice would mean something. Anything. That our country would stand by us no matter what and make sure we got a fair shake, a good job, an education, and a shot at the American dream. Lots of promises that weren't kept, don't you think?" He seethes.

"Little dramatic, don't you think?"

"Fuck you!" he swears with anger cresting. "You know what those heroic vets from the *good* wars did? They turned their backs on us. That's what they did. They said that Vietnam wasn't really a war at all because it was never declared. That in the same time period more people died on the nation's highways than in Vietnam." The words caused so much pain and anguish that Brown needed to take a few deep breaths before continuing.

"That they keep telling us that almost as many died at the Battle of Gettysburg than in the entire Vietnam War. Can you believe that? They will come up with anything that will diminish our sacrifice," Brown said tormented. "And you know what else? They said that we didn't have the heart—the guts. Not like they did. No guts no glory. That's what the old World War Two and Korean War farts say.

"Everything was a lie right from the beginning. They sent us there with our hands tied behind our back. We didn't have a prayer in the world of winning."

"At ease, Gunfighter! Release the hammer and holster that Colt. You have no beef with me," General Morgan said admonishing him. "I was the one who stood by you. Who carried you when you couldn't walk. Who taught you how to take the misery, the pain? Who showed you how to beat the fear? Control the anger. But something went wrong. Something . . . happened."

The anxiety of the moment engorges his eyes and shortens his breath. Brown feels the onset of an excruciating headache.

"You've turned your anger in on yourself. You've become your own nemesis," General Morgan said compassion returning. "That's what I've been trying to explain. First thing Mustang did was numb your butt. Next, he ran you so hard it scrambled up your brains, and finally he tried to kick you out of the saddle."

General Morgan takes a measured puff on his cigar. "That wild horse couldn't fool *me* though, or take *my* memory," he said proudly. "And from what I recall, you were very, very lucky during the war. One inch this way, one second that way. You understand me?"

"Yeah, I understand," Brown said still trying to give the good fight. "I understand that if an infantryman wasn't killed by an enemy bullet or shrapnel from a rocket, booby trap, or grenade there were the other ways. Like killer viruses, diseases with no names, and jungle sores that would rot you skin and boil your blood. There were poisonous snakes by the thousands. Spiders, leaches, scorpions, malaria borne mosquitoes, fire ants and charging water buffalo. There were river drownings, heat exhaustion, vehicle accidents. There was malaria, food poisoning, drugs, friendly fire, Dear John letters, PTSD and not the least Agent Orange. And Agent Orange which kills you one molecule at a time.

"No, from where I stand none of us *really* made it back. We should have all died over there in the rice patties and jungles. Should never have made it out of the valleys or off the Fire-bases. It would have made things a lot easier for everyone back here in the real World. Wouldn't it?"

"That's right, Gunfighter. K*eeee*-p it comin'. The self pity, self destruction, anger and denial. Maybe your wish will come true," General Morgan scoffs. "And where did you get the cockeyed idea it would end up like some Grimms Fairy Tale?"

"Well it does sometimes, doesn't it?" He never believed it would be a panacea but always hoped for the best.

"It's check-in time," General Morgan explains. "Time to take roll call, Gunfighter! Time to square your shoulders and start thinking about the unthinkable."

"I ain't no bloody hero," Brown said his defiance waning. "The heroes are already dead." He spins to throw an arm and pointed finger in the direction of The Wall.

Battle Of Cynthiana

CIVIL WAR BATTLE OF CYNTHIANA, CYNTHIANA KENTUCKY
—JUNE 12, 1864

General Morgan tilts his head causing the shadow of the hat brim to recede letting sunlight bath his face. His retinas begin to change from grey-blue to a marbleize black encircled by lines of yellow and blue. When Brown sees a shimmering silver five-pointed star appear in the center of Morgan's retinas, he feels himself levitating. Then, as though loaded into the breech of a cannon and fired, *"Ca-blamm!"* he spins faster and faster till he swoons with dizziness.

Landing firmly on both feet like a cat, it takes a few more seconds for the dizziness to abate. Regaining his senses, he looks around at an area that seems as foreboding as a cemetery at the bewitching hour. Not waiting for his eyes to fully adjust to the darkness, he takes a guarded step and hears the crunching sound

Plate 26   Brown spinning *(illustration by John Tylk)*

of dry leaves. A hole in the dark clouds lets a beam of moonlight pass through. In the dim light he finds himself standing on a hilltop covered with early morning fog that has boiled up from the lowlands.

"I'll be damned," he softly mutters, "it is a cemetery." The smaller markers were submerged under the thick atmosphere, but the taller granite monuments and statues stood above looking like zombies. Shivers run through his body as the chill of an early morning breeze begin to move the heavy atmosphere.

Splashing mist some thirty-yards away catches his attention. A fellow soldier, Okie, rises from the concealing fog to slide noiselessly alongside a tree. His right hand appears to be clenching a Ka-Bar Marine survival knife. Patiently, he waits for the enemy soldier to get closer. When the unsuspecting enemy passes, Okie lunges, using the old tried and true method of a choke hold and a knife through the back.

The soldier viciously swings his rifle around trying to knock away the intruder. It only proves to be an exercise in futility as the juice of life begins pouring from the gashing wound. With a vengeance, Okie continues to twist the knife blade ripping out organ after vital organ from inside the chest cavity.

The weakened soldier drops his weapon and finally stops struggling. Okie let's the dying man slide off the knife to crumble on the ground like a rag doll. It took hardly two minutes to finish off the enemy soldier.

"Look out!" Brown shouts when he catches the glimpse of a rifle barrel jutting from behind another tree.

Okie leaps just as the enemy rifle discharges. A bullet catches him in mid step, his body reverberates from the impact. The sound of the blast echoes through the valley sending birds fluting from their roosts.

Okie coughs, grasps his side and cringes. The Ka-Bar drops from his grasp as he turns with the pallor of death stamped on his face. Doubling over, he falls nearly on top of the dying enemy soldier.

Brown swings his rifle up and fires. The enemy spins from

the bullet's impact and disappears beneath the fog like a man splashing backwards into water. Brown cocks his rifle and waits for any more signs of movement.

"What?" he said startled. You don't cock an M-16 rifle. He stares at a Civil War era Spencer rim fire repeater rifle held so dextrously in his right hand. Then down to his knee-high cavalry boots, to his blue woolen pants and jacket. Checking the pistol belt, he finds the US belt plate, the saber handle, ammunition pouch, and Army Colt revolver.

Somehow, someway, and for some reason he is experiencing a Past-Life Regression. His thoughts and feelings had always been anchored around the time of the Civil War but he had never been sure.

As a Union Civil War soldier, he continues to scan the area for more danger, not so concerned about dying as with wanting to live longer in this time warp. There were some crucial questions he wanted answered.

"We'll secure the area, captain," a familiar voice said. A Japanese and a black man, both dressed as Union soldiers, move past.

"Yamane? Stewart?"

"Captain?" Stewart, the black soldier, said turning. Too stunned, Brown's unable to respond. "Were gonna keep movin', sir."

"Right." He nods. His hand touches his wide brim hat where he feels the officer's rope and double bars. "A captain?" That's when he decides it would be best to stop questioning and let things run their course.

With the urgency of the moment returning, he hurries over to Okie's side. Rolling him, he stares at the bearded face, the sunken eyes and the gashing in his chest caused by a 57 caliber minie-ball. There are no outward signs of life. No one could survive a hit like that. From Okie's jacket pocket, he pulls out a letter addressed to his wife, Annie.

"I'll make sure it get delivered personally, my old friend." Captain Brown slides the envelope into his pocket. The he retrieves the Colt revolver from Okie's waist band and shoves it under his own.

Glancing down, he notices a puddle forming around his boots fed by two streams of steaming blood. One stream flows from Okie's body, the other from the Confederate picket.

The mixing of the blood seems so poetic. "And how old are you Johnny Reb?" he addresses the mortally wounded enemy soldier who groans. "Both of you ain't nothin' but kids who learned how to fight and died like men."

Rising, he notices both soldiers have expressions that display an outward glimmer of calm. And why not. Maybe they are going to a better place. There will be no more force marches or numbing horse rides. No more winter nights where even a horse might freeze to death. No more fatigue, the kind no person could understand unless they've experienced it. No more thirst and hunger. No more fever, sickness and diseases. And most of all, no more heartaches.

"Both of you," he said swooning with emotion, "should've been home with your hunting dogs running across a prairie flushing out rabbits and birds. Out with a cane pole fishin' for bass or trout in some mountain creek. Or huntin' pheasants and deer for supper. But not this," he said slowly shaking his head, tired of three continuous years of war. "Not lying here in shredded uniforms your blood soaking into the ground. Not this."

Taking his hat off, he places it over his heart. "Dear Lord, please take care of them. They were just doing their patriotic duty. Born into heaven on Lord's day of June 12, 1864. Ahhmen."

Hastening to catch his command, he recalls bits and pieces about last night. Under a campfire light, the battalion commander uses a branch to draw a crude battle map in the dirt.

"Captain," the commander addresses Brown after the other officers are briefed, "I want you to take six of your best scouts up to Battlefield Grove Cemetery." He circles the location on the dirt map. "From there, eliminate all the pickets moving around to the east. Be in town no later than day-break."

"Yes, sir." Captain Brown had already begun to select his scouts. Among them would be his bravest and most disciplined: Yamane, a Japanese soldier, and Stewart, a former slave.

While puffing on the cigar, the commander stares one at a time into the faces of his officers. "Hopefully our movement will go undetected. With the element of surprise on our side," his voice rises, "the signal for the attack will be the cannonade. The bombardment will start promptly at first light." He relaxes on a log. "At that time, I want the forward scouts," he gestures to Brown, "to move through town and take-out those pesky bushwhackers and stay-behinds. Any questions?"

With wrinkled foreheads, scrunched lips, and fingers running absently through mustaches and beards, the officers talk among themselves as they continue to go over the battle plans.

The commander motions to an aide who produces a jug of dandelion whiskey. "Gentlemen, I dare say tomorrow we shall see The Elephant." He motions for the aide to fill everyone's tin cup. That completed, he stands and raises his cup. "I propose a toast to our upcoming victory."

In the early morning hours, Brown and his scouts had tethered their horses just short of Battlefield Grove Cemetery and covered the rest of the way on foot. Reaching the cemetery, they had a panoramic view of the valley overlooking the Licking River and the sleepy town of Cynthiana, Kentucky. Soon the legendary John Hunt Morgan and the Rebel Raiders would be theirs.

Captain Brown recalls reading a Northern newspaper about the wily commander. The writer had depicted the Raiders as a bunch of murders, robbers, horse thieves, and scoundrels whose comet-like rides were worthless to the overall cause of the Confederacy.

After reading the article, Captain Brown recalls thinking, "And what would a newspaper reporter from New York City really know about soldiering anyway? Respectable types who would prove to be mentally unfit for the responsibilities of the military and worthless in the rigors necessary to survive in battle?"

The thirty-eight-year-old widower had caught the imagination of the South with his spectacular wedding in December of 1863 to the twenty-one-year-old Mattie Ready. At that moment in time General Morgan was the unequivocal toast of all the southern bells and embodied the very soul of southern chivalry.

Brown ears' perk at the sound of rustling. The lead scouts have apparently stabbed to death another unsuspecting picket. On seeing the "all clear" sign, they continue toward the outskirts of town.

"Tex," Captain Brown whispers, "take two men and move to right. Yamane, Stewart, you're with me. We'll flank left."

"Got it, Captain," Tex replies and the others disappear through the wet, fog-covered brush.

From the northwest ridge overlooking the unsuspecting town, Captain Brown begins to hear the faint sounds of wheels squeaking and horses struggling under the weight of the siege guns, caissons, and other field equipment.

Reaching the outskirts of town, they creep along a rutted dirt road till they reach a main street. From the seclusion of an alleyway, Brown guardedly looks down the cobble stone street lined with single or two story buildings most of which serve the dual purpose of business and home. Some were made of wood, others brick, but all narrow. Nailed onto an overhang support were two painted wooden street signs which read:

The signs of trade such as a boot carved out of wood for the cobbler, a wagon wheel for the blacksmith and wheelwright, a burlap flour bag, shovel/pick affixed to wooden planks for the provisions store were haphazardly displayed with chain and iron hangers above the establishment.

The street is deserted except for a dray, drawn by two horses, that enters from a side street, crosses hastily and disappears. Its muted rattle and bangs seeming portentous.

Though near dawn, there is still no candle glow from inside the buildings. But far off to the southwest of town black smoke from several chimneys flows lazily into the crisp morning air.

In the time remaining, the scouts busy themselves with making last minute checks of their weapons, ammunition and gear. When satisfied, they relax and begin munching on hard tack, beef jerky, and some biscuits and jam saved from the last evening meal.

Soon the eastern sky starts to turn a crimson red as a farm rooster crows and a dog barks in the morning. Then a thunder-like clap erupts as the cannons on the ridge send a spotter volley of death rushing toward town. The cannon balls smash into walls and explode on the streets sending shrapnel raining through town.

The citizenry and Rebel Raiders awake to the realization they are surrounded by a fighting force of Union soldiers. During a pause to reload and adjust the cannons, church bells begin to toll. People hurry to shutter their doors and windows. Everyone from the commanders on down to the mothers and children must have said a brief prayer as the lanyards are pulled once more sending yet another volley thundering through the yellow morning sky.

Hearing shouts, rattling chains and racing horses, Captain Brown again peers into the street. A buckboard drawn by a team of horses careens around the corner. The teamster stands as he furiously whips the horses moving at full gallop. In the back are three Confederate soldiers holding on tightly. Hearing the whistle of an incoming cannon balls, Brown and his scouts hunch against the side of the building.

Three artillery rounds explode in quick succession. Mortar, brick, splinters of wood, and glass are hurled throughout the area smacking, hitting and slicing everything around. Choking dust billows through the air as the entire brick facade of a building collapses into the streets.

Through the settling dust, Brown surveys a grim street scene. The buckboard had taken a near hit, the blast having rolled it over. One horse lay dead with gashing wounds in its chest and neck. Though still alive, the other war horse is severely wounded, its left hoof almost completely severed. Losing strength, it drops to its knees. Gallantly it tries to regain its footing but fails. It settles back down then slowly drops its head.

Next to the wooden sidewalk rests the severed head of the teamster, the rest of his body lay under the wagon. One of the three soldiers lay dead, half buried under a collapsed awning. The other two must have been thrown clear because they appeared only bruised as they struggled down the street.

"Hats off. Put on your head rags." A few seconds later Captain Brown commands, "Alright, let's go." They move swiftly but guardedly into a street still filled with smoke, debris, blood and the dead. The increased rifle fire is a sure indicator of the advancing infantry. The bombardment continues but has moved to the roads leading to the bridge over the Licking River. Down the street they see Confederates moving helter skelter in their fluttering rags, some on horse back, some on foot.

Encountering the first bushwhacker, they jump for cover in doorways. To flush out the sharpshooter, Captain Brown scurries over to the next building. A bullet rakes the door frame just as he makes it to safety. He searches the roof tops, window openings, and doorways for the sharpshooter.

Taking into account the angle of the trajectory, he decided it came from a roof top three buildings down. He motions to the scouts the suspected location, then makes a dash for another doorway with a bullet again narrowly missing. But this time he catches sight of a puff of smoke. He signals the bushwhacker's position.

Stewart shoves open a shrapnel-ridden door and bolts upstairs to the roof top. As a distraction, Captain Brown fires at the sharpshooter while dashing for yet another doorway. Shots ring out and a moment later Stewart waves the "all clear."

A door opposite Captain Brown gets flung open and there stands a disheveled, battle worn Confederate officer. In his hands he holds a Spencer repeater rifle and an officer's cavalry hat with

Plate 27   **Morgan and Brown** *(illustration by John Tylk)*

a red feather tucked under a pinned up brim.

A cannon ball lands in the back of the building shattering windows in the house. Unflinchingly the officer pulls on his hat.

"It's him," Captain Brown gasps. The legendary General John Hunt Morgan stands within easy pistol range.

Spotting movement, the marauder spins to see Captain Brown with Colt drawn. Brown stares breathlessly, his mind screaming, "kill or be killed!" But he can't pull the trigger.

Mirrored in General Morgan's ashen, ruggedly handsome face is a war torn, anguish ridden heart. Captain Brown senses the compassion that pours from those misting grayish blue eyes. For what seems like an eternity, they measure each another with the clamor of the struggle only steps away.

The trance breaks when another marauder gallops over with General Morgan's Kentucky mount in tow. A mare, who's short back appeared immensely powerful, is the most magnificent beast-of-war Brown had ever seen. The thoughbred has a sculptured face with wide eyes that taper down to a dainty muzzle. The Mare with her bristling jet black hair could be none other than Black Bess. She pulls nervously against the reins, her nostrils flaring, her white teeth covered in froth. Morgan grabs the reins, and in a single flowing movement, jams his foot into the left stirrup and swings effortlessly into the saddle.

A cannon ball whistles overhead then smashes through the second story wall of house General Morgan has just left. The ensuing explosion sends Black Bess rearing to show the might of her hind quarter and the explosive speed it represents, while her 185-pound master appears no heavier than a feather. While prancing, Morgan strokes her reassuringly along her superbly proportioned neck. He spins her around, salutes Captain Brown, and charges down the street.

Screams come from inside the house. Captain Brown dashes across the street and through the entrance. Inside a woman comes stumbling down the staircase dressed in a off-white calico night gown with a baby cradled in her arms.

"I don't know what got into us," she said through tears when she reaches the landing.

"Ma'am?" Captain Brown said in confusion.

"Why, we lost all sense as soon as the cannons started firing. I plum forgot about our dear child and that last artillery round caught the crib afire." She turns her attention to the child. "I'm so sorry little pumpkin," she said smooching the baby.

"Should have listened to my husband before I came down from Chicago to visit my sister, Louise. Even though Kentucky is a neutral state, he said something might happen."

"*Couuu-gh!*" came the sound of a man at the top of the stairs.

"Need any help, sir?" Captain Brown calls up the stairs.

"No. Fire is out," he said. "Darlin', you okay?"

"I'm fine, Charles."

"Hurry to the cellar. I'll be right there."

"The battle is moving to the edge of town, sir," Captain Brown said as the husband descends the steps. "Just stay inside until you hear the church bells ring the 'all's clear.'"

"Mighty kind of you, Captain."

Surveying the room, he notices a gold pocket watch lying next to a half empty glass of water on a decoratively carved walnut table. "Your watch?"

"No, I don't believe so. Nor the Smizer's either. Must belong to that Confederate officer who stayed the night."

Taking the watch, Brown turns it around to read the inscription:

To my
beloved
– Mattie

"Mattie?" He looks over to the man. "Why does that name sound so familiar?" He closes the time piece. "Of course, his wife."

"Whose wife, Captain?"

"General Morgan's, sir. If there's no objection, I'd like to take this watch with me." Without waiting for a reply, he places the watch inside a jacket pocket. "By any chance, did you or your wife talk with the general?"

"Afraid not, Captain. Stagecoach came in late and the ride was very hard on my wife and child. And I mean this as no offense, but with baby Sara, we didn't want to pick up any disease from those filthy soldiers."

Making his way through the blood marked streets, passed dead horses and men, and the wounded, Captain Brown arrives in view of the covered bridge that crosses the Licking River. There he spots the Confederated standards as they drop. A wisp of a boy quickly retrieves the banner from a fallen comrade and holds it gallantly as the battle continues to swirl around him. Pockets of resistance are quietly routed as the Rebels run low on ammunition. The covered bridge quickly becomes clogged with retreating soldiers.

General Morgan gallops past calming his cavalrymen. A Union soldier rushes over, kneels and is about to fire at the commander when Captain Brown lunges. . . .

General Morgan sits honing his pocket knife on the leather sole of his boot. A cavalry boot softened to a distinct familiarity of bunions, joint movement and riding style. Draped loosely over his shoulders is the sun bleached wool cavalry jacket. Though old, patches and frayed, the jacket is still quite useable. With that rather large bone handle pocket knife, he probably cuts his meat, prepares a cud of tobacco, and kept his fingernails in genteel repair, but at the moment it mainly served as a companion to his evening meditations. Feeling Brown's stare, he closes the knife.

"That took a special kind of courage," General Morgan said

pulling on a gold chain that produces the gold pocket watch. He pushes the stem and the lid flips open. A sweetness spreads across his face as he gazes lovingly at the inscription.

"After our gala Christmas wedding in '63 things started unraveling," General Morgan began. "Went on a raid into Ohio and got captured." His eyes glowed with pain. "Spend six months as a POW. Then I escaped." Lips pursed, stretching neck, eyes wondering, hands gesturing, it appears he doesn't want to go on, but he does.

"Saw my beloved Mattie only . . . ," the words trail off. "I loved that women more than life itself." His mouth twitches and a hint of a tears forms along his eye. "Did I ever tell ya I had a daughter?"

"No. No you never did."

"I never really saw her, I was killed before she was. . . ."

For a moment it appears he might continue, when that passed Brown said, "I'm sorry. I really am."

With sweet nostalgia swept from his face, Morgan rises to stand lax but strong, his face with a indeterminate expression. "No more time for Brave-Heart chit chat." General Morgan pulls a cigar stub from his pocket, lights it and while puffing it back to life, asks, "Now do you recollect anything about the war elephant?"

"War elephant?" The question momentarily stumps him. Usually he would avoid delving into his memory, but now he did it like a dying man digging for water in Death Valley. And under the heat of the moment, recollections come bubbling to the surface.

"The elephant is coming," General Morgan states in a definitive voice. He puffs on the cigar and motions toward the advancing fog bank.

There is a moment of silence. "That's South China Sea fog isn't it?" The urgency begins to dawn. "And that pounding?" Brown said with emotions beginning to be overcome by anticipation.

"The elephant."

"It's making its way to the doorway, isn't it." He knows the answer.

They look across the park lawn where night shadows are beginning to gather and will soon coalesce to darkness. It wouldn't be long now before the thick cascading fog would swallow up the entire monument.

"The demons and phantoms are on the move as we speak," General Morgan explains in an even voice. "Gunfighter, you have to do *it* all over again."

"*It?*" Brown mumbles unsure of the meaning. "Oh, no. No way, man. Not that," he shrieks realizing the true meaning. In the 1970s he remembered reading about a coroner who proved that twelve Vietnamese refugees had died in their sleep because of nightmares. So he knew full well that memories could be lethal, just as deadly as a loaded gun.

"You got corn mush in that skull of yours, Gunfighter? Now you know, as well as I do, that when you get thrown from a horse ya get right back in the saddle." General Morgan's harsh expression melts into an encouraging smile. "I'll ride alongside. We'll fight through this thing together." With a strong hand on Brown's shoulder, he adds, "But this time to the finish." General Morgan turns to face The Wall, his expression thickening and his body becomes rigid.

"I gotta tell ya, though," General Morgan sighs, "Old Iron Butt has plenty of saddle sores." They smile feeling the warmth of camaraderie.

"What I'm saying is, the beast of war can sense weakness—fear. That like a deranged animal, it feeds on it."

General Morgan extends a hand and Brown greedily takes hold. Then finds himself shamelessly embracing. He pushed his face deep into the woolen grey frock coat, breathing in the heady scent of earth, wind and fire. He swallows past the lump in his throat. The penetrating warmth of General Morgan's hand on his back radiates courage throughout his body.

"Thanks," Brown said with lower lip trembling. "If there's no other way. Well. . . ."

"Let Mr. Colt do the talkin'?" General Morgan smiles. Drawing his ivory handle Army Colt revolver, he spins the chamber to check the load and percussion caps. He winks and they allowed themselves a laugh.

A chill runs through his body when he sees the fingers of the fog claw at General Morgan's cavalry boots. Then he feels the unnatural wind that blows the Confederate's tattered coat.

"We're about outta time."

"No way back?"

"Nope."

"So what's the plan?"

"Walk tall and go in shootin'."

"God willing," Brown said optimistically.

"What's to lose?"

"Lose?" Anger suddenly stings Brown. "You makin' fun of me!?" In that moment he hates the bastard, hates his cocky, sure attitude. Hates all the general stands for. Hates his seeming passion for hellish war. "Why you're nothing but a war monger. Like all the rest of 'em."

"Just when I think you understand, that ego of yours steps in. Listen up, Gunfighter," General Morgan said gruffly. "Life isn't a given. Every step, every move, every damn thing about it is a challenge." He pulls on his cavalryman's gauntlets, cocks his Spencer rifle and lets it dangle secured to a shoulder sling. He pulls out another revolver, spins the cylinder and inspects the load and percussion caps.

"Yeah, you bet," General Morgan said angrily. "I've been wanting to ride in with a full load, my powder dry for a *long* time. You know why? Because I have a commitment to live. How about you? Huh? You can't become a man until *you* confront that piece of hell stuck back inside that head of yours.

"Position of attention!" Morgan shouts. "Stomach in, chest out, shoulders back, chin in, head and eyes locked straight to the front." General Morgan's eyes narrow. "Let's *riiiiide!*

REBEL RAIDER

Give a Rebel Yell! Then dash through
the clutches of hell. Raise your
weapons of steel and make a toast.
The Torch of the South is on a
Raid. Black Bess's pounding
hooves of flint flash in the
night, blasting the genius of
the cavalry across O'Kentucky.
They shout, "Morgan, give us a
reason for this hunger! Give us
a reason to fight!" Oh, how glorious
it was in the summer of '62. And
that brilliant victory at Shiloh. Romance
flared and passion raged; Mattie Ready
fell in love with the Star of Dixie. That
commander rode farther and harder than any
other, then was cast into the Union's dank
dungeons. Escape, he did, and slithered through
wooded hollows, back to his beloved, and to
Kentucky's best. Wash your eyes with tears so you
may see, the ashes of the roses that lay at   your feet.
Battle blood now marks the land, and the horror of
it all pours into your veins! *Scream,* to show the ache
in your heart. The Thunderbolt of the South now takes his
last gasp; as glory and chivalry are being ripped to shreds,
Morgan falls to the ground, and so does the Southern race.

See the Elephant

At the sound of wicked laugher, Brown eyes roll. His heart sinks when he sees a stewing South China Sea fog pour from the rim of a witch's cauldron to slosh over The Wall and onto the park lawn. More spellbinding hysterics echo off the black tomb stones as the brew continues to spill ever more rapidly doubling back upon itself. His mind begins to float and swim around his head. Slowly at first then faster . . . fast*er* . . . *fasterrr*.

"*Remember . . . Rememberrrrrr . . . REMEMBERRRRR!*" comes a witch's shrieking chant. Spindly vein-covered arms with wart pocked hands labor against a stirring paddle, its cutting edge singing in a sweet serpentine voice. The words of an Asian song oscillate, and on each churn he hears clearly another *eerie, exotic, erotic* name that made up the war in South Vietnam.

EERIE, EXOTIC, EROTIC

DMZ
Rockpile
H u e
Phu Bai
Monkey Mt.
Citadel
Perfume River
Quang Tri
Khe Sanh
Street Without Joy
Cam Ne ◊ Lang Vei   **SOUTH**
Da Nang ◊ China Beach
        Marble Mountain   **CHINA**
Cong Thien ◊ Lo Giang
Dong Ap Bia ◊ Hill 937   **SEA**
        A Shau Valley
        Hamburger Hill
Duc Pho ◊ Quang Tin
Hoi An ◊ Tam Ky
Hill 45 ◊ Nui Lon Mounain
Que Son & Heip Duc Valley
Binh Son ◊ My Lai ◊ Chu Lai
Quang Ngai ◊ Central Lowlands
I Corps ◊ Bong Son ◊ Dak To
Hill 875 ◊ Ho Chi Minh Trail
Kon Tum ◊ La Drang . Pleiku
An Khe ◊ Da Lat ◊ Nha Trang
Qui Nhon ◊ Phuoc Binh ◊ Gia Nghia
Nha Trang ◊ Lai Khe ◊ Duc Co
Cam Ranh Bay ◊ Highway One
Ben Het ◊ Phan Rang ◊ Ben Cat
Tay Ninh ◊ Phan Thiet ◊ Ho Bo Forest
Central Highlands ◊ II Corps
Iron Triangle ◊ Cu Chi ◊ Cam Ranh Bay
Loc Ninh ◊ Bien Hoa ◊ III Corps
Long Binh ◊ Saigon ◊ IV Corps   **SOUTH**
◊ Can Tho ◊ Vung Tau
Ben Tre ◊ My Tho   **CHINA**
Mekong River Delta
Plain of Reeds   **SEA**
Khanh Hung
Ca Mau

The mysterious, swirling mist builds until it engulfs the entire scene from heaven to earth. Lightning begins to flash dully from inside the dense fog bank. Then a dazzling forked electric spark discharges with a huge *Bang!* jabbing the belly of the fog. On the heels of the crash, he hears the yearning, satisfying, aching sound of rolling thunder. Brown stands embroiled in a mixture of anticipation, horror, and fascination.

Under a moist palm, he feels his heart beating wildly. Though not exactly sure, he believes the fog is somehow conceiving, giving birth to the creatures that frequent his nightmares.

Within the stewing cocoon, he detects fog-creatures that creep, slither and swirl about the onlookers. Unaware, the viewers continue their slow, death-march-pace along the length of the Vietnam War memorial. Their hundreds of quivering and caressing fingers stroking the tens-of-thousands of names etched on the black panels.

The monument begins to crackle and spark from electricity created by the multitude of rubbing, caressing fingertips. Every touch uncovers another old wound, every spark ushers another load of tear, and every sorrowful plume of smoke feeds the insatiable hunger of the mother fog.

Similar to an earthquake, the ground begins to shudder. Concentrating on the pounding, Brown realizes the monster is moving in his direction. As it draws near, each hammer blow makes the monument heave with a deep guttural noise. The thunderous pounding persists, becoming heavier, more threatening as it nears.

Suddenly, everything becomes thickly quiet, void of even the most subtle sound of a bird's chirp or the rustle of leaves. Then, Brown feels a hot wind brush across his cheek. He gasps and stares breathlessly—a mammoth size, black Asian war elephant, towers over the monument. Its ivory tusks glisten like keen sabers in the surrealistic light. The beast of burden stands steadfast, its ears alert, trunk weaving snakelike through the air. With small glowing pink eyes it gazes malignantly over its prey.

Plate 28   Grim Reaper with helmet *(Illustration by John Tylk)*

Thunderclaps rumble threateningly while lightning zigzags its way across the sky ripping through the heart of the fog bank to slice away a section of mist. The disconnected cloud swoons and takes on its own internal glow. Assaulted by yet another bolt, it begins to jiggle. Brown shrieks as the formation hovers closer. *Whammmmmmmm!* With a final searing ball of lightning, it integrates into the face he knows so well. The keeper of all evil, the mask of life's most feared bandit, the terror that lives in every person's heart. Directly in front of him is the hollow-eyed, ace-of-spades nose—the hate-grin face of the Grim Reaper. Death personified.

The Grim Reaper raises an arm that transforms into a keen edge sickle blade, and mockingly, an army steel pot appears on its head. An ominous wind spreads its black cape like bat wings. Its jaw rocks open and a bolt of lightning shoots from the black void, striking a slab with a hammering blow. The Grim Reaper's teeth gnashed as he sucked in the damage with unseeing, all-seeing eyes. His jawbone rocks open again to send another bolt of lightning crashing into the granitelike wall.

The rogue elephant rears, arching its back like a stallion, its thigh muscles bulging under the enormous weight. It stands over The Wall poised for battle. The Grim Reaper gives a consenting nod and the mastodon's descendent gives a bloodcurdling trumpet then plunges with all its might to trounce the monument. The Wall quakes. It steps back to regroup. Then it charges headlong to impale the monument on its steely tusks.

A towering bolt of lightning ignites the sky, then swings like a machete, splitting the steel pot and Skull of Death. The force of the impact splinters and diverts the lightning bolt. Several shards slice through the flesh of the earth and, after a satisfying rumble, disappear. Meanwhile, the Grim Reaper dissipates into a cloud vapor.

Another bolt of lightning erupts from the sky. The war elephant rears and, with its trunk, intercepts the jagged thunderbolt. Holding tightly, it blasts out an angry, torture-filled

Plate 29   Rogue elephant *(Illustration by John Tylk)*

trumpet that shatters the sound barrier. Against a background of thunder and lightning, the elephant battle-rams the lightning bolt through The Wall, then begins to twist it savagely.

The remains of the machetelike thunderbolt suddenly shoot up from underneath the ground, spearing the monument's base. Brilliant streaks of silver-blue energy race across the length of granitelike slabs. An electrified shock wave washes over Brown as the ground ripples and softens.

The Wall starts to crack and splinter, creating jagged fissures from which the milk-of-hell flow like crimson molten lead. Lip locking onto a fissure, the elephant drinks greedily. And like a leech in the ecstasy of having found the main artery, the trunk wiggles and twitches while sucking its fill. The elephant pulls loose and whips its trunk around to shoot a stream of molten sacrifice down its throat.

An acrid smell shocks Brown's nostrils making his teeth chatter.

The words **KIA**
      MIA
             KIA rush through his vision, engorging his eyes.

The etched monument bulges with shapes that twist, push and claw. A complete hand, arm and shoulder pop from the black goop. Then an entire body tumbles forth, a tar-caked soldier wrapped in a treacherous turn of events begins to low crawl away.

Brown watches in frozen terror as body after body begins to ooze out of the sticky blackness of The Wall. Soldiers—long dead—are now free to crawl and stagger from their caged prisons. Hordes of tortured figures appear in clothes so tattered they appear like slashed flesh.

Gunpowder-black skulls start to develop eye sockets, their eyeballs flashing in consternation. Hellish aberrations continue to form, each frantic blink dragging them closer to the instant when they had put it *all* on the line.

Plate 30   KIA-MIA-KIA *(Illustration by John Tylk)*

Brave souls continue tumbling out of the past to again live through those last horror-filled moments before death. The Wall continues to belch KIA after MIA after KIA.

Brown hears the distinctive *"Whomp whomp whomp"* sound of an approaching Huey helicopter. Next he hears the "pop" of a smoke grenade. Swinging his head to and fro in confusion, the hissing purple smoke surrounds and invades his flared nostrils to sever the last threads of r
e
a
l
i
t y

FIREFIGHT

Incommmmmmmmmmmmmmmmmmmmming!

Gedown!

Get that machine gun up here

Move it   Move it   Move*iiiiiiit!*

CaBLAM!!!

I'm hit   *I'm hit*

Medic   Medic   Meeeeee-dic

Help me-**eee** Plea-**zzzz** someone, help me-**eee**

Go Go Go

Ra-tat-tat!

Incommmmmmmmmmmmmmmmmmmmmmmming

Gedown

Knock out that spider hole

Don't leave me Oh my God, don't leave m**eee-eee**

I don't wanna die . . . **Mommie, mommie**

Take the pain

Get those men up here

BOOM!

Civilians?   You nuts? **Ge***dim!*

Ra-tat-tat!

Dink 9 o'clock

Tell me-eee, Doc   Don't lie to m**eeee!**

Aaaaaaaaaaaaaaaaaaaaaaaaaaaaaaaaaaaaaaaaaa

Duc Pho

"*Y*ow-*www eee.*" The daydream/vision dissolves. "Now that was even a little too crazy for me." He laughs while shivering.

But why am I laying on my back? Where am I? Is this an army cot? he thinks touching the drum tight heavy canvas. And that sound? He detects the unmistakable noise of a diesel-driven generator. When his eyes adjust, he notices two lengths of black and white electrical wire strung across the ceiling connecting a row of 100-watt light bulb. Strung in the same fashion as a military hootch during the Vietnam War. And there is that signature sound of unsecured canvas flapping lazily against itself.

"No, way. Can't be. Impossible." Brown scrunches his eyes and clasps his hands over his ears in an effort to restart his senses. But the fact of the matter is, he actually does rest an army field cot. Which means, he hasn't escaped his illusions at all, but instead has plunged even deeper.

Through the heavy canvas roof he sees the outline of an intense midday sun. "God, it's hot," he exclaims, the hot air drying his throat. Rolling, he finds three other army cots with crumpled ponchos and liners, along with an array of combat gear.

Sitting, his jungle boots plunk onto the plywood floor. He finds himself dressed in sweat soaked jungle fatigues. Propped against the cot rests a complement of field gear along with his personalized steel pot. Curiously, he picks up the heavy helmet and begins turning it to gaze at the sewn on unit patches, church-key, wrist watch, quick loader, Pardon Cross, and combat infantry badge. Looking inside the helmet liner, he finds tucked under the head webbing letters secured inside a plastic field radio battery bag.

"This some kinda sick joke?" Brown questions.

"Familiar?" General Morgan asks sit on the bunk across from him.

"Is that all you got to say?" He runs his hand along the smooth black plastic of his M-16 rifle, noting the cleaning rod inserted into the rectangle hand guard and the three prong flash suppressor.

He coughs, choking on the stifling air. After massaging the stiff muscles on his sweaty neck, he reaches for a canteen.

"About time, sleeping beauty," a familiar voice rings out. "Anyone ever tell ya, you talk in your sleep?"

"Got some Goofy-Grape drink," Brown said, offering his canteen. Then he snaps his head around to gawk at Robin Hood, his former combat platoon sergeant. He sits on a steel folding chair behind a field desk with a PRC-25 field radio nearby.

Robin Hood is busy leafing through and filling out papers on a clipboard. After writing in a final note, he places the work among a scattering of other clipboards and loose paper strewn across the desk top. He spears the pencil behind an ear, snatches a clean piece of paper from inside a desk draw, and rams it into the manual typewriter.

"Where am I?" Brown asks, wiping the grape drink from his chin.

"This is your worst nightmare," he said laughing and reaching for a pack of *Lucky Strike* cigarettes. "Or, if you like, vacation capital of the world."

"No? I mean what time, day, date?"

"Well," Robin Hood takes a draw on the cigarette and checks his watch, "lemme see. It's ahh, 1300hrs, November first, 1967. And this here is Duc Pho." With the cigarette dangling form his mouth, he begins typing out a report.

"Duc Pho?" Brown said, savoring the words to jolt his memory.

They both cock their ears at the sound of an approaching Huey.

"Supply chopper?" Brown guesses.

"No-ooo?" Robin Hood pushes back from the desk and listens. "No, I don't think so," he said. "I'd say it's the guys coming back from the outpost."

The Huey comes in for a landing exceptionally low. Brown instinctively hunches as it flies over, its blade wash blowing the sides of the tent outward like an umbrella opening. Then as it passes, heading for the helipad, the tent's sides come whooshing inward to flap violently, dust kicking through the opening.

The Huey lands a few hundred yards away and its engines begin to slow down. Robin Hood goes back to typing, while Brown walks to the rear entrance for a breath of fresh air.

"Cabla-a-m!" The sound of a single explosion, shatters the tranquility.

Robin Hood and Brown look at each other questioningly.

"Incoming?"

"Outgoing?"

Ready to take evasive action, they waited for a follow up explosion or a firefight to start.

"I think it was a hand grenade."

"Hand grenade?"

If so, why did everything suddenly get so thickly quiet? A kind of crackling electricity comes through the air, and then a horrible explosion with an aftershock rolls over the tent.

They grab their pistol belts, rifles and helmets, then dash outside. At the helipad, they see soldiers scrambling from the now burning Huey which had just landed.

As they hurry, a huge brown and yellow flame swirls upward from the helicopter's engine compartment. At a height of some twenty-feet, it fans out like the hood of a king cobra preparing to strike. The lethal flame shimmers, then swing back swooping through the cargo bay to ignite the belly of the chopper with its flaming venom. The Huey's alloy skin incinerates and sparkles like silver-white phosphorous.

Two soldiers make a mad dash, trying to out distance the fire cobra, but its deadly fangs easily catch them. They struggle hopelessly only to fall then flounder on the ground, ablaze with hydraulic fluid and deadly high octane fuel.

Brown blinks, shakes his head in an effort to break the vision. "This is Robin Hood's nightmare . . . not mine!" he pleads, but General Morgan has vanished.

Behind the helicopter's M-60 machine gun sits a blazing fire-demon that shoots red tracers at the fleeing soldiers. Inside the cockpit, another fire-demon wrestles with the pilot who fights to free himself from the seat harness. The ammunition on board cooks-off and joins the deadly mayhem.

A wounded soldier comes staggering toward them, his smoldering clothes covered in flammable fluid. On seeing Robin Hood he gathers enough strength to sprint over with arms flaying. Nearing the ten-foot high fence topped with concertina wire that encircles the landing zone, the desperate soldier screams, *"Help me-eee! Help me-eee! Plea-zzzz."*

"Wait there!" Robin Hood instructs and motions for him to sit and conserve energy. Heedless, he continued, the best he can to keep pace with the sergeant who races along the fence toward the helipad entrance.

As Brown watches helplessly, the wounded soldier's run turns into a sloppy jog. The sloppy jog slows into a distorted trot. The distorted trot turns to a series of desperate jerky motions. His head droops precariously forward and starts to roll dizzily on his neck.

Robin Hood yells over his shoulder, "Stay there . . . wait!"

Oblivious to everything, the soldier continues the death-shuffle. Tripping, he lunges and grabs onto the chain link fence.

On the far side of the blazing chopper, an officer howls, "Everyone, stay back! Stay back! She's gonna blow!"

Robin Hood, like everyone else, heedlessly keep running toward the helipad.

Reaching the opening, Robin Hood swings through and runs madly over to the pleading soldier. Feeling strong arms around his waist, the wounded soldier releases his grip on the fence and collapses. Robin Hood gently lowers the mortally wounded soldier to the ground.

Delicately, he begins to peel back the oil-soaked fabric to reveal blood pumping unabated from a multitude of chest wounds. The soldier coughs. A heart whispers goodbye. With melting neck, his head rolls to one side.

Robin Hood slowly raises his eyes to the heavens as both soldiers freeze in time.

Slow Poke Kinsey

"Saddle up! Get ready to move out. Make sure your hand grenades are secure. Check your ammunition. Make sure your weapons are loaded and on rock 'n' roll!" Platoon Sergeant Denning's five minute warning rings through the line of reconnaissance soldiers resting along the side of a muddy trail.

"Here we go," Yamane says as he wearily secures a flare under a taut rucksack strap.

Brown does a double take. "Yamane?" His former squad leader, who squats a mere arms length away, turns at hearing his name.

Deep chagrin lines crease the skin around Yamane's dark glowing eyes. He spat.

This is *impossible*. Right? *Right!?!*

"Saddle up!" Yamane shouts through megaphone cupped hands. "Pass the word. We're movin' out." Again, he looks questioningly at his radio telephone operator (RTO). "Come on, Brown. Snap out of it. You look like you just saw a ghost."

"I did."

"Well," General Morgan said, materializing, "what're you waitin' for? An engraved invitation? Get a move on."

Setting next to him were a muddy pair of boots and wet socks. He reaches for a can of fungus powder and dowses his pale white feet that are cracked and wrinkled from jungle rot. From inside his rucksack he fishes out a pair of dry white cotton socks, slips them on, then pulls on the boots.

"Not too tight, Gunfighter." Brown stares puzzled. "The laces."

"Oh, yeah." He realizes he'd over tightened the boot laces. "Right." If they were too tight his feet would swell and cut off circulation or if too loose would fatigue his ankles and arches since it might be hours before he'd have a second chance to readjust them.

"And Gunfighter." Brown listens while meticulously adjusting the laces. "Stop trying to decide whether this is possible or not," Morgan coaches. "Take it for granted. It's real and as deadly as when it first happened." Morgan puffs on his ever present cigar. "You could die here," he said softly. "So, watch your step."

"Meet ya on the trail," Yamane calls as he trudges away.

"Your gear, Gunfighter." General Morgan points to a full compliment of combat equipment. "You'll be needin' this, too." He tosses an M-16 rifle and Brown's hands closes around its plastic hand guard.

"The Widow Maker," Brown said staring at the assault rifle.

"Widow Maker, Black Magic, Tonka Toy, Jammin' Jenny, call it what you like," General Morgan said. "None of my concern. But it's probably the noblest thing you'll ever carry."

"What?"

"High-minded rhetoric, religion, and a single stroke of a pen have caused more damage and destruction, and destroyed more lives than that weapon could ever."

"Yeah, I guess. Now that you put it that way."

"When all else fails, desperate men always turn to their trigger-pullers."

"Why don't I remember this?" Brown asks looking around.

"Memories fade with time."

"That's not what I mean," Brown said perturbed. "Did this *really* happen? Or is this somehow all made up?"

"This most definitely is *not* made up. The first time you were preoccupied with other things."

"This must be like a movie then," he said taking in the surroundings. "I mean every time you watch, you notice something different. Right? You always find a part you never saw."

Kneeling, he slips his arms through the straps of the near hundred pound radio-laden rucksack. Then, while using the assault rifle as a cane, works himself into a standing position. "Damn this thing is heavy." Yamane is already way ahead and he needs to hurry, but the heavy pack excludes jogging, so he resorts to long, gangly steps.

His boots push into soft, water soaked ground, his ankles compensating for the mushy surface. "I'm right behind ya, Yamane," Brown assures him though he's still yards away. Panting, he takes up the RTO position, approximately ten feet behind the squad leader. To get a better grip on the rifle, he wipes his moist palm on the dirty, torn fatigues. Looking around at the lush green jungle, he mumbles, "I gotta bad feeling about this."

Lifting the little D-ring on his suspenders, he pulls over the radio antenna and secures the tip inside the ring making the radio unnoticeable as possible. Outside of pointman, he knows the RTO holds the deadliest position in the war. Life expectancy: two-tenths of a second.

By monitoring the radio traffic, Brown concludes that their mission is to sweep an illusive enemy in the direction of Bravo, their sister company and blocking force.

"All right!" Yamane calls.   "Let's move into fire-team formation. Keep it spread out and stay in eye contact."

Brown's reconnaissance platoon pushes cautiously through thick underbrush and around saplings. It becomes so dense, they didn't notice Bravo Company until a couple of its soldiers pop up, seemingly out of nowhere, their helmets heavily camouflaged with twigs and leaves.

"Hi, guys." They grin. "Come to join the party?"

A buzz of conversation accompanies Reconn into the clearing. However, the conversations are cut short for Bravo Company receives orders to move-out. In fact, Bravo Company assembles and moves from the clearing so quickly that they appear like strands of spaghetti being sucked hungrily into a vein strung foliage mouth.

"Oh, my God." Brown cringes.

"Settle down, Gunfighter, and get a grip on that imagination of yours," General Morgan warns. "You'll be needin' your wits about ya."

A hollow, numb sensation sweeps over him as he continues to watch his fellow grunts slip one by one into the expectant jaws. A well-known adage plays in his mind, "while you search for someone to kill, that same someone is waiting to kill you."

The carnivorous trail continues to swallow the platoon whole. When the last strand disappears into the belly, the tongue rolls in and the jaw closes with a satisfying, "*Oooommm*" to leave a crimson sauce dripping around the edges.

The resulting silence tries to convince Brown that Bravo Company had never existed, except a black/white image of the scene has already been burned into the cells of his brain. Along with the trail's lip-smacking smile.

"Quiet!" someone calls motioning toward the trail. "Hear that?"

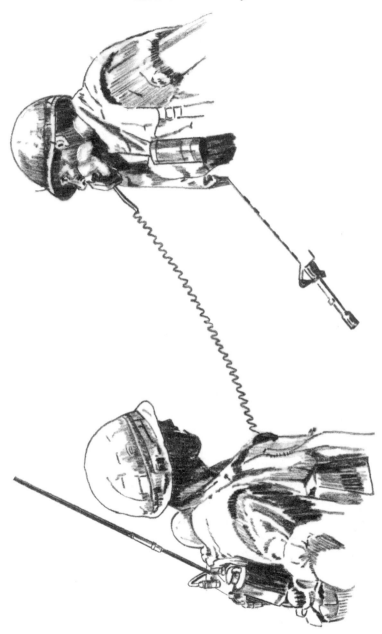

Plate 31 **Platoon Sergeant with RTO Brown (*Photo by Dana Stone*)**

Everyone's ears quicken at the sound and echo of a single muffled explosion. A barrage of M-16 rifle fire immediately cracks through the still jungle air.

"They made contact," Sergeant Denning bellows. "Everyone get down." Being the nearest RTO, Brown rushes over to passoff the handset. Denning quickly dials a different radio frequency. "Bravo two-five, this is Romeo two-five on your push. Over." He waits for a response. None. He tries again. Sporadic small arm fire and high-explosive detonations continue.

"Shit!" Sergeant Denning thrust the handset at Brown. He curls his lip while shaking his head. "Yamane! Take your RTO and Doc. They've lost radio contact. And be damn careful when you get near 'em. They might be spooked. And watch, the trail might be booby trapped," Sergeant Denning rattles orders. "Bedford, go with 'em. They might need an M-79 man."

The four soldiers double-time into the mouth of the jungle, the sounds of the firefight subsiding. Everyone has left their heavy rucksacks behind, except Brown who carries the radio. He quickly falls behind from exhaustion, his walk barely able to keep him within visual contact. The heavy rucksack and radio mercilessly pounded his back and drain his strength.

On reaching the rear element of Bravo, Brown slowly weaves his way past the grunts who appear edgy and a bit trigger-happy. The tough-faced soldiers crouch among expended brass cartridges, every other weapon aimed toward the opposite side of the trail. Like moments before the firefight, an eerie silence engulfs the area.

"Two-five, two-five, this is two-two kilo. We've alpha. Over," Brown radios their arrival.

"Roger, two-two kilo this is two-five. Sierra Romeo? Over."

Brown gives Platoon Sergeant Denning a brief situation report. Moving along the trail, he comes to a small blackened crater near the middle of the path, where blood mingles with exploded earth and where the air is heavy with the smell of gunpowder and decay.

Pausing to study a boot slashed by shrapnel, his eyes follow a blood trail that leads to a shrapnel-riddled, rucksack-mounted radio. Alongside with eyes wide and empty lay the RTO in a pool of blood.

Yamane, Bedford and Doc Prien begin feverishly working on three other soldiers lying nearby. Brown kneels next to the motionless RTO, the GI he had heard earlier talking on the radio.

"He's dead."

Brown turns to the speaker, a grunt who has

LIFE'S A BITCH THEN YOU DIE

written in bold magic marker on his helmet.

"Slow Poke is dead, man," the grunt repeates wiping sweat from his eyes. "My buddy bought the farm."

"Brown!" Yamane shouts. "Get a chopper in here. We need a medevac. Hurry!"

"You mean. . . ?" Brown said baffled. Though he carries the radio, he knew practically nothing about how to use the PRC-25 field radio. On top of that, he'd never called *Six*, the call sign for the company commander, and bringing in a dustoff was far beyond his ability.

"Yesss!" Yamane shouts. *"CALLLLL!"*

"Right away." Brown releases the antenna to let it reach full height, then grabs the handset. Boldly pressing the squelch button, he speaks, "Six, this is two-two kilo. Over."

"Two-two kilo, this is Six-kilo, I hear you loud and clear. Over," Bravo company commander's RTO replies.

"Roger," Brown responds trying to control his jitters. "We got one KIA and at least three WIA. Need dustoff. This is an emergency. We got soldiers dying out here. Over."

"Two-two kilo, this is six kilo, roger," the company commander's RTO replies. "Chopper inbound. What is lima? Over?"

Plate 32   RTO KIA (*Photo by Dana Stone*)

"Location? Shit." Brown lowers the handset. "Yamane, where are we? They want a location."

Yamane waves him over. After placing Brown's hand on a bloody bandage wrapping a soldier's wounded leg, he said, "Hold it tight until Doc ties it off."

"Oh my God." He swoons with dizziness. Fighting to keep his mind occupied, he turns and busies himself with watching Yamane scan the complex topographical map. He sees a grease pencil mark on the plastic map cover which marks an earlier position.

"Ah, let's say, Tango-nine, Bravo-two," Yamane said his finger planted on a spot. "That'll give us a rice paddy just over there." Yamane nods toward the west. He glares at Brown. "Well? What are you waiting for?"

Still griping the bandage, even though Doc has finished, Brown jerks his hand away and quickly wipes off the blood. After the communication, Brown peers around at the other two severely wounded soldiers. They lay in a daze, their blood soaking into the ground, and the bandages oozing more.

"It could've been a train, a car, a falling tree. Right? I mean who's to know," the dead RTO's friend said without a hint of emotion. "When it's your time to go man, you go." The grunt leans over and pulls the eyelids closed on his deceased buddy. "You know what I mean?"

Avoiding looking at the corpse, Brown stares at the soldier with eyes rimmed in exhaustion-purple, his combat fatigues marked with fresh blood. "It was just time for Slow Poke to go."

"You got it."

And why not? Brown thinks. Makes as much sense as anything else.

"Brown!" Yamane shouts. "The rice paddy is about a half klick in that direction." He points. "Times running out. Better get goin'."

"Right," the wounded platoon sergeant babbles. "That's affirmative. The perimeter is secure. Everything's A-okay."

"Roger that, Sarge," Doc said playing along. "No problem, everything's shipshape. Got a chopper inbound, so hold on there buddy, you're goin' home." Doc pulls out a syringe of morphine. "Hold still." He jabs the leg just above the wound.

"What time it it? I gotta give Six a SITRAP." The delirious sergeant thrashes his arms as he twists around. "Where's my RTO? Hey, Slow Poke! Where the fuck are ya?"

"Relax, Sarge, Slow Poke is busy helping someone else," Yamane continues to reassure him while lightly patting his shoulder.

"Gunfighter," General Morgan said to Brown. "Get a move on."

"Yeah." Brown stands to face the anxious soldiers of Bravo Company.

General Morgan leans over and whispers, "Act confident, and talk like you know what you're doing. They'll follow, no questions asked."

"Alright, listen up!" He takes a deep breath as he notes the volume of his voice. "We've gotta bring in a Medevac. If you're not needed here, follow me."

Brown starts to push through the brush and after a few yards dares to glance back. With a sigh of relief, he finds the soldiers are indeed following his orders.

Shoving and pushing, he forges a trail through the thick underbrush till he comes to the edge of the tree line. In front of him unfolds a horseshoe shaped flooded rice field with plenty of landing space for a Huey. Time is short, so he'll have to throw caution to the wind. With this in mind, Brown does the only thing he can, which is to slide into the calf-deep water and quickly move about forty yards from shore. If the enemy were present, he will surely draw fire.

Continuing the air of confidence, he turns to the soldiers waiting his instructions. "All right," he bellows from the middle of the rice field, "I want two of you on each of those land points." He points while walking backwards, almost feeling the cross hairs of an enemy rifle on his back. "The rest of you spread out along the edge of the paddy."

Near the middle of the rice field, he begins to hand-signal like a traffic policeman to get the soldiers into position. The entire time his skin crawls knowing the impending dangers. "Farther to the left. That's right. Keep it movin'. Keep it movin'."

While directing traffic, he keeps moving and bobbing not wanting to become, literally, a sitting duck in a shooting gallery. "Okay. That's fine. Let's keep a sharp look out. You over there," he shouts and motions. "Don't bunch up. Keep it spread out!"

Listening to his even baritone voice, Brown begins to feel a sense of power. These GIs don't know a thing about him, yet never dare to question either his authority or ability.

Yamane, Bedford, and Doc halt just inside the tree line with the wounded. It amazes Brown how they had taken complete control of the entire evacuation. Without the platoon sergeant's leadership, it appears the entire unit had been effectively paralyzed.

The distant *"whup-whup-whup"* of a Huey's rotor blades cut through the air. A tremor of terror runs through Brown, the responsibility lay heavy on his shoulders. Until arriving in Vietnam, hardly four weeks earlier, he had never even seen a field radio, let along operate one—now this, an entire combat medevac.

The words of the helicopter pilot's vibrating voice blares over Brown's radio receiver. *"Two-two, this is Minuteman on your push, over."* He recognized the voice of Peacock, the helicopter's pilot. He searched the cloudless blue sky in the direction of the beating noise and spots the chopper.

"Roger, Charlie Charlie, this is two-two kilo. Over," Brown replies.

"Two-two kilo what's your lima. Over?" Peacock asks.

"Nine o'clock your location. Identify smoke. Over." Brown tosses a smoke grenade onto a raised dike. It *pops!* and begins to spew its deep red smoke.

"Roger, two-two kilo, I identify choo-choo cherry. Over," Peacock replies in his vibrating voice.

"That's a roger Charlie Charlie. Alpha secure, lima zulu cold. Over," said Brown, verifying the color of smoke and that the landing zone is secure.   Secure?   He looks around and mumbles, "I hope."

In an effort to relieve some tension, he stares at the colorful smoke that flows whimsically through the air and thinks he sees the shape of a dancing angel.

"Okay, listen up!" he shouts diverting his attention back to the perimeter. "If there's any VC still around, they'll probably open up. So look alive!" The Huey banks and speeds in for a landing. It sends the remaining red smoke either scurrying across the rice field or threading up through its beating blades.

The severely wounded are hurried into the rice field on rifle poncho-stretchers. Following behind are Bedford and another able-bodied soldier who helps a slightly wounded GI with one leg wrapped with bloody bandages. The dead RTO is brought out last. Jolted by the hustling, his head bounces unsupported by the poncho-stretcher.

Nearing the chopper's blade wash, everyone stoops to protect their faces from the high wind and splashing water. They struggle onward with their burdens in calf-deep water clothes flattened against or furiously flapping around their bodies. Rather than set in the rice field, Peacock hovers the chopper with skids only inches above the water. The medics step off the side of the rocking helicopter and balance their feet on the landing skid while they help hoist on the dead and wounded. Meanwhile, the door gunners keep their M-60 machine guns trained on the tree line.

As the last of the dead and wounded are loaded, Yamane hands outgoing mail to the door gunner. The door gunner in return hands off a plastic bag.

Everyone clears away as the chopper blades hit a feverish pitch. The chopper lifts, turns and bounds away to speed low across the open field. Occasionally it jinks right and left to avoid any possible ground fire, then springs up and out of sight over the distant horizon.

After making arrangements for a replacement platoon sergeant, the reconn soldier starts back. Moving guardedly back down the trail, Brown takes his usual RTO position where he detects the scent of death wafting from everyone's fatigues.

"How can you stand all that blood and guts, Yamane?" Brown asks. "That was . . . . well. You know. And when you made me hold that bandage . . . uhhh."

"It's really not that bad," Yamane contends, without breaking stride. "If a man is dead or wounded, just pretend he's a *mannequin*. Block out any thought of him or the wounds as real." Yamane, suddenly noticing a speck of bloody flesh dangling from his sleeve. He flicks at it madly as though it were about to burn through his skin.

Composed, Yamane slows to face Brown, his eyes gaunt, face grim. "Anyway, this is war. That's what it's all about."

Back on the main trail, they silently maneuver around the booby trap's crater, past patches of pulverized bloodstained earth laced with remnants of army clothing, and a shredded boot.

Slowing, Brown contemplates the place where Slow Poke Kinsey had been killed and others severely wounded. A place, a day, and a time that would be forever etched in the forefront all the participants minds. But from this moment forth, no one who passes here will know what happened at this spot on December 29, 1967.

KINSEY, JOE EDWARD   **29 DEC 67 32E 096**

Tet Offensive

Plunging ever more perilously into his illusions, Brown finds himself once again inside a grey mist. Shifting his stance, he notes the excruciating weight of a fully loaded rucksack, thirty magazines of M-16, a bandolier of M-60 machine gun ammunition and his fragmentation jacket. Stuffed inside the fully loaded pack will be the usual five days of C-rations and an array of other necessary survival items. Strapped to the outside will be an entrenching tool, sandbags, extra canteens of water, a flashlight, smoke grenades, illumination flare, poncho and liner, a climber's ring, and a PRC-25 field radio with an extra battery. On the pistol belt is an ammo pouch with grenades, a compass, a field dressing, two quart canteen, and a bayonet. Strapped to his thigh is a gas mask. The combined weight easily surpasses one-hundred pounds.

Plate 33 Brown running (*Illustration by Jean Altepeter*)

Positioning his steel pot low so as to cut across his line of vision, he contemplates the sprawling rice field. As a safety precaution, he pulls the charging handle on his M-16 rifle to eject and reload a fresh round. He flips the selector switch to rock 'n' roll—full automatic. Then after a cleansing breath, he starts to hustle across the field, conscious of the mother of all land mines, his mind.

"Get me outta this place," he pleads while staring at the billowing black smoke just ahead. "This is Operation Miracle, Defense of DaNang. Wake up, man!" he shouts at himself. "Come on. *Wake the fuck up!*"

Entering the smoke cloud, he takes a whiff of nauseating napalm mixed with the stench of blood, guts, and burning flesh. He begins passing a procession of bloody, wounded or dead Americans being carried, encouraged or helped along by their buddies. Among them is a shirtless GI with a bandaged right shoulder and left chest. The soldier's face is ashen, crushed in, and has a gaze seeming of another world. His head swivels and levels on the intruder. Like a wet tongue welded on frozen steel, Brown's eyes get stuck on the man's icy gaze. Then an evil scowl crosses his face as he presses on.

All around lay expended ammunition casings, torn clothes, fractured steel pots, blood drenched field dressings, and twisted chunks of steel that had once been military vehicles.

"Incommmmmmmming!"

"Meeeeeeeeeeeeeeeeeeeeeeeeeeeeeeeedic,"

Get those men up here!

"I don't wann die! Oh pleazzz, don't let me die."

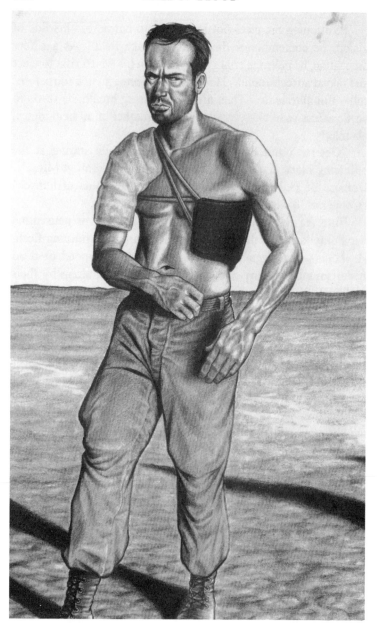

Plate 34 **WIA** *(Illustration by Curt Chiarelli from Dana Stone photograph)*

The universal screams of battle flows across the fields of crimson slaughter.

"Move it!" Brown yells at himself as he plunges deeper into the billowing smoke. "Move it, move it, move it!" Picking up the pace, he recklessly splashes through the boot-deep mud and water of a flooded rice field. Nearing the epicenter of the battle just minutes past climax, he slows. Sporadic explosions and small arms fire could still be heard but becoming more and more dispersed and distant.

The sky clears to reveal an enormous rice field, littered with moaning NVA and American soldiers. Familiar images float into focus. He passes an enemy corpse whose skull lay cracked open like a chicken's egg, its gray matter spilling out. A dead GI lay with face submerged in the muddy water, an arm stretched over the paddy dike with hand still wrapped around his rifle.

"Bull? That you?" Brown utters with his throat constricting. A translucent shadow rises from the corpse and floats upward as the clouds part to create a stairway to heaven.

BULL

H e r e,
in the land
of war, will
I be forgotten
on its battlefield,
as soon as the
grey light of dusk
creeps across m y
blood, and my remains
are washed away by wind
and rain? Is my loss seen?
The grief seems s o cold.
Death is different here, not so
easily understood.   Please, let
m e be remembered.   L e t m y
legacy be passed on. Pray for me
now, and I'll pray for you later, because
the thirst of W A R has n o t been quenched.

Plate 35   "Bull" in rice field (*Illustration by Jean Altepeter*)

Plate 36   Dying NVA *(Illustration by Art Rydell)*

At the sound of laboring breath and shuffling feet, Brown turned to see two weary soldiers awkwardly carrying a dead GI in a rifle poncho-stretcher. Brown didn't want to stare but couldn't help himself. His eyes follow and shudders when he realized their destination.

A "field cross" erected from combat equipment, and beyond lay dead American GIs in a row that seemes to stretch to eternity.

Some corpses were already tagged-and-bagged, while others wait their turn in shredded clothes that appear like another layer of ripped flesh. They lay so silently naked, quietly exposed, and utterly helpless on their mud-splattered poncho. Brown thought it shameful to stare, though he found it impossible to divert his attention.

Plate 37   Dead GIs *(photograph by Dana Stone)*

He reaches for a piece of paper protruding from the pocket of a DEAD MARINE. Unfolding the paper, he reads:

Take a man and put him alone,
put him ten-thousand miles from home
empty his heart of all but blood
make him live in sweat & mud
this is the life that I live
and my soul to the devil I give
I am already here and it's too late
I've traded all my love for hate.
You peaceniks have your parties and drink your
beer while young men are dying here.
You paint your signs and have your fun
and then refuse to use a gun
as if you have nothing to do with it.
Then I am supposed to die for you,
but there's one thing that you don't know
and that's where I think you can go.
I'll hate you until the day I die
you made me hear my buddy cry
he was lying there in his bloodshed
then they said, "this one is dead."
It was a large price for him to pay
just to let you live another day.
With his life your freedom he buys,
but who gives a damn when a MARINE dies.

(Found on unknown KIA, June, 1969 Quang Tri Province, Vietnam)

A grief-stricken soldier kneels on one knee, his face nestled within his crossed arms. In front of him lays a dead GI covered haphazardly by a muddy poncho. A note next to the corpse reads:

Dear Ray,

My congratulating thanks to you for the many times you'd saved my life and those of the other guys in our squad.

I know them all: Spencer, Slade, Sloan and the rest have you deep in their heart for all their lives.

Especially me, cause I'll never Forget holding you in my arms when You died.

I couldn't understand why the Best had to leave us.

You made me proud and I'll Always love ya,

           SARGE!

(From letter found at Moving Wall, Chicago 1986 - author unknown)

Under an overcast sky at twilight, Brown finds himself inside a foxhole behind a gravestone in a Vietnamese graveyard. The area has a calm, peaceful kind of feeling like when inside the eye of a hurricane. But he knows the demons and phantoms are only at bay. Warily, he notes the dense, restless, churning fog that encircles them.

"Where's that smell coming from?" Brown asks, scrunching his nose.

"From under your feet, Gunfighter," General Morgan said standing next to him. "It's what you get for desecrating the dead."

"I didn't pick this cemetery for a night logar." He looks at the bubbling mud around his boots. "Think we're gonna get hit?"

"Area's swarmin' with enemy. You guess is as good as mine."

The conversation gets interrupted by the sound of a helicopter bearing down on their perimeter. A Loch gunship known as a Fire-fly, dives out of the darkness, swooping low over Brown's company. Its high-intensity belly light seeming to be searching. Searching for what? Do they spot movement? Advancing NVA? It fires an illumination flare.

Good idea, Brown thinks, now everyone can double-check the perimeter and their field of fire. "Can never be too careful." The flare dangles on a parachute some 300 feet up, and begins making a slow descent.

Then seemingly out of nowhere, a Huey gunship appears and just hangs there, deadly and menacingly, as if droll were dripping from its machine guns. It appears as though it's trying to make up its mind. About what?

"Oh shit," Brown swears under his breath. The gunship drops its nose, and moves into full throttle. It charges Brown's perimeter, firing rockets and strafing with M-60 machine guns.

"Incommmmmmmmming!

         Gedown!

            Incommmmmmmmmmming!"

Morgan drops and pulls Brown behind. The gunship roars past, strafing the edges of the perimeter.

Staying low, Brown peers over the day's bloody battlefield. It appears empty, only lost souls out there. So why this? In the fading light of the flare, Brown detects movement. There running wildly into the open rice field is Ziggy and Dennis. That's it. Normally, only the enemy would spook at the sight of a Fire-Fly. The gunships think we're NVA.

"Nooooo! Ziggy-yyy! Stop. You're running the wrong way," Brown yells at the top of his lungs. *"Gedown!"*

Both choppers reel around and come straight for the perimeter, low, full throttle and at full death. Regardless, Brown starts to climb from the foxhole.

General Morgan grabs Brown's pistol belt and pulls him back just as the gunship starts firing off rockets and strafing the perimeter.

Like a squirrel, Brown curls inside the foxhole, making himself the smallest target possible. Rocket shrapnel zings past and moments later, bullets zip across the back of the hole, showering dirt over his steel pot and down his back.

As soon as they pass, Brown pops up to watch a line of red tracer fire lead up to, and pour over the dark silhouettes of Ziggy and Dennis. The two lurch like rabbits, plummeting to the ground with bullets riveting their bodies.

Doc Labarbra, Yamane, and Platoon Sergeant Denning run fearlessly into the rice field and converges on the two wounded.

Captain Price, Brown's company commander, fires flares in an effort to wave off the gunships.

"They need me out there," Brown pleads.

"No, they don't, Gunfighter," General Morgan said.

"But they're my buddies."

"You're the RTO. Your job it to stay on the horn."

He stares at Morgan. "Yes, of course, you're right. We might be attacked." Then after a moment of reflection, he said, "I'm just chicken, ain't I—afraid to go out there?"

General Morgan makes no reply, and for the next ten minutes Brown struggles with the decision.

"Okie," Brown softly calls when his friend comes jogging back from the field after helping with the casualties.

"That Ziggy," Okie said squating at the edge of the foxhole, "must've been higher than a kit. You know the last thing he said before he died? 'Don't let 'em find the grass in my rucksack.'"

Brown stares astonished. "You're kidding."

Okie sighes. "Brownie, that gunship mangled him bad." He stands and walks slouched to his foxhole on the opposite side of the perimeter.

The medic, who had just arrived a few hours earlier, slides into the foxhole next to Brown. "Did you know Ziggy?" he asks.

"Yeah, sure did. A real good buddy of mine." Brown represses his emotions. He detects the scent of drying blood on Doc's clothes. "Doc, I couldn't go out there. I don't think," Brown swallows hard, "I don't think, I couldn't stand to see another man die. Not right now. Not today."

Brown sucks-in his grief as the sound of the Medevac chopper fades into the night sky. Dropping back into the foxhole, he continues to struggle with the thought that, regardless, his buddy would've wanted him near during those last moments.

PRIEN, DON	31 JAN 68	36E 023
O'CONNOR, RICHARD E.	31 JAN 68	36E 029
MANGIOLARDO, MICHAEL J.	31 JAN 68	36E 031
BOUTWELL, AMOS HAYES	08 FEB 68	38E 021
BOWMAN, JOSEPH B °	08 FEB 68	38E 021
CARRASQUILLO-DENTON, A.	08 FEB 68	38E 022
CERIONE, JAMES STANLEY III	08 FEB 68	38E 023
CLOVIS, FRANKLIN	08 FEB 68	38E 023
DAHM, RALPH ALBERT	08 FEB 68	38E 024
DENSLOW, GEORGE R.	08 FEB 68	38E 025
DURR, BRIAN FRANCIS	08 FEB 68	38E 026
DYKES, ROBERT LEE JR.	08 FEB 68	38E 026
HALE, LANNY EARL	08 FEB 68	38E 029
HASELBAUER, JOHN IRVINE	08 FEB 68	38E 029
JERVIS, JOHN LEROY III	08 FEB 68	38E 030
LOPP, JAMES LEONARD	08 FEB 68	38E 032
McKINNEY, DAVID LEE	08 FEB 68	38E 035
PARKER, JAMES EARL	08 FEB 68	38E 036
POSO, JOHN RICHARD	08 FEB 68	38E 037
PRATT, WALTER RAYMOND	08 FEB 68	38E 037
TROYER, RODNEY PHILIP	08 FEB 68	38E 041
WILCOX, JOHN ARTUR JR.	08 FEB 68	38E 041
PUMILLO, MICHAEL	09 FEB 68	38E 059
GONZALEZ, RAMON H.	13 FEB 68	39E 025

Combat Photographer

There were the throaty *thump* sounds of enemy mortar tubes *thump thumping* in the distance.

"Incom*mmming!* **Gedown!**"

Everyone dives for cover. The enemy artillery rounds begin to explode throughout the area sending shrapnel slamming and slashing jungle, earth, and bodies alike.

Alternately low crawling and when safe enough running, Brown makes his way toward the shambles of a bombed out NVA bunker/trench situated along the top of the ridge. Small arms and chattering machine-gun fire rings out across the hilltop. Rolling into the trench, he finds himself in the midst of a South Vietnamese Special Forces Mobile Strike Force (MIKE Force).

Plate 38   Dead NVA *(Photograph by Dana Stone)*

Settling on something uncomfortable, he lifts up and slides his hand underneath, touching some type of hard obtrusion. Scooting over and twisting around for a look, he finds an enemy canteen. And there next to him is a dead mud-covered NVA in the early stages of rigor mortis. Dried blood around the head and ears were the only noticeable signs of injury. Probably died from a brain hemorrhage when the bunker took a direct hit from the initial American artillery barrage.

Taking a whiff of air, he detects the always present battlefield stench of burnt flesh mixed with decaying body parts, and gunpowder fumes which permeate the soil.

Turning to the sound of movement, he sees an American commander giving some final instructions to the MIKE Force soldiers. Then in unison five of them pull the pins on their hand grenades. "Ready? On the count of three," he commands. "One . . . two . . . three!"

With only arms protruding above cover, they toss their grenades in the direction of the suspected enemy. Simultaneous with their explosion, the commander jumps up, screaming and yells to rally the Vietnamese allies. Hardly free of the trench, he is fell by shrapnel to the stomach, leaving the MIKE force temporarily without leadership.

Medic!!!

Plate 39   WIA American soldier *(Photograph by Dana Stone)*

Brown recognizes the tall American who jumps to command in place of the wounded officer. It is none other than combat photographer Sean Flynn, Son of Captain Blood. One hand pins two cameras against his chest while the other swings forward. Simultaneous with the movement comes the bloodcurdling scream, *"Charge!"*

The South Vietnamese soldiers rally to hustle over, around and through the trenches and bomb craters closing on the NVA position. Brown watches in awe as the soldiers run through a hail of enemy fire with bravado that borders on madness.

The area fills with the orange-silver flashes from repeated explosions. Shrapnel once again indiscriminately seeks out every unprotected body part. Brown, running close behind is suddenly blinded by a huge explosion that hurls him through the air.

Plate 40   Sean Flynn yelling *(Photograph by Dana Stone)*

"Plummp!" comes the sound of him landing flat on his back in a flooded rice paddy. Instinctively he holds his rifle clear of the muddy water. With aching body, he slowly raises to check himself for injuries. Waves of nausea wash over him when he finds himself in blood-laced water and in another place and time. Rolling onto his side, he feels the cool paddy muck ooze between and around his fingers.

A strange sound, similar to corn popping, catches his attention. Not far away, he sees a rocket-punctured armored personnel carrier. The targeted APC quickly becomes a raging furnace, cremating the still-shrieking crewmen trapped inside. Brown watches helplessly as a secondary explosion sends flames rocketing skyward.

"Gunfighter!" General Morgan hollered. "What're you doing? Get movin'!"

Brown struggles to his feet and makes a mad dash for an old French concrete pillbox five-hundred yards away near the main road.

An M-48 tank with its powerful 90-mm cannon steam-rolls into view, a sun-bleached human skull jiggling on top of one of its many antennas. The armored monster clanks onward, its engine straining against the tonnage. On the steel deck lay a tangle of bloody American corpses. Some faces were bloated, already ripe from the intense heat. The tank's crew gawk at the spiritless hulls of their brothers-in-arms, dumbstruck and momentarily paralyzed by war's flesh-and-blood reality.

Glued to the spectacle, his eyes follow the iron hearse as it clanks past. Brown's senses are once again consumed by the ever present smell, sight and sound, taste, and feel of the ensuing battle.

Plate 41

Tank *(Photograph by Dana Stone)*

He falls-in to trudge behind the tank. Soon, he comes upon a Vietnamese girl who squats on the side of the road, her black silk clothes moist with fresh blood. She beseeched Brown with a moan and a feeble outstretched hand. Kneeling, he wraps both hands around her clammy palm. Her mouth twitches as she succumbs to fate. Gently, he lays her on the ground and places both hands across her chest. Then stays with her for a moment of silence.

Hearing screams in the distance, he sees an exodus of villagers streaming from a hamlet that spits crackling, roaring flames. Oblivious to Brown, a peasant farmer crushed with pain, floats past. His eyes are blind to all but the limp dead child he cradles so tenderly in his arms.

Plate 42   Vietnamese carrying dead child *(Photograph by Dana Stone)*

A traumatized boy halts and delicately pushes from his line of vision the bloody field bandage wrapped around his head. He wipes a mixture of blood and tears from his cheeks and struggles forward.

A GI, obviously aged beyond his years, hands another limping boy an open C-ration can of peanut butter. Then he gently lifts the little boy who buries his face deep inside the nape of the soldier's neck. Composing himself and with one sweaty little arm still held firmly around the broad shoulders of the soldier, the little boy begins to lick his peanut butter treat.

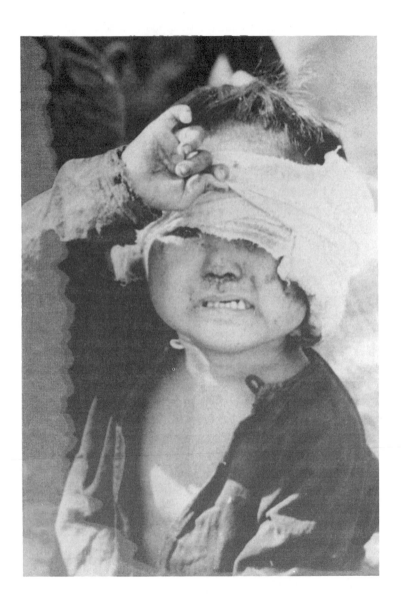

Plate 43   Boy with bleeding head *(Photograph by Dana Stone)*

Plate 44   Soldier carrying boy *(Photograph by Dana Stone)*

A pint-size man with a face resembling the American rock 'n' roll legend/singer Buddy Holly and with ASSOCIATED PRESS scrawled in ink on his helmet, darts past. It is the renowned combat photographer, Dana Stone. Strapped around his waist is a leather NVA officer's pistol belt with U.S. Army fanny pack and canteen. His fatigue pockets bulge with rolls of new and exposed film, and as he runs, several Nikon cameras swing on varying lengths of leather straps to beat a rhythm against his chest.

Dana hustles over to a woman squatting with her naked child resting between her legs. He drops to one knee, aims, and snaps photo after photo of a nurturing mother resigned to life in a war's freefire zone.

Plate 45   Mother squatting with child *(Photograph by Dana Stone)*

Journalists would report the battles, write the books and in-depth articles, and create film documentaries but could they truly cover the war? Brown thinks not. He watches as Dana hurries away, with the camera at war. No, the type of photograph that Dana Stone and his colleagues shoot would speak directly to the soul. They would ultimately stand alone as a representation of the true meaning of war and why we need to fight for peace on earth.

"A*aaah*, man. Not this."

At Brown's feet lay a dead Viet Cong with a bayonet driven through his eye socket. On the corpse's chest lay a crossbone-and-skull ace of spades with the printed words *GUNFIGHTERS—DEALERS OF DEATH.*

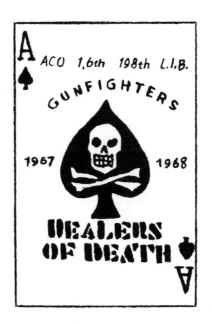

Plate 46   Ace of Spades *(Illustration by Art Rydell)*

Plate 47 Bayonet in face *(Illustration by Art Rydel from Dana Stone photograph)*

A gunpowder-grey mist swirls, and in a clearing just ahead, he sees the Hanging Tree. A limb creaks in protest under the strain of three VC whose broken necks are cinched with hangman nooses.

"Damnit to hell. Why didn't they finish it," Dana shouts, walking in Brown's direction. Dana stops short and draws his Ka-Bar. In a single sweeping motion, he leans over a dying NVA who lay gasping for air, places the keen blade against the man's neck, and slits his throat. Dana watches the soldier die while he wipes his blade clean with a broad leaf.

"Don't get me wrong. I ain't no dink lover," Dana said to Brown. "But it ain't right to kick and beat someone like this and then just let 'em suffer."

Brown nods with solemn respect in his eyes.

Back to work, Dana kneels, grits his teeth and searches for another photo opportunity. While evaluating his options through thick eyeglasses, he begins to clean the camera lense with a chamois cloth. His mind flashes a decision. Hurrying away, he pauses, aims, and snaps picture after picture of the battle's aftermath.

Plate 48   Dana Stone *(Photographer unknown)*

Plate 49   Man in trench *(Illustration by Art Rydell from Dana Stone photograph)*

ASSOCIATED
PRESS
DANA

VERMONT

The ABUSE *potential* oF A CockTAIL!

I smoke To ReLeAse Nervous Tension

Plate 50   Dana Stone's helmet cover *(Illustration by author)*

Plate 51   Woman with dead husband *(Illustration by Curt Chiarelli
from Dana Stone photograph)*

Dana's ears perk. Turning, he spots an incoming Huey. "Ohh-h shit! They're gonna ream my ass for this." Dana takes one last panorama of a row of American corpses, though he knows the brass frown on such explicit photography.

"Makes 'em look bad," he said motioning to the command helicopter. He swings the Nikon to take Brown's picture. "Wouldn't wanna do that, now would we?" As a precaution, Dana rewinds the film, pulls it out and loads a fresh roll of 35mm film.

An officer and U.S. Army journalist, escorted by a one star general, jump from the chopper. Hunched, the three make their way through the blade wash. Immediately, the general becomes engrossed in a field debriefing. The officer meanwhile busies himself with examining the platoon's roster.

The journalist, with a different job at hand, starts interviewing, jotting down notes and observations. Unlike the combat photographer, a journalist could be hours, days or even weeks away from the original action and still produce an award winning article. They could, in essence, produce article after article without even venturing into the battlefield.

Both junior officer and journalist are dressed in crisp new jungle fatigues and stand in stark contrast to their surroundings. "Cherries," Brown mumbles, "both of 'em." Probably the first time in the field with "God" himself, the division commander. The general signals to the officer. After a short conference and a few gestures the junior officer nods his understanding and courteously takes his leave.

While this happens, Dana tries to lose himself in the landscape, but the officer diligently scans the field, and finally spots the combat photographer within the chaos.

"Hey, you!" the officer's voice rings military gruff, and he jogs over.

Dana pretends to be unconcerned as he takes a few fluff photos of the soldiers smoking their cigarettes.

"Hey, I'm talking to you, shorty!" He closes on Dana with the journalist in tow. "Whadoya think you're doin'?" he says in a controlled voice not wanting to draw any undue attention.

Dana turns slowly. "You talkin' to me?" He lowers the camera as they square-off. From what Brown can make out, the officer and journalist have heard a great deal about Dana Stone and his remarkable ways with the camera. Regardless, the brass didn't give Dana carte blanche, there was the unwritten "Code Of Silence" that everyone must observe.

Like James Dean in the movie *Rebel Without A Cause*, Dana stood cocky while dishing out his special brand of back talk to both the officer and the curious journalist:

DANA STONE

"Right, you got it,
Dana Stone, combat photographer.
Sure, freelancing is cool,
but I only snap what I feel's important.
And there's a story only I know behind each one.

Fuckin' A . . . it's dangerous!
In the bush, knowing your shit talks, bullshit walks.
I've been pointman,
that's why the marines call me Mini Grunt.

Hey, man, who doesn't burn when they don't get it?
Why the hell ya think they're in the trench? *
Scared to death, that's why.
What'd you think, they're snoozin'?

Yeah, I snapped that, too.
Their buddies took off and the VC overran 'em." **

Dana sidesteps the officer and defiantly yells,

"Goddamn it, General,
where's the fuckin' leadership, huh?!"

The officer's head jolts as if hit by a left hook. Recovering, he blocks Dana's view, making hand gestures that said he should "settle down and not stir up any unnecessary trouble." Then he proceeds to reprimand Dana, probably more for the general's benefit than his.

In response, Brown hears Dana defiantly rant:

"Crazy! Who's crazy?!
I'm the one dealing with reality, man.
Do you know the story
behind the boy with the bleeding head?***
You couldn't even guess.

Up to fuckin' here, man.
You get to where ya don't wanna look, but ya do.
Look at the shots, will ya.
Where the hell ya think I stood to take 'em?

How could I walk away?
The red clay of Khe Sanh, the death, bullshit, atrocities!
Anyway, you know what I really fear?
My darkside . . . yeah, I fear That even more than dying."

In the end, even while escorting Dana to the waiting chopper, the officer shows grudging admiration for this gruff combat photographer. He is a man, the officer knew, who would match bravery with any man around and often took point-position simply because he knew more about the terrain and the booby traps than most of the soldiers.

   * *refer to plate 49 on page 189*
  ** *refer to plate 37 on page 162*
*** *refer to plate 43 on page 180*

COMBAT PHOTOGRAPHER

CAPA, ROBERT *(France)*	25 May 1954
REESE, EVERETTE DIXIE *(USA)*	29 April 1955
HUYNH, THANH MY *(Vietnam)*	10 Oct. 1965
CHAPELLE, DICKEY *(USA)*	4 Nov. 1965
CASTAN, SAM *(USA)*	21 May 1966
FALL, BERNARD B. *(France)*	21 Feb. 1967
MINE, HIROMICHI *(Japan)*	5 March 1968
ELLISON, ROBERT JACKSON *(USA)*	6 March 1968
EGGLESTON, CHARLES R. *(USA)*	6 May 1968
NOONAN, OLIVER E. *(USA)*	16 August 1969
CARON, GILLES *(France)*	4 April 1970
BELLENDORG, DIETER *(German)* MISSING	8 April 1970
STONE, DANA *(USA)* MISSING	6 April 1970
FLYNN, SEAN *(USA)* MISSING	6 April 1970
SAWADA, KYOICHI *(Japan)*	28 Oct. 1970
HUET, HENRI *(France)*	10 Feb. 1971
POTTER, KENT *(USA)*	10 Feb. 1971
BURROWS, LARRY *(Britain)*	10 Feb. 1971
SULLY, FRANCOIS *(France)*	24 Feb. 1971
KHOO, TERRY *(Singapore)*	20 July 1972
HERBERT, GERARD *(France)*	22 July 1972
LAURENT, MICHEL *(France)*	28 April 1975

Hanoi Jane

"Surprised, Gunfighter?" Morgan said smugly, them back inside the grey mist cocoon.

Brown looks quizzically at General Morgan. "Whatdoya mean?"

"Why that was Dana Stone and Sean Flynn," Morgan said. Brown remains confused. "The legendary photographers themselves."

"And?"

"Well, didn't the media make you lose the war?" Morgan asks. Uncertain of the general's meaning, Brown stays silent.

"Tell me, Gunfighter, did Dana and Sean appear to you like men bent on making you lose the war?"

"Well no. Not exactly," Brown concedes diverting his eyes.

"See Dana and Sean, and their ilk didn't have to go to war. But they did," General Morgan starts to explain. "And if you think about it, who better to tell the *true* story?"

"Yeah, you're right. Like they say, a picture is worth a thousand words," Brown said beginning to understand Morgan's deeper meaning.

"The first actual combat photos were taken during the Civil War, and they gave the public its first actual glimpse of what happens on a battlefield," General Morgan explains. "And from that moment on, the way we think of war changed. Photo's don't lie. So now that you've had some time to think about it. . . ." He takes a puff on his cigar then leans closer. "The question is, Do you still blame the media?"

"I never actually said I blamed 'em."

"You know what I mean," Morgan said gruffly as he rolls the cigar in his mouth. "Shall we blame General Westmoreland?" Morgan asks sarcastically, already knowing how Brown feels about the retired commanding general.

Brown shrugs.

"'Hanoi Jane' Fonda? The Peace/Anti-war Movement?" Puffing smoke rings into the air, he starts slides his finger in-and-out of one donut hole after another. "How foolish of me, your father of course and don't forget the part big business played?"

Morgan keeps goading. "How about the politicians? Now that's a whole rat's nest of hypocrites. They made all kinds of money through the backdoor and yet never let one of their *own* die in the war."

General Morgan keeps pressing. "President Lyndon Baines Johnson?" he said slowly relishing the name. "How about him? He or his wife, Lady Bird Johnson, had part ownership in that big Texas construction firm that did the lion's share of construction in Vietnam. Sweetheart deals closed with a handshake. And after all Johnson's the one who professed an outhouse couldn't get blown up without his *direct* order."

"They're all to blame. Damnit!" Brown screamed at the top of his lungs. "All of 'em," he said, eyes wild with rage. "Every single one of 'em. They made deals, career moves, and money. Lots and lots of money. Their greed turned this country upside down and inside out. Everything got twisted around. Don't you get it? Johnson, McNamara, Kissinger and the rest of 'em. And just like they did to those Nazis after World War Two, those three should be on trial for war crimes. Especially Kissinger who should return his Nobel Peace Prize. Because it was a sham.

"And if you know so much," Brown continue to seethe, "tell me this, when was the last time a nation blamed its infantryman for the loss of a war? Huh? I mean think about it. Most of us were only nineteen-years old and couldn't even vote for chrissakes. We had no political base, no lobbyist, nothin'. They knew they could blame us and get away with it.

"Hell, man, they controlled the government. Owned the media. They could twist, slant, spin-doctor stories anyway they wanted and who would know any better. They could cast blame on anyone they felt like. So why not blame the loss of the war on Lieutenant William Calley and the infantrymen? It was all too simple.

"I mean who lost the battle of Waterloo? Napoleon. Right. See *real* men don't go around passing out blame to those under their command. And answer me this, when was the last time a country held up its POWs, over their combat soldiers, as war heroes?" His stomach begins to growl as it churns with anger.

"They build libraries for those who started that war and give cardboard boxes to those patriots who fought it," he said pleading for understanding.

"Don't you see," Brown rants on. "When we came back the hippies spat on us but veterans, the ones from the *good* and glorious wars, might as well have done the same thing. The old vets said that we didn't have the guts, work ethics, principles, morals, virtues, brains or integrity." The words spat from his mouth. "The old guard said we were out of control thugs. That we just plain out-and-out didn't have what it took to win a war." Brown turns exasperated, feeling the onset of a headache.

"Shit, man. I mean look at us. How many of my brave fellow combatants are homeless, out of work, crippled, divorced, have children with deformities? This country virtually wiped out the High School Class of 1967. And how many committed suicide or died from complications directly related to the war—after the war. Some three-hundred-thousand by my last count.

"Now tell me, how many hippies are living the good life? The American Dream? Why shouldn't I hate them? For chrissakes, look what happened to me. To us." Brown spreads his arms wide to expose his aging body. "We're all old men at thirty with our insides rusting out."

Seeming indifferent, General Morgan turns to the sound of a distant helicopter cutting through the night sky. A wind starts, and they both contemplate the gray-white fog bank that begins to churn. After a deep contemplative breath, the general calmly looks back at Brown.

"Okay," Brown says, "maybe I shouldn't use such a strong word as *hate* but we've been left out, man. Whenever anyone wants to defame us they whisper, 'he's a Vietnam vet.' Which translated mean **LOSER** in big bold type. What did we do so wrong to deserve this. I mean, we did everything the country asked of us. And often times more."

General Morgan takes a puff on his cigar. "Similar thing happened to me during *my* war."

"The Civil War?" Brown said baffled.

"Near the end of the Civil War, they called me back to Richmond, Virginia to face a possible court martial." His face slackens from the humiliating memory. "They broke my heart. Same as they did to yours."

"I didn't know."

"See, war is life at full gallop. And a lot of things get lost when a country is at full gallop. The important thing here is, war or no war, you must at all times stay true to yourself."

Brown searches his soul. "Well, I'm proud to say that I joined the United States Army with intentions of being a peacekeeper. And I think I did a good job at that. And, at no time in my life did I sacrificed my morals for the sake of making more money."

"So the real problem seems to be misguided anger."

"But why did *they*," he gestures with pointed fingers, "the politicians and generals in all their infinite wisdom, have to start the war in the first place?"

"Inevitable."

"Inevitable? You joking?"

"Think of Vietnam as a name on a dart board. America wanted, no wrong word, American *needed* a war to reassert itself as a dominant world power. After all, nearly every generation of Americans since the Revolutionary War has had their war."

"Damn." At that moment it feels as though his mind has just broken through a log jam and the "river of constructive thought" begins to flow.

"You just gotta quit passing the buck, Gunfighter. Chose life over death. Chose forgiveness and enlightenment over anger and blame. Learn the lessons of war. And . . . well," a faint smile crossed his face, "I've always believed there's a lot more to learn from losing than winning. Loses are character builders," General Morgan said philosophizing.

An F-4 Phantom jet shrieks into view and begins to spill its payload of misery, while in the distance Brown hears the heavy "crump" of howitzers belching their brand of death. The surrounding air takes on the combined stench of burning cordite, Willy Peter and napalm.

Huey meat-wagons sweep in and begin to load the WIA assembled next to the KIAs that lay in gory rows. On takeoff, the Medevac's blade wash smears mud over a scene of flapping jungle fatigues. A blood splattered note snags on Brown's pants. It reads:

PROMISE

Remember that day I borrowed your
brand new "used" car and dented it?
I thought you'd *kill me*, but you didn't.

And remember the time I dragged you to
the beach and you said it would rain and it did?
I thought you'd say 'Told you so,' but you didn't.

And remember the time I flirted with all those guys
just to make you jealous, and you were?
I thought you'd leave me, but you didn't.

And do you remember the time I spilled that
strawberry malt all over your car's rug?
I thought you'd scream bloody murder, but you didn't.

And remember the time that I forgot to tell you
the dance was formal and you showed up in jeans?
I though you'd walk out on me, but you didn't.

Yeah, there were a lot of things you didn't do.
But you put up with me. You protected me.
And you loved me.

And the last thing you did before you left
was promise me you'd be back.
But you didn't and I miss you so much.

(author unknown)

Yamane

"Your squad's got point, Same Same," Platoon Sergeant Denning instructs Yamane using his moniker. "All right, let's saddle up, we're movin' out!" he calls to the rest of the platoon. "Brown," he said, addressing his platoon RTO, "let's go."

"Green! Okie!" Squad Leader Yamane shouts. "You guys have point." The reluctant, though obedient, slumped over soldiers move into the point position.

Under the clear morning sky of March 16, 1968 the second platoon has received its marching orders. They are to set up a blocking force on top of Hill 45. The thumb-shaped hill, named for its elevation, stands in the middle of an open plain just west of LZ Baldy. Situated along a meandering river, it marks the outer edge of the American area of operation and the beginning of the South Korean AO.

Trudging along in his designated position behind Sergeant Denning, Brown feels as though at any moment his back might snap from the weight of his equipment. And if that happens the bulging rucksack would probably finish him off by crush him to death. His shaky legs strain and can only muster enough strength for a ground scraping foot shuffle. Bumping the rucksack with a learned motion, he tries to settle the equipment better, a little more comfortably against the sore back muscles.

As they plod across the open rice field with elongated necks and heads swing freely back and forth, the soldiers appear more like sleepwalkers than a formidable advancing army.

"Shit," Brown swears almost losing his footing after skidding on a few loose rocks.

"You okay, Brown?" Sergeant Denning asks his red faced RTO. "Here, lemme help." He lifts the hundred-round bandoleer of M-60 ammunition from Brown's shoulder.

"Thanks, Sarge," Brown said. "Still haven't woken up." He wipes the ever present perspiration from his brow before the salt begins stinging his eyes. As they march toward the slowly rising sun, he grumbles, "If it's another scorcher, I'll never make it."

"Well find some shade by noon."

"Better."

Lifting his gaze, Brown sees their objective, the steep sided Hill 45. At this range it took on the appearance of a huge land-wart. In all probability, it is a pile of dirt dredged there from the adjacent river bed, rather than a natural formation. A wide vegetation-less scar left by the tracks of armored vehicles leads to the plateau top.

"Shit, man, I can't keep this up." Brown pants trying to catch his breath. The incline starts slowly, but quickly steepens. Like the soldiers up front, he leans farther and farther with each step. Soon, with his rifle butt literally bumping on rocks and his knuckles occasionally scraping the ground, he resorts to using his free hand as a third leg. This also helps to lessen the weight on his already cramping back and thigh muscles.

"Yeah," Sergeant Denning said to Okie and Green, "Okay." Both point soldiers step to the side of the trail, turn to face everyone, then wearily collapse. Squad leader Sergeant Yamane takes pointman as the platoon continues to grind at a snail's pace.

"Hurry up, Slow Poke," Okie jests, using the slang term for an RTO, from his resting spot. "Daddy long legs is gettin' away from ya."

Brown's loud exhales is all the response necessary. Platoon Sergeant Denning continues opening the gap between them. Moving slowly onward, he resorts to using both rifle butt and free hand to aid his movement. "Fucker's tryin' to kill me," he swears under his breath. With a rolled shirt sleeve, he wipes the steady stream of sweat from his brow and away from his salt burning eyes.

"Oooow-ch." Brown loses his footing, his knee jamming into loose stones. "Damn!"

Regaining adequate footing, he struggles onward. Near exhaustion, he arrives at the edge of the crown still crawling on all fours. Unable to stand in an upright position he rests on his hands and knees. Looking up, he sees Sergeant Denning heading for the far side of the plateau. The other soldiers begin to fan out across the rest of the hilltop.

He stands to find his muscles vigorously protesting. Stars run through his vision as waves of nausea cause him to drool. Using the rifle as a cane to steady himself, he spits, and starts panting like a dog trying to catch his breath.

"You ain't tired already, are ya Brownie," Okie's says calling from down the hill.

"Me?" He didn't dare turn around for fear of losing his balance. "Just waitin' on your sorry old ass."

Walking again, he spots Yamane and his signature ducklike stride, moving to the right some thirty-yards away. Then for some unknown reason Yamane simply stops, turns and looked directly at Brown.

"Yamane," Brown calls smiling and gesturing with his hand. A wide audacious Japanese-American grin spreads across his face. Yes, that's just like Yamane, in the thick of it, he'd have that reassuring smile.

"What's this?" someone calls up front.

His eyes dart past Owens, to Dawkins and finally to Hicks, commonly known as Beanie Weenie, who appears to be reaching for something low to the ground.

"No," Yamane shouts.   "My God, don't touch it. *Noooooooooooooo!*"

A deafening blast shakes the ground. A hurricane-force death cloud of swarming pellets and shrapnel sweep across the hilltop. The blast rocks Brown back with lead banging into his fragmentation jacket, steel pot and shattering the radio handset.

Instinctively, he drops to his knees and lowers his head not wanting to lie down for fear of being unable to get up. Golf ball-size clods of dirt begin to rain back to earth. He breathed in the dust and coughs.

An immense cloud of debris envelopes the hilltop. It seems like an eternity before the hill begins to come back into view. He lets loose with another racking cough and tries to filter the air through his shirt sleeve. Through the haze, he sees there is not one soldier left standing.

Stretched out next to him is the motionless body of Owens with eyes wide though lifeless. The back of his head rested in an ever enlarging pool of blood. A perfectly round hole in the middle of Owen's forehead marks the entry of the lethal projectile. Brown touches Owens' warm face with no response.

"Incommmmmming!"

"Mortars! Incommmmmmming!"

"Everyone Gedown!"

"Doc," Brown shouts. "This way." They bolt for a depression left by an artillery round. Both soldiers jump inside and cover their heads as fine debris continues to rain back to earth.

"Medic! Medic!"

"We've got wounded!"

"I'm hit, I'm hit!"

"God, help me!"

"Medicccc!"

For a fleeting moment, Doc and Brown stare into each other's eyes.

"That was no mortar. Probably a booby trap anti-tank mine or artillery round," Brown decides. The light of determination sparks and Doc jogs away to disappears inside the dust cloud.

"Help *meeee!* Ahhh! Ahhh!" A chorus of moans seize the hill.

Coming to his senses, Brown pries himself loose of his rucksack and damaged radio. A morning breeze quickly begins to dissipate the dust, however a suspicious white haze continues to linger over the kill zone. Then the full force of reality strikes.

"Yamaneeee!" Brown bolts through the haze, past the already dead and wounded till he spots his mentor and squad leader. There he lay all alone in the dirt, trying in vane to crawl, but for some unknown reason can't. He collapses just as Brown skids to his side.

Unable to raise even a feeble hand, Yamane looks at Brown and whispers hoarsely, "I . . . can't . . . breathe."

"What? Can't breathe?" Brown said puzzled. "Why?"

Yamane's face tightens, his lips begin to resemble those of a fish out of the water making breathing motions. Still confused, Brown quickly looks for someway to help. That's when he notices Yamane's left leg that has been shattered and transformed into a mass of blood, muscle, tendon and bone. It set cocked to one side in an unnatural position with only a small piece of flesh still connecting it to his body. Grabbing a field bandage, he rips open the package and tried to decide where best to apply the it.

Now it's Brown's turn to say, "*I can't breathe!*" The mysterious white cloud had been killer CS-tear gas.

Bewildered, he drops the bandage and gets to his feet. Overcome by dizziness, he ventures a breath. His lungs flame in protest. With legs rapidly turning into jelly, he lunges away with his last remaining strength. He staggers, trips over a dead soldier, and collapses just clear of the gas cloud. Gasping for air, he begins to dry heave. With stars swirling about his vision, he works himself into a kneeing position. Forcing himself to think, he unlatches then secures the gas mask. After a few charcoal-filtered breaths, he wobbles back to Yamane's side.

"Yamane," he calls hoping for a response, but Yamane's body only moves slightly. In training they told him, "whenever possible, do not move the wounded." He seriously doubts he had the strength anyway. So, he quickly pulls off his gas mask and places it over Yamane's face, then grabs Yamane's gas mask for himself. Barely able to see because his eyes are watering and burning, he tries to apply the bandage like a tourniquet above the knee.

"Yamane, come on . . . brea*the*!" he cries. "The mask will clean the air. Breathe." In desperation, he grabs Yamane's arms and tries to drag him out of the gas, but the rucksack quickly lodges itself on the shrubbery. "Artificial resuscitation. Of course." He pulls Yamane's arms over his head then back to his waist. With both hands, he pushes on the rib cage. He repeats this several times but with negligible response.

"Medic!" he screams. "Doc. Someone. Help me!"

"Gunfighter," General Morgan said, dropping to one knee on the other side of Yamane. "There's no one to help. You're on your own."

The mild wind finally dissipates the CS gas enough for Brown to pulls off both of their gas masks. He opens Yamane's mouth wide to make sure he hasn't swallowed his tongue. No obstruction. Brown clinches Yamane's nose, lip locks, and starts mouth-to-mouth resuscitation. He blows hard and, with his free hand, pushes Yamane's bulging stomach down to help in the exhalation. Between breaths he keeps on encouraging. "It's okay. You're gonna make it. Just relax. I'll breathe for you?" He continues until he becomes light headed.

"Yamane!" he pleads. "You're not even trying. Come on, man, breeeeeeathe." He picks up the pace and blows even harder into Yamane's throat and pushed harder on his stomach. "It hasn't been that long. You can still do it."

Beginning to feel something seeping onto his knee, he looks to see a pool of blood. "Ahh, man." Yamane needs a tourniquet fast but he can't do without oxygen. Brown spits to clear his mouth and sees that his saliva is laced with blood.

For the next ten minutes, Brown continues mouth-to-mouth resuscitation, stopping only to wipe blood from his own mouth. "Hang in there, man," he continues to plead. And between every five breaths, he calls, "Doc. Someone help me. Medic!"

His only hope lay in continuing the resuscitation till the chopper arrives or that someone would take over so he could apply a proper tourniquet.

"Medicccc! Anyone help me! He's bleeding!" he cries but still no one comes.

"Chopper inbound! Hurry it up!" Sergeant Denning's bellowing voice can be heard across the hill. "Let's get these men rolled onto ponchos. Move it!"

"The dustoff is almost here," Brown tells Yamane. "Hang in there, buddy. You'll be okay."

"Pop smoke!" A red smoke grenade explodes. The helicopter Medevac swoops for a landing, sending a mixture of exploded dirt and rocks zipping across the hilltop.

"Lemme give ya a hand there, Brownie," Okie said suddenly leaning over them. Together they scoot Yamane onto a poncho, making sure to arrange the left leg in the correct position.

"Doesn't seem to be bleeding that bad now," Brown said encouraged.

They grab the edges of the poncho and hoist. "Wait. Lemme give him a little more air." Brown leans over and gives Yamane two deep breaths. "That oughta hold him for a while."

They hurry their burden to the helicopter and lifted Yamane onto the platform where a medic helps pull him aboard.

"He gonna be alright?" Brown asks

"Don't worry," the medic assures him. "We'll take good care of him."

"He'll be needing some oxygen." Brown looks around but doesn't see an oxygen tank. "I gave him a few breaths a little bit ago but I don't think it will last much longer."

From everywhere wounded soldiers start arriving at the LZ. Spotting Dawkins, head bandaged and in a state of shock, he hurries over to help carry him over to the waiting chopper.

"Sarge," Brown shouts and waves over the roar of the helicopter's engine as it starts gaining speed. Needing assistance because of a shoulder wound, Brown hurried over to help Sergeant Denning onto the helicopter. "Sarge, Yamane's onboard with ya."

"I'll take good care of him," Sergeant Denning assures, as he settles on the platform next to Yamane's lifeless form wrapped in a bloody poncho.

"Get him some oxygen as soon as possible!" Brown instructs as the engine gathers speed ready for take-off. "Alright."

The Huey lifts with blade-wash punishing everyone with a cloud of dust and debris. Brown's clothes flap violently as he turns his back to the gale force winds and covers his face with a forearm. As soon as the wind lessens, he turns to watch forlornly as the helicopter banks, speeds across the valley of green rice fields, and turns into a black dot on the horizon.

"Yamane!"   He raises his hand.   *Yamaneee!*
Yamaneeeee!

    I

      LOVE

          YOU."

"Do you recall what happened next?" General Morgan asks with them again in the cocoonlike cloud bank.

"Yeah. I think so," Brown said surprised he could bear the memory, also surprised he isn't flooded with emotion. "You know what I remember most?" he said. "I remember that night sneaking from my foxhole back to the spot where Yamane had died. For an hour I just sat there meditating I guess. Not doing much of anything just sitting and occasionally running my fingers over that hollowed ground."

"Contemplating the passage of time and the meaning of life. You sat there quietly measuring every inhale and exhale of your lungs, every heart beat."

"Yes," Brown concurred. "I'd never sat so still in my life."

"And for the first time you saw your surroundings."

"Yes. Yes, in a very clear way. Vietnam was a virtual *Garden of Eden*," Brown said. "The trees, veins, flowers, bushes and fruit grew like this were somekinda greenhouse. And everywhere we'd go there would be another cool mountain stream with cascading waterfall, another river brimming with fish or a rice field that extended in the distance like a lake of green."

"And the sky was blue."

"The truest blue you could ever imagine," Brown said.

"And the sunsets, why they were simply amazing."

"I was like the whole western sky was made of cathedral stained glass."

"There was no roof out there."

"We slept under the stars," Brown continues in concert, "and they twinkle." He smiles at Morgan. "I swear to God, one night I saw the cow jump over the moon." It amazed him how those times, events, and places could be so captivating.

"And to wipe off the morning dew."

"And stand in the mountains."

"To watch the sunrise over the white rolling South China Sea fog is to know. . . ."

"To know there is a God," Brown said finishing verse. They smile and embrace the moment. "It might sound a little crazy but you know," he looks directly into Morgan's eyes, "I felt more alive and at peace with myself at that moment than I ever had in my entire life." With tears welling up in his eyes he turns away. "Is that bad?"

"No. I don't think so."

"Until now, I only wanted to remember the horrible parts. I only wanted to talk about the pain, the suffering, the death, atrocities. Revel in the denial.

"But it really was beautiful, wasn't it. It really was a special time." His eyes are ablaze. "For the first time in my life, I had actually found a place where I belonged."

"The worst day of your life can also be the most important day of your life?"

Brown listens.

"Would you have really wanted to change anything, Gunfighter?"

Brown listens patiently.

"Do you believe in destiny?"

YAMANE

D a w n's
early l i g h t
b r i n g s a
sky t h a t
s p a r k l e s
sapphire blue. T h e sands
o f time trickle a s a baby is
created. The sun marches to zenith,
a sweet smell of jasmine in the air,
and the sand dances merrily about.
The c h i l d is appeasing destiny. A
raging ball of fire spews a horrible
blood red. And inside a blinding
sandstorm the peacekeeper lay
dying. Da w n explodes, sending
spirals of light   cascading
through the wide eyes of a
newborn. Is it now this child's
turn to give his life away?

Plate 52   Benji Yamane *(Illustration by Jean Altepeter)*

CRAWFORD, WILLIAM DON	13 MAR 68	44E 033
HICKS, GARY DALE	16 MAR 68	45E 004
OWENS, DEWEY RAY	16 MAR 68	45E 004
YAMANE, BENJI	16 MAR 68	45E 046

Larson Airfield

Under the hot afternoon sun at the edge of a desolated airfield, Brown stands gazing northward up a country gravel road that parallels the runway. Then, out of the timelessness of the road, rises a water buffalo pulling a rickety stake bed wagon with iron clad wooden wheels that strains under a blossoming pile of hay. Forging onward, white dust rises about the beast of burden's knees, dust stirred by its strange, drag-footed, incompetent-seeming motion. Walking alongside with a wooden switch in hand, its skinny leathery-skin master guides the slow moving vehicle onto a connecting artery. He is probably headed for a village, though no hooch, shack or any other type of building is in sight.

Looking south down the road, Brown spots an approaching rolling cloud of dust. Barreling into view is an army Jeep with bikini canvas top, an ARVN behind the wheel. The Vietnamese soldier downshifts and spins the wheels to careen through the barbed wire gate. Bringing the Jeep to a skidding halt, the soldier jumps out and disappears inside the dark guardhouse bunker.

The tarmac that stretches over a mile across an open field is heavily cracked with its many pot holes filled with tar soaked gravel. At the far end of the strip and off to one side, sets the burned-out hull of a DC-3 in the process of being gobbled whole by the encroaching jungle.

The ghoulish looking wreckage has taken on the appearance of a jungle-choked carving similar to those found at the ancient ruins of Angkor in Cambodia. Depressions in the ruptured skin serve as planting pots and through the ruptured aluminum jut fifty-foot tall trees. Pythonlike thick vines encircle and crush the fuselage while scraggly bushes with budding tips sprout from inside the cockpit protruding through the broken window panes. Where the wings had once been attached, hydraulic hoses, copper tubes and electrical wire dangled like bones, veins and arteries.

Brown's imagination takes control:

"Mayday! Mayday! Do you read? Over," the pilot's frantic voice blares over the radio.

"This is Tam Ky landing field, we read you loud and clear. Over," the airport authority calmly replies.

"This is Flight 666. We need an emergency landing. Left engine has flamed out. Right engine rapidly losing pressure."

The year is 1954 and the machine-gun riddled, burning aircraft is limping back from the ensuing French battle of Dien Bien Phu. Having successfully air dropped precious ammunition and foodstuffs, it was raked by Vietminh anti-aircraft fire.

"Landing gear shot out. I don't know if I can hold her. Clear the runway. We're comin' in for a crash landing."

The disabled aircraft wobbles as though surfing on an ocean swell. Its flaming left engine suddenly explodes, sheering off part of the wing. A plume of smoke jets from the remaining engine which then coughs. It sputters. The pilots watch as all gauges drop to zeros and the propeller locks down. The engine catches fire and flames race back licking the fuselage. The pilot and wounded co-pilot give each other a knowing look that says, "Damn. Should have ditched when we had the chance." As the plane rolls and dives out of control, Brown visualizes the pilots against a backdrop of red and yellow. . . .

"Brown! Get smoke out there," Platoon Sergeant Denning shouts.

Grabbing a smoke grenade, Brown focuses on a small object in the bright blue afternoon sky. The object quickly grows into a huge forty-foot Chinook helicopter which flies in line with the burned out DC-3. He tosses a red smoke grenade onto the tarmac and grabs the radio receiver.

"Larson Field, this is Moby Dick, I identify Choo-Choo Cherry," the Chinook pilot's voice calls over the radio.

"This is two-five kilo, that's affirmative. Out!" Brown stares one last time at doomed Flight 666. "I wonder if anyone made it out alive?"

The huge Chinook helicopter hovers some thirty feet above ground then begins to vertically drop to settle on the airfield. Its thundering twin thirty-foot blades churn up a cloud of dust and debris for hundreds of yards. Brown crouches, turns and positions his steel pot to take the full force of the violent debris storm. "Hurry up. Cut the engines, for chissakes!"

When the blades slow, Brown shakes and brush off the accumulated dust. Turning around, he watches as the huge rear hatch begin to drop like the jaw of a very patient Moby Dick size whale. From inside its depths, the soldiers of Charlie Company obediently stand ready to disembark.

"Will ya get a load of that," General Morgan said, standing next to Brown. He points to a GI who has

ROCK BOTTOM

printed boldly with a black marker on his helmet cover.

A certifiable Pointman Gunfighter—a soldier who has been Pointman over forty times. Brown analyzes the short, fair complexion, bespectacled gunfighter in grungy jungle fatigues who slugs down the ramp into the brilliant sunlight. A huge, bulging rucksack dwarfs the GI and comically reminds Brown of his childhood box turtle, Orville, that on occasion, he would playfully hold upright so it could appear like it was walking on its hind legs.

Brown mentally and visually inventories what Rock Bottom carries inside and out of the rucksack and wrapped around his body:

* Five days of C-rations (cans of Ham and Mothers, and Choke and Puck for those desperate moments), a bread-can stove, and heating tablets supplemented with C-4 explosive scavenged from a claymore mine..
* Six packages of Kool-Aid (received from the World)
* Two pairs of extra socks (also received from the World)
* Towel, poncho and liner
* Map, climber's ring, pocket knife, mosquito repellent, foot fungus powder
* Cigarettes with matches, shaving kit, mirror, comb, sewing kit, soap
* Letters from home along with writing paper and pen
* Wallet filled with MPC money and pictures of his girlfriend
* Ten empty sandbags
* Pick handle only (someone else carries the metal pick head)
* Gas mask
* Fragmentation vest
* Pistol belt with two ammo pouches, compass, bayonet with sharpening stone, first-aid field bandage
• One riot (CS) grenade

* One smoke grenade
* One flare
* Six quarts of water and iodine purification tablets
* Flashlight with colored lenses
* Steel helmet, cover and liner
* Salt tablets, malaria pills (the daily-daily and weekly ones)
* Four hand grenades and booby trap wire
* Two 100-round belts of M-60 machine-gun ammunition
* M-16 rifle, extra firing pin, cleaning supplies and sling
* 800 rounds of M-16 ammunition dispersed between magazines, and bandoleer of clips with quick loader
* Claymore mine and detonator
* Wrist watch

The near one-hundred brutal pounds of war-hardware means Rock Bottom has plans on doing some heavy "commie killin'," and also has full intentions of walking out of Operation Blue Dragon alive and kicking.

Similar to the Vietnamese beast of burden, his worn boots barely clear the ground as he kicks up dust. Rock Bottom leans farther than the other grunts humping nearby because of the above-and-beyond hardware. And Brown notes the signature gait of a veteran infantryman. It's a kind of short stride mixed with a bumpety-bump of legs muscling under enormous weight. Oddly enough, the OD towel and machine gun bandoleers draping his shoulders resembles that of the water buffalo's harness.

Rock Bottom's lower jaw bobs in rhythm with his grunt walk and there, at the edge of his mouth, is the ever present drool. From past experience, Brown knows Rock Bottom can keep up that slow, ground eating pace from dawn till dusk, dusk till dawn, day after hideous day, and without complaint.

And dangling on the right wrist is a brass *good luck* Montagnard bracelet. The same hand which also lightly clenches a wobbling assault rifle that seemed as if it might drop from his grip at any moment. However, Brown knows those curled fingers and loose wrist are firm as steel; no need to waste energy keeping the connecting muscles and tissues unnecessarily taut. Actually, Rock Bottom handles the rifle as adroitly as might a gunfighter of the Old West. One who knows how, when and where, and whose trigger finger never falters. A warrior who aims with his mind and fires with his heart.

Rock Bottom stands apart from the other shabbily clad, teeth grinders, the ones with hollow, remote stares and ruddy faces lined with dead serious creases. His demeanor reflects an attitude of *I'm cool.* And he is because he grasps the lay of the land.

And like all the hard core veterans by simply saying, "Fuck it. Just fuck it. Don't mean nothin'." He could begin the emotional spiral of PTSD that would disconnect him from this harsh existence for days, weeks or even months at a time. Possibly forever. Disconnect himself from relentless progression of loss. Disconnect himself from the wounding, maiming and killing. A form of mental disconnection which will serve as the ultimate weapon for survival. A kind of mechanism that will help him accept that hell part of war where his buddies are there one moment and gone the next. Accept that they would simply vanish from existence after getting hauled onto the platform of a Medevac chopper that lifts, banks hard and disappears over the horizon.

Rock Bottom has endured forced marches, lousy food, monsoon rains, diseases with no names, killer viruses, normal sickness, skull-bleaching sun, jungle rot, festering cuts, ringworm, rashes, bloodsucking leaches, scorpions, spiders, red ants, poisonous snakes, malaria, mosquitoes, and ten-foot-tall razor-sharp elephant grass. He has survived crossing rivers swarming with poisonous snakes. Has survived combat assaults, search and destroy missions, the tunnels, firefights, ambushes, booby traps, sniper fire, friendly fire, and the deadly Pointman position over forty times.

So, whether he finds himself humping a mountain, lobbing a grenade, feeding ammunition into a machine gun or enduring the cold nights of the monsoon, it doesn't matter that much.

And what about rest? Never stands when he can sit, never sits when he can lie down—that could mean lying on a cold rock, hard ground or in water—never stays awake when he can sleep.

Though he lives like an animal bent on survival, deep inside he is still human. He does care, has feelings like everyone else, but a veteran grunt, under no circumstances, will show them. A veteran of the bush learns early on how to suck in pain, block out emotions, handle the fear. Learns how to numb himself because "that's what you do in war." To beat the beast of war you must understand the beast. "Fuck it. Just fuck it. Don't mean nothin'."

In the field, full mirrors are a rarity, chipped fragments suffice for reflection. So Rock Bottom probably has only a vague idea of his singular appearance as he nonchalantly joins his fellow soldiers.

The NFGs, new fuckin' guys, secretly envy this combat-ready soldier, a man who displays that special demeanor of a true to life warrior.

But Brown also knows that outsiders—those who have never hit the dirt in a split second after hearing the shout *Incoming!* Those who will never lie on the ground of a freefire zone to feel the cool eager fingers of mother earth caress them while they wait for the enemy mortars to explode—would view this kind of grunt quite differently.

He imagines whispered comments: "Those grunts are inhuman. Deranged killing machines who have no feeling. Just animals really."

Looking away, Brown's stare happens upon the Larson Airfield's commemorative sign.

Soon the awesome fighting force of the entire 1/6th 198th Light Infantry Brigade, Americal Division encircles the sleepy little airfield. His eyes drift over the dust-covered scene, and falls on another soldier. This GI is awkwardly managing to walk straight and strong across the airstrip, painfully aware of the stares that study his every move. Obviously, an NFG with no hope of hiding the fact. The pronounced things were his healthy

Plate 53   Larson Airfield (Illustration by Art Rydell)

appearance, lack of a steel pot, and the sticklike way in which he carries his assault rifle.

"Brown," Sergeant Denning calls, "got a letter for ya." He gives it to Brown. "Get on over to our position and dig in." He points out the general location for their night foxhole.

"What's intelligence say?"

"Clear pretty much. Mortars maybe."

"I heard there was a human-wave attack here last October?"

"Yeah, from what I've heard."

"Think I better go tight and deep, huh?"

"Good ideal. Might get probed or snipered at."

"Wanna roof?"

"No construction stakes. So don't worry about it."

"Any sandbags left."

"Yeah, they're stacked over by the bunker. Grab yourself some," Sergeant Denning points. "Better get a move on, Brown before it gets too late."

Brown shoves the letter into his side pocket deciding it will serve as the dangling *carrot*. First he will dig the hole, fill the sandbags, relax while checking over his rifle, eat something, and then he'd read the letter.

Darkness comes swiftly as the sun drops behind the mountains and it isn't until twilight that Brown opens to read:

Hi Freddie,

Sorry I was so long in answering your last letter. I wrote my first one in a month yesterday. I suppose you have been hearing about C Troop. We lost one track to a mine and one tank to a recoilless 75. It went right through it and set off all the ammo inside. Everyone came out of it. The driver jumped out of the tank without a scratch and then a PC ran over his legs. Last week we were on Seagore Island. I loved it out there. Cool all day. We rode the track along the beach in the water. That's okay when the big

*waves hit the front of the track and splash all over
everyone. Going across the dunes, we just go like hell.*

*My track is about the slowest one, but I kept it
floored all the way and once I got going I was okay.
We went swimming one afternoon. The water was
beautiful, but salty. The only thing is I can't swim.
I went in anyway. We got mortared a few times but this
great mortar crew that I drive around took care of
that. We had our first round out before they had their
third one in. And we were right on target. Well
enough about the Cav. How's everything with you? I
have been hearing a little about the 1/6th but not
enough.*

*Hey, ya know the only money I have spent all month
was on laundry, hair cuts, a few beer and sodas, etc.
And a few dinky dows. I think that is the least I
have spent since I started making my own money.
Well, we have worked with the 196th Bde. The
ARVNs. Maybe we will work with the 198th 1/6 next.
Hey why don't ya put in a 1049 for the 1/1 Cav. C
Troop. Ya may get it in May after your first six
months are up.*

*Well I guess that's all for now. We are west of
Tam Ky and it is a little hotter than on the coast. So
I'll see ya later and hope to hear from ya soon.
Ha, I have a new A.P.O. number 96325*

> *An ol leg buddy,*
> *Ernie Brown*

Picking up an issue of the *Stars and Stripes-Army Times*
newspaper dated April 10, 1968, Brown reads the headline,
"Americal kills 129."

CHU LAI, Vietnam — Americal Division cavalrymen recently topped one of their most successful weeks of fighting with a lopsided victory in a daylong battle with North Vietnamese regulars near Tam Ky. Ground forces of the division's lst Sqdn, 1st Cav combined with the air support of a 17th Cav troop and an infantry unit from the 196th Inf bde to kill 129 NVA soldiers in 12 hours of fighting. The action closed out a six-day period in which the cavalrymen killed a total of 293 enemy soldiers. Friendly casualties in the near continuous action were listed as light.

"Brown," Sergeant Denning said, sauntering over. "When you get a chance, the lieutenant wants you to read this and write them back a letter." He hands Brown an envelope. "Okay?"

"You got it, Sarge," Brown said. Inside is the letter with a note which reads:

To: Fred Brown

     Fred could you answer this we have written a letter to his parents but they want one from one of Scott's friends.

The letter reads:

Dear Sir: *March 31, 1968*

We are PFC George S. Dawkins mother and father. George was wounded on March 16. As of now they tell us it was a gunshot wound to the head and neck. He has been evacuated from Vietnam to Japan. We hope and pray he lives. George told us in a letter 15 March, they were up around Tam Ky. Gary Hicks of N.C. was a friend of George, he got killed, also George had a friend Fred Brown, from Chicago in Company D 198th Inf. Bde. Could you have Fred write us. We don't know his US Army number.

Sir, were you with George when he got hurt? If so, write us and tell us all about where at, and just how it happened. Was it from a sniper or one of our boys. George liked you very much. So if you know of any of the boys that was with George on this day or night of the 16th March, please have them write us of some of the things they did, up till George got hurt and how. We know he was a radio and an RTO he wrote us about a friend Smith. But Fred Brown and Gary Hicks was very good friends.

May we have all George's things pictures and bill fold. He also had a radio back at Chu Lai.

Thank you,
Mr and Mrs Clyde C. Dawkins
Biscoe, N.C.

Alerted by a sudden rock crunch coming from the gravel road, Brown drops and swings up his rifle. Through the darkness he scans the field-of-fire past the barbed wire fence and beyond the rows of concertina wire. With his finger tight around the trigger, he continues to scan back and forth across the area trying to detect the slightest movement.

To his relief, a small gray/black dog comes into view. It is hardly more than a bundle of bones with a tail appearing like the frayed bristles of a discarded cane broom. The mongrel continues past with jerky movements caused by its stiff probably arthritic joints.

For the fun of it, Brown swings over his rifle and dry-squeezes the trigger.

"Take care pup." He watches as the dog gets eaten away by the darkness. "Ain't much worse off than us."

Sloan

CcccCrrack!!

Rummmble!!

The lightning flash is followed seconds later by a tropical thunder clap that rumbles through the thickly humid, drizzly atmosphere.

"How ya doin?" General Morgan asks.

"Tired. Hungry," Brown said his face drooping. "Just tryin' to make it one step at a time."

"Take care of the seconds and the hours will take care of themselves."

The scene unfolds as more lightning flashes and the ground shakes from the rolling thunder. Then, as if by the mere turn of a faucet, the drizzle bursts into a full-blown torrential rain shower. Although Brown has lived in the field throughout the month-long Asian monsoon season, it occurs to him that until now, he has never heard thunder before in Vietnam.

As he shivers from the cold rain that drains off his steel pot to run down his back, he remembers how as a child his mother had given him the impression that rain could somehow harm a body. He could hear her saying, "You'll catch a death-of-cold if you don't get out of those wet clothes." Silly nonsense. Thank God. Or else I'd be up Shit Creek without a paddle by now, he thinks amused.

Brown and his platoon have secured an area around a flooded rice field, skirted on two sides by thick vegetation, that will serve as a pickup zone. In a short while, they will be choppered to LZ East, Hill 488, a mountain overlooking an area the Vietnamese call Valley Of Living Death.

Principally, the valley is a heavily-traveled infiltration route from the Laotian leg of the Ho Chi Minh Trail. The Americans try to control the enemy flow with three fire support bases: LZ East, LZ West and LZ Center. Brown's platoon would be assigned to LZ East. Based on the circulating rumors and reports, the Vietnamese moniker for the area seemed more than appropriate.

After wringing rain water from the towel, he whips it back across his neck and shoulders, first feeling its chill then the returning warmth. Brown tries not to dwell on what happened the last time he'd worked the Valley Of Living Dead. But the memories persist and valley names continue to provoke bone-chilling visions of horror, mutilation and a blood bath. A firefight in Que Son and Hiep Duc valleys could easily turn into a full fledged battle that would last for days or even weeks at a time.

Always the observer, Brown searches the faces of the soldiers in second platoon. He knows that in all likelihood, tomorrow there would be one less man. Maybe more. Maybe a lot more. Maybe *his* number would get punched. He'd buy the farm. It was common knowledge that those valleys could suddenly run red and devour an entire infantry company in an hour.

He studies the expressions on the soldiers' faces and wondered if there were some way to tell on whom the angel of death would place a hand. Possibly somehow they already know of their impending death because of a premonition or something that came to them in a dream. Would the premonition show on their faces as a forlorn or obscure look of doom that spoke, "My days are numbered. I'll be dead in three." After all, the battalion average casualty rate was three WIAs a day and one KIA every third day.

The towel is again drenched. He wrings it out and places it back around his neck. Needing to keep his mind occupied, he continues to look from one soldier to the next. It occurs to him that even though they are all issued the same clothes and have access to the same equipment, everyone's individuality is still alive and well. A helmet invariably tilted slightly back or to one side. The name of a girlfriend or some perverse statement printed boldly on a helmet cover. A sleeve rolled high enough to expose a tattoo. A shirt unbuttoned to the navel. The front of a T-shirt ripped open and looped together with shoe string. Or maybe a faithful hunting knife arranged for easy access. The stance, walk, shoulder position, physique, and equipment arrangement also became very individualistic.

In a war where constant replacements, rotations to the rear, serious wounds and death didn't foster familiarity. Little differences of style and mannerism were often all that were remembered of the soldier: "Wilson bought it." ". . . Wilson?" "Yeah, you know, the guy who always cleaned his nails with a bayonet and had DEATH WISH written on his helmet." "Oh yeah right, guess he got his wish."

At Argo High School, Brown's sister, Roxanna, had been in a play, *The Diary Of Anne Frank*. He remembered hearing about the final cast party, how emotional everyone became, how the tears flowed and hugs went all around. Granted some were seniors, and quite possibly would never see each other again, but basically the cast and crew were together for maybe twenty practices and six performances.

In contrast, he never shed a tear nor saw anyone else shed a tear—for any reason—even though they'd been welded to a combat zone twenty-four hours a day, some like him for the last six months. He knows relatively nothing soulful about any of these other soldiers and visa-versa.

His eyes drift to the other side of the flooded rice field to Private First Class Sloan. The soldier stands silhouetted against the lush green jungle, his breath condensing in the cool air. He's primarily known as a "good follower," a soldier who would do the task, whatever it was, without complaint.

The six-month field veteran stands in a classic grunt warp. Even without the weight of the rucksack, his back is curved, shoulders slumped and neck elongated with droopy head. His combat gear rests in a mud puddle next to him looking more like a shrub than war equipment. His clean and well-oiled rifle rests, butt on the ground with prophylactic-covered muzzle, against his body.

Clutching a crumpled pack of Winston cigarettes, Sloan clumsily pulls one out. Noting a break in the soggy filter, he discards the tip and places the remaining portion between his chapped lips. For the purpose of camouflage, his helmet is covered with an array of sticks and leaves which he minutely adjusts to create an overhang for the cigarette. That accomplished, Sloan searches for and finds a dry book of matches. After several failed attempts, one limp match burst to life. Greedily, he cups his hands around the flickering flame and inserts the cigarette through the opening. A series of satisfying clouds of smoke get puffed into the air.

Flicking the dead match, Sloan takes a deep satisfying draw and rolls his head back with an air of reminiscent pleasure. For the remaining life of the cigarette, it will stay planted firmly between his lips. There is a real fear of inadvertently soaking it with water and possibly jeopardize this special, very precious, contemplative moment.

Sloan, like so many others, will often stare for hours on end at his letters from home, reading them repeatedly, and in between the lines, till they virtually disintegrated in his moist fumbling hands. By his expression, Brown decides, Sloan is reading his priceless correspondence from memory.

" . . . . went to the beach the other day and saw a classmate of yours, Julie. Back from college for the weekend I guess. Said she's doing real good. Anyway, she said Hi and said she might write.

From what I've heard it's really hot over there. Be sure to drink a lot of water and try to stay out of the sun. Oh guess who else I saw. . . . "

Sloan contemplates the overcast sky, shivers, and shoves his hands deep into his pant pockets. Then the side of Sloan's mouth curls, displaying a look that could pass as a silent cry.

With eyelids closed, Sloan slowly rolls his head around to stretch his neck, his body moving ever so slightly. What's he thinking about? Brown wonders. Or better yet, what picture keeps popping up? Is it the one where he's saying all the good-byes? Where he drops on one knee to wrap his arms around his baby sister?

"I love you so much," Baby Sister says through teary eyes.

He can't respond, afraid he might betray his quaking emotions. So with his face pressed tight into the nape of her warm neck, he lightly strokes, then crushes her long chestnut hair in his hand.

"I'll be back before you even know it," Sloan tries to sound up-beat as he whispers in her ear. The words may have fooled baby sister, but his shaking body doesn't buy it. A lump the size of an apple restricts his throat and he can't stop the feeling of a red hot knife being pressed through his heart. He slowly releases her, but that only makes her hold on tighter.

"I love you so much," baby sister sobs.

"I love you, too." Nothing can stop the tears that begin to roll down his cheeks. Again, he buries his face deep inside the nap of her neck to draw on her fragrance and warmth, his arms

lifting and squeezing her against his body. He wipes his cheeks on her frilly white blouse before daring to raise his head.

After pasting a wide grin on his face, he holds her at arm length and in a jittery voice says, "Will you wait for me?" With his finger he delicately wipes tears from her cheeks. "I'll be back before you even know it."

Baby sister stares with big round Bambi eyes, her cheeks already chapped and red. Then she bolts and runs to clutch her mother's skirt.

Stands like a gallant knight in shining armor, Sloan watches tears roll down his mother's cheeks. "Mom, you said you wouldn't."

"Keep your head down," she said hanging onto the barest threads of composure.

After a final glance at his loved ones, he turns. The last words he hears are, "Write. We love you."

"And I love you too, mom," he says barely audible.

Second platoon hasn't had a "walk in the sun" for months. They seemed to have bought a ticket for a carnival horror ride that never seems to end. The trick question was not so much whether Sloan would finish the ride, but rather, when it ended who would the man called Sloan be?

The "thud-thud-thud" of the approaching Hueys sends Brown's heart rate beating in unison.

Sloan saddles his gear and steps into the flooded field. As he splashes toward the chopper, he takes one last choking draw on the cigarette, pulls it from his mouth, and scrutinizes the red tip before spreading his finger to release it into the water.

While trudging through the mud, he gazes back over his shoulder toward the tree line. Written on his helmet is:

OLD MEN
RAGE WAR
THE YOUNG
MUST DIE!

THE MOMENT

If he joins a cluster-fuck
who will keep watch, listen for the
rustling of bushes, the crack of a branch,
or scrape on the ground? Instead, he must
embrace his loneliness. If he tries to be cool and
"let it all-hang-out," chances are Charlie Cong is
gonna take a crap. Instead, he must accept the
sadness—aloneness. Staying strong enough to die,
will give him the courage to live. This is no place for
emotions, they only get in a trigger puller's way.
He must stay busy, while seemingly do
nothing. He must control the isolation that
pushes him to the borders of madness.
Let his mind, body and soul
unite! If not, this may be his
last . . . moment.

Plate 54   **Sloan** *(illustration by John Tylk from a Dana Stone photo)*

Dig-it

"Oh my god," Brown mumbles woozily feeling his body vibrating. "Where am I now?" He opens his eyes to peer downward from the open-sided Huey slick that flies some 1000-feet above a lush green valley floor.

"Que Son and Hiep Duc Valleys," General Morgan said, appearing next to him on the helicopter's deck.

"Known as the Valley Of Living Death. How could I ever forget?"

Flying within the trough of the connecting valleys he notices in the distance a Huey and Puff the Magic Dragon gunships. Their machine guns, rockets and motorized Gatling guns spilling an unrelenting blood stream of death. Not far from the duet of death, is a Phantom F-4 jets screeching out of a power dive after belching its payload of thunderous napalm. The napalm bombs hit the ground exploding into a raging ball of fire that lurches, and in one big gulp, consumes an entire block of real-estate. Meanwhile, a vintage Second World War Tiger prop airplane, flown by the Vietnamese Air Force, does the honors. Machine guns blaze away as it sweeps low dropping off its brand of doomsday. And in yet another sector, an artillery battery mercilessly bombards a target with their special version of *whirring* shrapnel.

Brown has a panoramic view of the ensuing battle a virtual smorgasbord of ceaseless bawdy rumbling war. The billowing black smoke provides an appropriate backdrop for the display of deserts.

A yellow plume of smokes begin to spew from the peak of a commanding hilltop. The color mushrooms skyward, marking the mountain landing zone. Brown's chopper begins its final approach to Hill 488.

From his vantage point, the hilltop has the appearance of scared and burnt flesh. Its grotesquely raw dome is ravines gouged, barbed wire choked, and denuded of all meaningful growth. The mountain peak sets in stark contrast to the quiescent blue sky and lower elevation lush green triple canopy jungle.

"Place gives me the creeps," Brown says out loud.

"*The Alamo*," Morgan said. The nickname derived from an assault against the hill a few months back that left only three Marines alive at dawn.

His gaze remains transfixed on the abomination as the chopper careens for a landing. Brown takes a deep breath and exhales slowly, half expecting *incoming!* as they try to land. Unconcerned about the blinding prop wash, Brown and the rest of his platoon hustle from the chopper even before the skids settle on the ground. Leaving nothing to chance, they hurry from the LZ in search of cover.

"Gunfighter!" someone shouts, "draw!" Brown turns to a GI, who stands with back to the prop-wash, casually smoking a cigarette.

"Dig-it?" The soldier smiles in response. "Damn, man. Is that you?"

"What's the world coming to when you don't recognize an ol' leg buddy?"

"Sure I do. How could anyone forget an ugly face like yours."

"Fuck you." They smile. "I could recognize that candy ass walk and sissy way you carry a rifle anywhere."

"Better watch it. Them's fighting words." Brown raises the rifle and bares his teeth.

Dig-it extends a raised palm. "Put 'er there buddy." They clasp hands.

"So how's it hangin' man?" Browns asks pleased with the momentary diversion.

"Shit," Dig-it swears while motioning to the dismal surrounding. "Whatdoya think?" He wipes a piece of tobacco off his stubby beard. "Be glad when we blow this joint. Tell ya what. We ain't had shit for rest since we got to this piss-ant two days back. Ain't but fifteen of us trying to secure this whole fuckin' thing. And the whole fuckin' time they keep fuckin' probin' us with them fuckin' rockets and fuckin' mortars."

Stunned by the physical deterioration of his friend, Brown finds himself unable to pay close attention to the conversation. While continuing to talk and smoke, Dig-it unbuttons his pants and begins to urinate.

"You know what? No matter what you do, after you take a piss there's always one last drop that ends up running down your leg. Ever notice that?" Dig-it grins displaying rows of tartar covered rotting yellow teeth.

With emotions weaving back and forth from outright hilarity to out-and-out fright of the confronting reality, Brown continues to stare dumbfounded.

"Hey, man, what the fuck you lookin' at? Huh?" Dig-it gives a good-natured huff. "You don't look like no sleepin' beauty yourself."

"Well, I don't look as fucked-up as you," Brown said, and

they laugh. "They haven't actually tried taking this hill, have they?" Brown said becoming serious.

"If they really wanted it?" Dig-it said motioning with the barrel of his M-16. "They could take it all. Easy."

His matter-of-fact posture sends shivers running through Brown's body giving him a pucker factor of seven. The situation conjures up visions of Mexican soldiers scooting up ladders to pour over the walls of the Alamo. And of Davy Crockett, Colonel Travis and Jim Bowie firing muskets, then resorting to swinging their rifles like clubs in the midst of a losing battle.

As the conversation continues, Brown can't help but note the sallow face with dark brown retinas surrounded by snakes of red in a sea of yellow and how deep the eyes are sunken into their purple skin sockets. There is no mistaking the exhaustion in this filthy dirty, bone-numb grunt. His friend is so far beyond normal exhaustion that there was no hope for a revitalization. Dig-it flops his penis back inside his ratty pants and buttons the fly. That's when Brown notices the droplets of urine all over his dusty boots.

Dig-it raises his chin to acknowledge a shout from his squad leader. "Hold this Brownie." He hands him two bandoliers of M-60 machine gun ammunition. Hoisting the rucksack off the ground, he struggles to get it on his back.

"Fuckin' thing gets heavier every day," Dig-it said, then adds, "Last night at LZ Center they killed some twenty-five NVA in the wire and they got six more in the perimeter."

Brown helps drape the two bandoliers over his shoulder.

"They all had fuckin' brand new AK-47s and Chicom hand grenades galore. Can you dig it? This ain't like fightin' the dinks back around Chu Lai where there's only one fuckin' carbine and a handful of shells between 'em." He field strips the cigarette butt, and starts to search for another.

"Lucky?" Brown offers him a cigarette from a C-ration four-pack.

"Wish I felt lucky." Dig-it places the offered cigarette between his lips and pulls out a Zippo lighter inscribed with the words:

YOU HAVEN'T
LIVED
TILL YOU'VE
ALMOST DIED

"Enemy anti-aircraft fire," Brown notes, listening to the throaty sound of them pounding away in the valley. Both soldiers move to a vantage point and stare with sorrowful fascination into the bowels of the ensuing battle.

"I can just make out LZ Center from here," he says pointing northwest through the battle clouds.

"Weeeeeeeahaaaaaaaa!" came the sound of powerful engines of a Phantom jet pulling out of a bombing run dive.

"Music to my ears." Dig-it studies the cigarette he rolls back and forth between his thumb and forefinger. "It's like the whole valley is playing a fuckin' death march."

"Just for us," Brown said.

"Yeah." His eyes follow the flight path of the F-4 Phantom. "Fightin' never stops. Day-in. Day-out. Around the clock. A*lllll* the fuckin' time." He looks at Brown through blood shot eyes. "One NVA division after another is moving through here from the Ho Chi Minh Trail. And those suckers do not run and hide like the local VC. They'll stand right up in your face and fight ya to the death." Taking a draw on the fresh cigarette, Dig-it glances over to his reconnaissance platoon which has started to board the chopper.

"Brown." Dig-it breathes loudly through his nostrils. "You know that guy, the one we used to. . . ." his voice chokes in mid sentence. Dig-it's eyes drifted over the valley where vultures, cruising in a circle, waiting for someone or something to make them a meal.

"Can't help but watch those buzzards." Spastic muscles make the side of Dig-its mouth winch. "They'll start wide, then, little by little they swoop lower and lower. The circles get tighter and tighter." He jumps the rucksack to let it settle on his back. "I keep picturin' one of those damn birds perched on my head, feasting on my eyeballs.

"Gotta shake it off," Dig-it said shaking his body like a dog after leaving the pond. "Hey, still wearin' that good luck Montagnard bracelet the dink chick give you at Nuc Mau, huh?"

"Yeah, sure do," Brown said spinning the bracelet on his right wrist. "Never take it off my wrist."

Dig-it stares with a woebegone expression. Brown touches his shoulder and Dig-it returns the gesture with a light punch to his arm. "No way to weasel outta this one. Dig it?"

"We'll make it," Brown said encouragingly and smiles.

"Please Mr. Custer, I don't wanna go," he sings the lyrics from a popular song about General Custer and the Battle Of Little Big Horn, "Forward ho-*ooow*."

Silence falls between them as they look at each other. "Say, it's been good seein' ya, buddy." Dig-it trudges away with boots clopping to join the other soldiers of his squad already on the chopper.

"Hey, Dig-it!" Brown calls. "You dropped something." Brown picks up a crumpled pack of cigarettes that slipped through his friend's ripped cargo pocket. He hurries over and hands it off. "We're gonna make it. You hear. Take care."

"Fuckin' A," Dig-it says with widening eyes. "You know me."

The words have a hollow sound, and for a fleeting moment, Brown's eyes burn. He watches his tired old friend hump away, his feet leaving a trail of dust. Before boarding the chopper, he turns to give Brown the two-finger "Peace" sign."

The flying debris from the accelerating chopper blades forces Brown to turn and cover his face. After the chopper lifts and moves away with the wind subsiding slightly, he turns to watch. Dig-it sits on the platform bowed like an old man staring woefully, the cigarette still planted between his lips.

The Huey banks and at eye level, heads in a straight line for LZ Center. Gradually, the helicopter takes on the appearance of a tadpole swimming in a valley of clear water.

Once more Brown becomes aware of the thunder of war and the distinctive "Thump! Thump! Thump!" of the NVA antiaircraft gun.

Brown shudders in disbelief as he watches green enemy tracer fire target Dig-it's chopper. The Huey shakes abruptly as it gets raked by enemy rounds and at that instant a soldier falls from the platform. "Dig-it?"

For a moment it appears as though the pilot has regained control as the helicopter levels out. But like a sitting duck, the anti-aircraft gunfire continues its onslaught, again riddling the fuselage. Forward motion slows as the Huey's blades lose speed. Then for an instant it seems to just hang there, suspended in midair like a toy on a string.

Flames belch from the exhaust and the helicopter noses forward like a sinking battleship. It then plunges, gathering speed as its blades shear off resembling a fireball headed for the lower hells.

"Oh my God."

WINTER KILL

I t was the
call o f the
Am e r I can
Eagle. S o
with   t h e
style of a badass, a flag and
cigarette in hand, his
mother walks him to war. Now
as Nam's acid etches through his
mind, the transformation ignites
his eyes. Everything has become
a crock of shit, and all he can trust
is his sweet-16 and a full magazine.
For months he's marched in jungle
jungles and muck, waiting while
avalanches of water soak him.
And he has been rehearsing
death, but with t h e vision of
a clumsy animal's annihilation.
He's found that special kind of
sorrow, that special kind o f
alone, when the winter's wind
b l o w s before summer i n
this . . . special kind o f W a r.

Plate 55 Dig-it *(Illustration by Art Rydell)*

EGGERT, RUSSELL WILLIAM	05 MAY 68	55E	010
FREEMAN, JAMES PAUL	05 MAY 68	55E	011
NORMANDIN, DUANE M.	05 MAY 68	55E	025
QUICK, ROBERT EUGENE	05 MAY 68	55E	027
REINHARDT, BARRY THOMAS	05 MAY 68	55E	028
WEDDENDORF, ROBERT G.	05 MAY 68	55E	035

Death Battalion

Brilliant white phosphorous glistens as it incinerates and scorches. Jellied-gasoline napalm bombs belly-flop, roll, rumble and engulf large swatches of jungle, its fireball fingers collapsing lungs and turning flesh into rawhide. Artillery rips, gouges, and slices at the very arteries of the jungle. To the men of war it's as though vampires stalk the battle-saturated Valley of Living Death. Hunting. Patiently hunting. Gloriously hunting.

A sporadic volume of horror clamors and echoes up from the bowels of the valley floor. The constant battle drones fuse with the shouts of leaders and the terrifying screams of the newly wounded; the ones who lay bleeding to death that clench their teeth and gather enough strength to raise and fire their weapons one last time. But the most uncanny sounds of all comes from the wounded with hope already drained. From those who suck in the pain of their mortal wounds and stare in wonderment at their exposed intestines. From those who pray or repeatedly mouth the names of their loved ones. From those who lay calmly with eyes glazed, body shattered only one heart beat away from eternity.

On occasion there is a thick eerie silence, a kind of a pause or exhale in the battle which gives everyone a chance to take a deep cleansing breath, say a quick prayer over a fallen comrade, and for themselves, then hastily reload. Then the silence gets swallowed, replaced by completely new and inventive sounds which rumbles, froths, and boils anew from the connecting valleys. The caldron-rim mountains again throb and pulsate with crimson slaughter and horrific destruction.

Morgan? Brown says to himself looking around hastily from the helicopter's platform. Where are you. I'm not doing well. I need you.

LZ Center looms into view and seems to embody the symbol of skull and crossbones. On nearing the landing pad of perforated steel planking, Brown half expects to see brimstone and fire, and the red devil himself with raised pitchfork directing the chopper's descent.

Stoically Brown disembarks, his hand mashes into a semi-wet? He looks . . . *blood*. KIAs zipped tight inside black body bags are carried past and loaded even before he clears the PSP.

Two officers standing off to the side argue. "Acute situation reaction," the younger of the two says slowly punctuating each syllable. "Walking wounded. Shell shock. Battle fatigue. Bloodless wound. You understand me?" he said in a stern accusing voice. "You're pushing them beyond living. As for me, I have an obligation!"

"There is no choice here, dammit!" the senior officer fires back. "You know what I'm up against." His eyes drift toward the landing pad and to the body bags. "I can't pull back now. And desperate measures are necessary. Believe me," he stares intently at the junior officer, "I don't enjoy getting my hands dirty, any more than you."

"Then plan better!" the junior officer shrieks. Their eyes lock. "You knew the bomb allocation was low before this started. So you had a choice. I'm warning you, sir, if you continue to push these men," he pauses for punctuation, "you won't have to worry about *their* choices. They won't have any left. And while you're at it, why not rename the unit? Give it some Second World War blood and guts name like *Death Battalion.*"

Brown half expects to hear someone shout, *"Cuuuuuut! That's a wrap. Print it."* Then wearily, "And let's call it a day."

The actors would shake off the tension with some light hearted jousting. The ones inside the body bags would unzip themselves and walk away with fake blood dripping off bandages and extra body parts in hand. Everyone from the director to the stellar actors, from the camera men to the bit-part actors would laugh and joke at the intensity and authenticity of the scene. "Cool. Congratulations." "Academy Award on the way, man." "High five!" "How did you learn to act like that? God you were great." And the director smiles at his support staff and says, "If we keep this pace we'll finish ahead of schedule and receive a big bonus."

A benign infection begins to rage inside Brown as he watches two soldiers grab a body bag and swing it like a side-of-beef onto the deck of the chopper. A thousand KIA voices thunder through the wake of silence, professing to the remaining soldiers, "You ain't gotta chance in hell."

Brown slumps away, noticing that the putrid smell from the chopper pad lingers in his nostrils. He rubs his nose and sniffs only to realize where the odor really comes from—it's the smell of his own decay.

At the assigned bunker, Brown lets the heavy rucksack slip off his shoulder and free-fall to the ground. He freezes in place as his mind spins out of control. For the next few moments, he fights against the sheer enormity of the doom and gloom. Fright and panic sweep through his mind leaving in their wake weakened knees, frayed nerves and a stomach alternately getting filled with butterflies then all tied up in knots. He fights against an

Plate 56

Brown *(Illustration by Curt Chiarelli)*

overwhelming sense of emptiness and futility—a vision of a clumsy animal's annihilation. The continuity of his mind is scrambled and it leaves him with little self control.

Peeling loose the fatigue shirt that's sweat pasted to his back, he fans the skin till some circulation returns. With rifle in hand, he plods around to the front the bunker and scans his field of fire. Below lay a mountainside strewn with the remnants of a tree shattered rain forest now choked with concertina wire, laced with trip wires connected to booby trap mines and grenades, and command detonated claymore mines.

Turning to the sound of shuffling feet, he sees trudging toward him eight of the hardest-*run* grunts—bathed in grime and gore—he'd ever seen. Their fatigues hang shabbily over their sore flesh and bones and showing through the fabric's many rips and tears is blackened dried blood and red bruised skin. Only two of the grunts haul a rucksack and remarkably one is even without a weapon. Everyone still wears a pistol belt, though the ammunition pouches appear empty, and bare of hand grenades.

One of them staggers from weakness and, by the way his head rolls drunkenly, it seems he might literally die from exhaustion even before hitting the ground. Just in the nick of time, another grunt grabs his arm to awaken and steady him.

All the while he watches, there is the distinct impression that if they dare stop their slow motion drag-pull shuffle, they might not have the strength to get restarted. The feeble grunts continue to trudge, their dragging feet leaving behind fleeting clouds of dust.

A scene flashes in his mind of Civil War soldiers, looking just like them, straggling back from the disastrous Picket's Charge at the Battle of Gettysburg on July 3, 1863.

One soldier who clutches a C-ration meal in a bandaged left hand, peels off and floats ghostlike past Brown headed for the adjacent bunker. After propping his dirty rifle against the sandbags, he leans back and, using the sandbag wall as a skid plate, slides to the ground. Dropping the ration meal next to him, he leans against the bunker.

Plate 57   Rock Bottom *(Illustration by John Tylk)*

Remaining within the hypnotic state of mind, he stares into space. Then ever so slowly, he pulls off his steel pot. Removing his glasses with taped-up nose bridge, he begins to lick the lenses. With them sufficiently wet, he attempts to remove the smudges with a relatively clean spot on his filthy shirt. As he rubs, rivulets of sweat course down his rough bearded face and dribble off his dirty chin.

From a bulging cargo pocket, he produces a can of beer. He reaches for the BUDWEISER stamped can opener secured to his steel pot. That's when Brown notices the name

ROCK BOTTOM

written in black permanent marker on the helmet cover and realizes this is the veteran from Larson Field. Could that have been only a few weeks back? Rock Bottom's grungy beard made him appear a good decade older.

Though small in stature, not giving the physical appearance of being big, bad, and brave, Brown knows Rock Bottom has the mind of a warrior. The kind of mind that can disconnect from danger and can shun the terror of death. But Brown also knows that the last month had been saturated with too much war. Saturated with too many moments with the prospect of death, and now, even Rock Bottom appears to have come unglued.

The bandaged hand is swollen but can still grasp the warm can of *Pabst Blue Ribbon* beer He drinks long and hard with some dribbling down his chin. Stopping only to catch his breath, he finishes the warm sudsy drink in under thirty-seconds.

Turning the meal box upside down, he shakes out the contents and grabs a ration marked SPAGHETTI WITH BEEF CHUNKS IN SAUCE.

With a practiced motion, he runs the P-38 can opener around the can's edge then pulls back the lid which is still attached to the can. From a shirt pocket, he pulls out a filthy spoon, sucks it clean and spits out the dirt. Holding the spoon in his arthritic moving hand, he begins to shovel the fat-caked food into his mouth.

Brown yearns to talk, but thinks it best to wait. Let the starving man eat. After a drink of strawberry Kool-Aid, Brown reaches for his own rations. He selects a can of PORK, SLICED COOKED WITH JUICES and a can of crackers.

Making a concerted effort to get the soldier's attention, he exaggerates every movement while fumbling with the rations. "These SP packs are sure tough to open when your hands hurt," he said. Clenching his teeth on the edge of the plastic bag which contains the C-ration accessories, he finally succeeds in ripping it open.

Rock Bottom lifts his eyes lazily while placing another spoonful of spaghetti and meatballs in his mouth.

"Hi. How ya doin'?" Brown ventures a greeting.

Through cracked lips that had left dried blood on his beard, he responds sleepily, "Huh?"

"I got more food if you need it," Brown said nodding to his rations.

"Haven't eatin' for days. Nearly starved to death." He looks at the half empty can. "And now . . . ain't that hungry," Rock Bottom said, his teeth glistening with red sauce.

"You Charlie Company?"

"Yeah."

"I'm Delta. Used to be Reconn but when the replacement came over in March, they turned us into Delta Company. Was a Slow Poke RTO for awhile, but lately I've just been a grunt. You know that radio can get your back after a while. What with the extra battery it can weigh as much as twenty-five pounds. And that's a lot of extra weight to be carryin' around all day long." Brown finds himself babbling.

"That fuckin' Yamane," he said the name fondly. "He with ya, ain't he? That little Jap and me go w*aaaaa-ay* way back." A glimmer of a smile touches his face as he relaxes against the bunker. "We were both mechanized back at Fort Hood, Texas. And there were those times. I'll tell ya what. One cool Jap. He knew his way around the motor pool. Wanted to go with him to your platoon . . . but you know."

"Yamane's dead."

Rock Bottom expression freezes.

"Killed back in March on Hill 45. I was with him."

A haunting expression eclipses Rock Bottom's ashen face as the horror of it starts to pour into his blood engorged eyes. Apparently losing his appetite completely, he sets the food off to the side and begins to fumble with a pack of *Winston* cigarettes. One at a time, he fishes them out and in dismay finds them either soaked with fear-sweat or broken. Settling for a droopy filter-less one, he slips it between his lips.

Exhausted from the effort, his eye lids flicker and it appears like he might pass out.

You idiot. Shit! Why did you have to go tell him like that? Brown hollers at himself. Thinking fast, he dove into his pockets and pulled out a book of matches and lit one.

"Here ya go, man." He moves the flame under the cigarette and after a few puffs, comes to life. Lethargically Rock Bottom takes a long, deep suffocating draw, then pulls it from his lips with a shaky hand. Raising his head, he looks straight through Brown like he doesn't even exist. Settling against the bunker, the cigarette slides from his fingers and onto the moist ground. Clumsily, he opens a can of bread, turns it upside down and taps out the contents. Then crams a wad of dough into his mouth.

"Grape Jelly?" Brown holds out a can. Rock Bottom nodes, so Brown quickly opens it up.

"Thanks," he said spooning the jelly into his mouth.

While chewing, Rock Bottom said, "You know if you're killed, they nail your coffin shut. Closed casket funeral." The nonchalant remark felt like a savage slap to the face.

Actually, the last thing either of them need to talk about is this, yet sadly enough, nothing really matters any more but *this*. In the intermittent silence, life continues to suck at their vital organs with their youthful vitality continuing to drain away.

"We ran right onto a fuckin' machine-gun nest. Not a damn thing we could do. Two guys were cut off and there was no way to get 'em out. Nothin'," the words trail off. His eyes implore Brown to search for the deeper story. "A couple more guys got wounded trying to take out the bunker. One of 'em took a direct hit in the face . . . his head just disintegrated. It was no ordinary machine gun, man, it was a 51-caliber antiaircraft gun. I mean those things don't just wound, if a round so much as nicks ya, you're histroy. Bye-bye." He lifts a feeble hand and waves good-bye.

Searching for the lost cigarette, he finds it on the cold ground nearly sniffed out. Puff, puff, puff. He pulls it back to life. "If we'd gotten outta there, we wouldn't have been surrounded, but we just couldn't leave the guys behind. So we got stuck, couldn't pull back and were too close to call in artillery. We dug in and for the rest of the fuckin' day and night, we held our position. Then the calling started."

Rock Bottom takes a sloppy drink of water. With appetite renewed, he eats more spaghetti and meatballs. His mind wanders back to the valley. "Help me! Help me! Oh, please dear God. Pleassss-e," came a plea that is from another voice. "The captured guys just kept calling." He takes another spoonful and slowly chews.

"A whole fuckin' night of 'em screeee-min'. I mean there was nothing—not a fuckin' thing we could do but get ourselves killed tryin'." Rock Bottom stares at the fat caked food. No tears come to his eyes, the crying seems to be taking place much deeper, deep inside the heart. "You know what I'm sayin'?" He breathes deeply and exhales loudly. "A whole fuckin' night of hearing my buddies scream."

Rock Bottom runs the spoon around the inside of the can trying to get the last morsels of food. He grabs another ration can. "Lookie what I got." He smiles showing the label PEACHES IN SYRUP. After opening it, he drinks the heavy syrup, then starts grabbing the peach slices between filthy dirty fingers.

Moving closer so he can hear better, Brown lowers himself into a dink squat.

"Just before dawn, we figured our guys were dead or close to it, so we brought in artillery and overran the machine-gun emplacement," Rock Bottom said. "Nothing could have prepared us for what we saw. Nothin', man. There they were. Three," he raises three finger, takes a second to think, then raises one more finger. "Maybe four guys. I don't know where they all came from. You know there's other units out there besides ours.

"Anyway, there were body parts all over the fuckin' place. One guy was hanging by his ankles from a tree limb . . . skinned. Literally. Like a rabbit.

"Another had both arms missing. Our pointman, Gunner, and this other guy were on the ground with their hands and legs tied behind their backs. They'd both been kicked and beat the whole fuckin' night. Just before we got there, they put a bullet in one guy. Gunner was still barely alive, but they'd cut his belly wide open. We found him barely alive holding his intestines in his hands. Ya know what I mean?" Rock Bottom's eyes said there is more, much much more, but he stops. Maybe the rest never made it to his brain—maybe it never would.

"Motherfuckers knew we'd be comin'. We heard the mortar tubes, so we *di-di-ed* outta there and right into a fuckin' ambush. Only thing we could do was drop the gear and make a run for it."

"That's what I've been tellin' ya, Gunfighter," General Morgan injects, materializing and squatting next to Brown. "The best part of valor is knowing when to run. But to do that, you must go deeper inside yourself. Deeper than you ever thought possible and find that source of realism you never thought existed. Then someday go back and face the reality of that action."

The empty ration can slips from Rock Bottom's bandaged hand. He slides sideways against the bunker and onto the ground where his head comes to rest upon a protruding rock. Out for the count.

FERGUSON, LEROY	09 MAY 68 57E 020
HARRIS, ROBERT EARL	09 MAY 68 57E 023
DUCE, ROGER	10 MAY 68 58E 015
MENCONI, WILLIAM LEE	11 MAY 68 58E 023

Dear Ma

"What?" Brown snaps awake bolting upright. Sitting quietly next to him is General Morgan.

"Where?" he questions as they both stare from their mountaintop perch into the black depths below.

"Que Son Valley."

"Still there," Brown said despondent. He settles himself better on the rocky ground and grabs his M-16 rifle.

"You were asleep on guard duty, Gunfighter," Morgan chides. "If you were caught doing that in the Civil War you could be shot by a firing squad."

"When was the last incoming mortar?"

"A couple about a half-hour ago."

"This nearly constant mortaring has me goin'."

"Listen Gunfighter, I don't mind helping out some, but you need to stay awake. I can't do this alone."

"Sorry. I didn't mean to fall asleep." Brown begins to meticulously scan the field of fire down the side of the mountain to the edge of the dark tree line. And while looking around his ears try to detect and identify any sound, no matter how minute.

Satisfied that everything is safe, he takes a drink from his last canteen of water. Lifting his Marine soft cap, he pours some over his head to let dribble over his face. Then, he shakes his head and pats his cheeks. "Man, I feel half dead."

"Why don't you write a letter home?" General Morgan suggests.

"Yeah, sure. I could do that." Brown reaches for his helmet and slides out a plastic bag from under the head straps, the only place he'd ever found where things could be kept dry. From the plastic bag he pulls out a piece of paper. Laying the rifle across his lap for a writing surface, he flattens out the sheet of paper then takes a pen from his shirt pocket.

"Code of Silence?" General Morgan questions.

"I know. What happens in the bush stays in the bush. But it doesn't work for me."

"Go ahead then, I won't fight ya. Talk it straight, Gunfighter. Your mother is a good woman. She'll understand."

Dear Ma,

Here I am in the boonies. We are doing good. We haven't lost too many men so far. We have taken two hills over. We got light resistance.

Now tomorrow we will try to take over an old 101st Airborne Fire Base that the NVA took over.

You know this fighting and dying, it plays tricks on a man's mind. I go through changes. At one time I don't care if I live or die. Then another time I am so afraid, I shake.

I have received Dad's letter and all of yours.

"Wow! (They come up to me and say) Ha, Brown, can I read some of your letters? I didn't get none."

That sesame seed bar sure is appreciated. Wow! It tastes good. Ma, I hate to say this but that lemon flavored Kool-Aid needs sugar. Read closer okay. I had to throw it away. I don't have hardly any Kool-Aid left, okay?

Ever since I've been in the field it has been Hump! Hump! Hump! When we assaulted one hill I could hardly walk up it, let alone run after NVA. But I have stopped and slept every chance I get. I feel okay now.

Plate 58 Brown writing home*(illustration by John Tylk)*

Me and the lieutenant are tight. I guess because I led our platoon up the hill. We were the second platoon up so I only got a few rounds over my head. A couple guys behind me were wounded though.

When we stopped on the hill the NVA started mortaring and rocketing us. Bla! I will not tell you how close the rocket was to me. But we killed six NVA, captured twenty AK-47 rifles, two M-16s, an M-60 machine gun, mortars with ammo and a rocket launcher.

It was a bring down. We moved into our night logar and they were mortaring us all the time. One Medevac after another. You should have seen me work out on my hole. Scoop. Scoop.

Tomorrow we are going to take the hill, World War II-style. We have to go through barbed wire obstacles and knock out bunkers. The hill is bare. Not too much cover from mortars, rockets, and small arms. We knocked out one of the 51-caliber machine gun, antiaircraft today. The jet just blew him away. There is still another one over there, I hope he doesn't let us have it.

Everything is rough and rugged. These last three days we have been mortared three times heavy. We are mortared almost constantly.

We are low on food, water, and sleep. I went almost one day without eating. We have no food now. I don't know when we will get some.

Everyone realizes the dangers coming. We all are excited. We took two hills, tomorrow the third and last.

We got the smell of winning. We will show them what we have tomorrow. I don't know who is in the lead but if it is us, you know what the chances are.

I am pushing for R&R. Hurry! Hurry! I hope I don't get wounded before R&R. I got $100 cash and a $400 money order. $500 total. Good huh. Wow! Clean sheets and a bed under a roof, air conditioning, TV, room service, Wow! I just don't know what to think. But after R&R I don't think I will come back to the field. I will have them break my arm on R&R so I will not. After this mission, I have done my share. I want a fair shake. If they will not give it to me. No sweat. I will give it to myself.

It is 11PM now. I have guard until 1AM. In the books they say you should not be on guard over 90 minutes. But they didn't take into consideration that I am writing home.

Did I tell you I found a cross? I sewed it over my Brown's Chicken patch. I camouflage it. It feels good. It is a real nice cross. It was digging a hole with my entrenching tool next to this old bunker when I bumped in to it.

Oh well. I am working with three new guys. I got them thinking for themselves. They are learning what to do and what not to do. They have turned out good.

Every once in a while you write, BRUSH YOUR TEETH AND WASH!. Wow! It has been well over a month since I washed and the same way with my teeth. But I sweat so much all the dirt just runs off. My teeth. Bla. I will not mention them.

That was alright for Roxanna coming home, wasn't it? I will send her a present from R&R. Good idea Huh. I will send everyone something. Okay?

You should see those gunships. Jets and Sky Raiders working out! Wow. They are something else. The jets open up with a burst of 40-mm cannon and you hear it.

Then a Wheeeeea. The blast of the jet engines. Shee woww! The Sky Raider knocked out an ambush a couple of days ago. The NVA were setting up to mortar one of our companies. Then we walked up. They tried to ambush us but we blew them away. They mortared us but Blam! and no more mortars.

Wow! 45 minutes left. Hurry time hurry. I am tired.

They are firing all night on the hill we are going to take. I feel so good. We are finally doing away with some NVA. They are a hard shell to crack. They will not run but stay there till they get you or you get them.

I realize more and more. This war will not be won by man power. Life is nothing to them. China and North Vietnam have unlimited man power. Russia has unlimited supplies. We only have so many men. Out of these men only one out of every ten get out and fight. The rest stay at base camp under roofs. We call them REMFs (Rear echelon mothers...) you get the idea.

Wow! I am getting tired.

Well, I better close. Thanks for the candy and Kool-Aid and all. Running low on Tabasco sauce. It makes even Choke and Puck takes good. Haa Haa. Honestly, I don't know what I would do without it.

Bye until later. Don't worry about me getting hit.

Bullets hurt. Okay?

Your son,
Fred leo

Peace Wants To Die

Brown stares perplexed at the bloody strip of T-shirt wrapped around his right hand and to the numerous lacerations and blood running down his forearm. Then to his left hand which is also bleeding from open scabs and to the machete held tightly within its grasp. Before him lay the explanation, a narrow trail bordered by razor edged elephant grass.

In a flood of afternoon light some fifty-yards behind, he sees the rest of his platoon. The dazed and confused soldiers appear intoxicated, incapable of walking a straight line. Some appear so inebriated that their buddies have to either carry part of their gear or help coax them along.

"You're pointman, Gunfighter," General Morgan informs him.

Continuing to absorb the explosion ripped, denuded jungle that surrounds him, Brown starts to piece together a time line. "The lieutenant got hit by a mortar." He stares at a once majestic tree with top sheered off and main trunk ruptured by shrapnel. The charred and dying remains of its broken branches now carry only wilting and shriveling leaves. "So that means first platoon, instead of us, took the hill at 0500 hours this morning."

Sweat pours out of his body like rain and dribbles off his shirt as he starts to hack with a dull machete at the ten-foot tall elephant grass to open the path. "We're in the middle of a twenty-one day battle where my battalion will take nearly eighty-percent casualties." He wipes sweat from his salt irritated eyes and off his eyebrows.

"I feel sick." He stops, places his hands on his knees and lowers his head. "Feel like I'm gonna pass out." An intense skull bleaching sun shines through the clear blue afternoon sky. The elephant grass effectively stops even the slightest breeze and the fine grass-dust parches his throat making the stifling hot air hard to breathe.

His mind has gone from hard-boiled to runny and sunnyside-up in the last two hours. At the moment, he's barely capable of keeping his eyes from rolling back inside his head, let alone making them focus well enough to pick out the muzzle of an enemy AK-47 rifle, a booby-trap trip wire, punji pit or a suspect ambush.

Stepping on a protruding rock his ankle twists, sending him staggering sideway with his leg muscles threatening to cramp under the exertion. He grabs a sapling to steady himself till his quivering muscles regain their strength. The rucksack seemed to be gaining weight with each foot drop and now feels like a ton of bricks on his back.

Woozily, he makes his way over an outcropping of huge boulders. Noting a depression in the granite, he turns and pushes back to nestle his rucksack inside the crevice. Resting, the machete slips from his bruised hand to spear into the ground, the

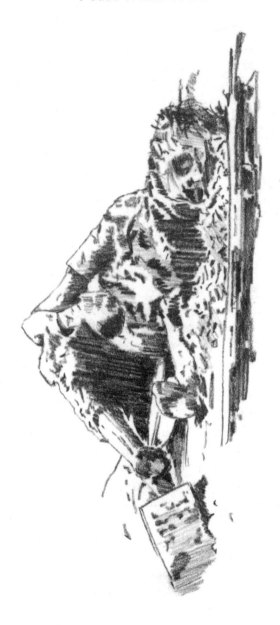

Plate 59   Crispy Critter *(Illustration by Art Rydell, from Dana Stone photograph)*

handle clanging against the rock. Since the steel helmet is too hot to handle, he merely pushes it back enough to expose his forehead. Leaning back into the gear as far as possible, he places both hands on his spine and, with a practiced move, decompresses his back and neck vertebras.

Taking a slow deep breath, he closes his eyes and rolls his head to face the sun. Dropping his head, Brown keeps his eyes closed to watch shooting stars orbit the afterimage halo of the sun. He blows sweat from his lips and grimace when salty liquid rolls down his arm and into an open cut.

Unable to keep his hands from shaking, it takes both to steady the canteen for him to sparingly drink. This is the last of the water. He pants like a hard-run dog, mouth wide, tongue hanging out.

A mile or so back, he had stumbled upon a crispy critter next to an abandoned NVA campsite. A white phosphorous, Willy Peter, or napalm bomb had fried the enemy soldier to death. All that remained were bones draped with parchmentlike-skin. And just a few kilometers back, he had noted some bloody body parts, possibly an arm and shoulder, or leg and thigh, dangling from a shattered, defoliated tree. Morbid thoughts persist to eat away at the thinning threads that hold his sanity intact.

"Call it, man."

Like deep within a dream, Brown slowly raises his head. "Peace?" A soldier wearing a head rag made from a T-shirt humps over. "Where'd you come from, man?" Brown gazes at an ashen mosquito-pocked face and notices the momentary vacant look in the deep set eyes—the thousand-yard stare.

Peace scrutinizes the trail. "What's goin' on?" he asks nodding in the direction of the meandering path. "Spooked or is somethin' up there?"

"Nothin'. Just beat," he huffs.

Peace shrugs his shoulders and stares at Brown. "You look white as a ghost."

I don't believe it, Brown thinks. That's exactly what I was thinking about him.

Plate 60 **Peace** *(Illustration by John Tylk)*

Peace pushes back his head rag to wipe sweat from his brow and eyes Brown's canteen. "Whatdoya got there?"

"Goofy Grape," Brown said, referring to the flavor of Kool-Aid in the quart canteen. "Not much in it. But it's yours if you want it."

"That's my favorite, next to Freckle Face Strawberry," Peace said. "I love Freckle Face." He takes the offered canteen and drinks.

Brown watches as Peace's Adams apple bobs and marvels at how everyone drank with a prescribed amount of dribble flowing down their chin and onto their chest.

"Good shit," Peace said, finishing the canteen and wiping his mouth. He pulls a canteen out of his pistol belt pouch and shakes it. "Half full. Here, take it," Peace said, handing it to Brown.

"Sure?"

"I drank all yours. And what are buddies for?" Peace smiles. A tear begins forming on the side of his eye, and with a quick hand movement, he whisks it away. Adjusting the head rag, he turns to scrutinize the trail.

Strapped to the back of his rucksack is his steel pot. On the helmet cover is an artsy drawing of a peace sign. Brown remembers how all the guys had thought Peace had made a stupid mistake when he drew the symbol upside down. "What an asshole," someone said and everyone laughingly agreed. When questioned, Peace calmly raised three fingers, pointed to his middle finger, and explained, "It means 'Fuck Peace.'"

They both glance back at the survivors of Second Platoon, Delta Company, 1/6 Light Infantry, 198th Battalion, American Division strung out along the jungle path. Their eyes return to the trail up front that snakes and disappears behind the outcropping of boulders on which Brown rests.

Without another word, Peace reaches for Brown's machete and takes point leaving something in the wake of his smile that makes Brown's stomach churn.

Plate 61 **Peace's helmet** *(Illustration by Art Rydell)*

"What're you doin?" Brown mutters. No one just walks up and volunteers for point. No one. That would be crazy. Like asking to be dragged-out and shot.

"Take care buddy," Peace said rounding the corner and disappearing from view.

When the third squad leader approaches, Brown asks, "Muton, what's the deal?"

"Deal?

"Yeah, Peace just took point."

"And?" Muton said, his usual self belligerent and short-tempered. "Wanna stay on point?" When Brown didn't respond. He mellows. "Listen, man, he got a *Dear John Letter,*" he said his left eyebrow raising.

Three more soldiers pass and disappear around the corner while they talk. Muton begins to follow. "Tell ya what. More of us been killed by them damn 'Dear John' letters than by the fuckin' bombs."

Brown struggles to pull the weight back onto his shoulders. Just then a large explosion shatters the silence with shrapnel pinging off the bolders.

"Mediccccccccc!"

PEACE WANTS TO DIE

Told her he'd be back
in a flash, after scaling
a   few   commie   for
Christ. A million-dollar
wound? might be back
even sooner. She bought
it. With a pucker factor of ten and the elephant hot on
his ass he wasn't so sure he did anymore. The truth?
He stood between a rock and a grenade. Her S.W.A.K.
perfumed love-sick letters meant *everything*, then came
the Dear John. That kind of bombshell makes taking point
through Injun country a
walk in the sun. Now a
booby trap done blew
his leg and balls clean
off. And as they rush
him in a bloody poncho
to the dustoff, he grasps
Brown's arm professing,
"It's all over, man." They
position him near the
LZ to the echo of an
M-16 nailing a coffin
shut. But Brown can't
help but wonder if that
bitch knew all along the
boy wasn't gonna make
it a-back, back, back.
May he rest in peace.

POHL, WILLIAM ANTHONY	13 MAY 68	59E 029
GILBERT, RICHARD LEE	14 MAY 68	60E 010
JOHNSON, DANIEL GENE	14 MAY 68	60E 012
MAURER, JAMES ROBERT	14 MAY 68	60E 014
HAYES, FRANCIS JOSEPH JR.	15 MAY 68	60E 023
PICARELLI, JOSEPH HENRY	15 MAY 68	61E 001
PHELPS, LARRY DELTON	16 MAY 68	61E 017
SEGAL, JEFFREY BERNARD	21 MAY 68	65E 001
O'NEIL, TERRENCE EDWARD	23 MAY 68	66E 012
TAYLOR, CLIFTON THOMAS	23 MAY 68	67E 003
CHITWOOD, JERRY MICHAEL	24 MAY 68	67E 007
HAYDEN, ROBERT ALLEN	24 MAY 68	68E 002
MICHALKE, RUSSELL AUTHUR	24 MAY 68	68E 005
TURNER, PHILIP GERALD	24 MAY 68	69E 003
MOODY, HERBERT WAYNE	25 MAY 68	67W 001
BASTARACHE, FIDELE JOSEPH	27 MAY 68	65W 005

Grim Reaper

While checking the map, illuminated in red filtered light, Platoon Sergeant Robin Hood sucks and chomps fretfully on the wooden tip of his unlit Hav-a-Tampa cigar. "I don't know," Robin Hood said shaking his head in confusion.

Brown looks at the topographical map. "Where'd we lose it?"

"Not sure."

"Gonna haveta double-back?"

"Looks that-a-way." Sergeant Robin Hood switches off the military goose neck flashlight.

They both gaze along the trail that peters out inside a ten-foot stand of elephant grass. In another place and time, they would easily pass as a crusty cowboys of the Old West who have followed yet another blind-trail.

"We're all so wasted, ain't no one who can even follow a *fuckin'* trail," Brown swears. Taking advantage of these few precious seconds, he bends to places hands on his knees to relieve the weight from the rucksack.

Clicking the flashlight back on, Robin Hood moves the tip of his grease pencil along a black thin line that represents a foot trail on the topographical map that weaves its way up the mountainside. "That's where we should be," Robin Hood said tapping the map with the pencil.

"But we ain't."

Approaching midnight the remnants of Second Platoon, Company D, 1/6 Light Infantry halts on a ridge adjacent to Suicide Valley. The darkness, along with the patches of thick towering elephant grass has contributed to the inability of any of the last several pointmen to stay on the trail. In less than two hours, they'd lost the narrow path three times, and each time they had gone through the arduous task of doubling-back.

"It's gettin' too late for this shit," Brown said. He stretches out his aching back. "Should've found a night logar before this, Sarge."

"The CO thinks the NVA are tailing us," Robin Hood explains. "That we'd be safer on top of this mountain."

"And you listened to him? Why didn't you ask me?" Brown felt the sting of betrayal. "For chrissakes, Sarge, he just got here. And I've been humpin' the bush for the last six months."

They both look at the other soldiers cloaked in extreme exhaustion, barely able to keep their balance.

"I'm hungry."

Robin Hood places a hand empathetically on Brown's shoulder, leans close, pulls the cigar from his mouth and spits. "Listen Brown, you're the best pointman we've got."

"You mean, the only Gunfighter you got left."

"You got this built in navigation system. I tell you where we wanna go and you get us there."

"If I do, you owe me a can of peaches and pound cake."

"All I've got is a can of pears. No pound cake. But I got some beans and dicks and Tabasco sauce."

"That'll work."

"Brown, seriously," they face off, "you're the only one who can get us up this mother."

A pregnant silence falls between them. The reality of the situation rolls slowly like droplets of water trickling off a block of melting ice. The cool water seeps into the crevices of Brown's numbed mind. He shudders. Then the liquid hits circuitry that sparked with the ultimatum. He faces the platoon sergeant who, again, is chomping fretfully on the wooden tip of his cigar.

"Brown?"

Avoiding the posed question, he slowly pulls off the heavy steel helmet and runs his fingers through his short matted hair. Brown looks up at the dark starlit sky, over to the jungle and finally to the dead-end trail.

It has been one of those long legendary kind of days where one moment a soldier is brave and the next he's shaking like a leaf. Where everything is calm one second and the next someone screams *Incominnnng!* While continuing to let the cool night air wick sweat from his brow, he contemplates the half moon rising.

"How soon before we get that three day stand-down at the Chu Lai Beach USO? Huh? Haven't showered in a month. Look," he drags his hand over his forearm, "my skin is peelin' off."

"All I can do is ask," Robin Hood said. "But I'll tell ya what, when we get there I'll throw in a Steam 'n' Cream at the village."

"Promise?"

"And all the beer you can drink."

"I'm only nineteen and I lost my fake IDs"

"I know the owner." They chuckle. Robin Hood attaches the flashlight to his rucksack suspenders and stuffs the map into his pants cargo pocket knowing he was winning. "Well."

"Well, what are we waitin' for? Let's dance." Brown replaces his steel pot, bumps the rucksack and shifts the bandoleer of M-60 machine gun ammunition to make it settle on a different set of worn out muscles. With stars of overexertion swirling through his vision, he again rests his hands on his knees. It feels like he is having a sensory overload, as though some type of internal circuit breaker is shorting out big time and about to blow-off. The chest muscles around his heart clench and jitter for a second.

After a few deep calming breathes, he forces his mind to focus. Squaring his shoulders, he checks to make sure the rifle selector switch is on automatic and the taped together ammunition magazines are tight and secure.

The aftermath of the late afternoon firefight still hung heavy on his mind. His buddy, gong-ho Klick, and the pointman were both killed shortly after the opening volley. A half hour later, with the dead body of Klick draped over his shoulder, Robin Hood had worked his way past Brown headed for the Medevac. Blood was still oozing from Klick's fatal AK-47 chest wound, streaking down his face, and dribbled off his blond hair onto Robin Hoods clothes.

"Stay glued to my ass," Brown said returning to the moment. "That's an order." Robin Hood gives a reassuring nod.

Without anymore discussion, Brown turns and squeezes past the other soldiers on the narrow trail to take the pointman position and begin the search for the elusive mountain trail.

"There, Gunfighter," General Morgan said materializing a few paces to the front.

In the pale moonlight, Brown acknowledges him and turns off the main trail to follow a faint path leading up the mountain. With his rifle, he pushes past the elephant grass and heavy foliage until he comes upon a worn little footpath.

"This is it," Brown said as he looks around the area to reassure himself.

"Get your distance," General Morgan said.

"Right." In order to concentrate and hear better, he quickly moves a good fifty-yards out in front of everyone. Then to detect movement better, he starts to mechanically swivel his head from side to side. For the next hour, Brown maintains his distance, repetitious posture and pace while snaking his way noiselessly up the narrow, dimly lit, steepening mountain path. Only on occasion does he stop to slow his heart and breathing rate so they don't effect his hearing

Because of his near hypnotic state of mind, Brown wasn't concentrating on the trail itself, so is shocked to find himself at the edge of a huge clearing. He pauses, scans the rocky surface, and wonders when the mountain's crown had been cleared of foliage. "The last time I was here, it wasn't like this."

"Don't reckon it was, Gunfighter," General Morgan said. "Looks like a field cleared for plantin'."

"I don't like it." Brown kneels and waits for Robin Hood to catch up.

Platoon Sergeant Robin Hood pulls alongside, and they both check the terrain covered in loose rocks scattered by numerous artillery bombardments.

Brown gestures and mouths, "Move off to the right."

Robin Hood nods, and they begin walking noiselessly and cautiously as possible in an ever-widening V pattern. After a good hundred yards of planting one foot after another, they come upon the earth of a freshly dug NVA slit trench line.

Ever more guarded, Brown hunches and in slow motion moves to the edge of the excavated dirt that stretches along the edge of the enemy trench. Peering along its length, he spots an unattended assault rifle.

"What?"

"Over there," General Morgan alerts.

Confused, Brown turns to see only a few yards away, two inattentive soldiers manning a machine gun just beyond a bend in the trench. The last he'd heard, their sister company would try to rendevous with them. And since there was no shooting they must be Americans, right? "Say!" Brown pipes up, "you guys from Charlie Company?"

Both startled soldiers jump and whirl their machine gun while yelling feverishly in Vietnamese.

"Aaaaaaaaaah!" Brown gives out a bloodcurdling scream and pulls the trigger on his M-16. The black-widow jumps to the command and begins to spit death. Moments later the mountaintop erupts with small arms' fire. Then out of nowhere, a mysterious black-capped figure swoops past Brown heading down the trench seemingly to follow his red tracer fire.

Momentarily, he stops firing to search for the black figure when General Morgan shouts, "Get down!" and shoves him to the ground. "Don't look at that thing!"

Enemy green tracer fire streaks past where Brown stood only moments before. He lifts the M-16 over his head, approximates the angle and fires along the trench, hoping to pick off any confused enemy soldiers. In a practiced motion, he ejects, spins around the taped together magazines and reinserts the fresh side, pulls back the charging handle and opens fire.

The rifle chokes and stops firing.

"Oh shit!" Feverishly, he ejects the magazine, fishes out the double feed rounds, reinserts the magazine and begins firing. Again the mysterious black-capped figure swoops heading for the trench. It disappears inside the NVA trench. Just then a machine gun barks from a bunker near the crest of the hill.

"Robin Hood!" Brown hollers over the noise. "Where are ya?" Brown detects enemy movement on his far left side and fires. For the third time, the black-capped shadow pops into view. What the hell?

The machine gun position that Brown knocked out moments before suddenly sparks back to life. Its bullets begin to ricochet off the inside trench walls lusting for him. He pulls a hand grenade off his ammo pouch, yanks out the pin, jumps from the trench and lobs it directly into the machine-gun nest. Instinctively, he spins around, drops and lets loose a rifle burst directed at a movement on the hilltop.

A bullet zings past sounding like the *buzz* of a bee. He rolls, breathlessly waiting for the grenade detonate. It doesn't explode. "Shit!"

Tracer fire from the machine gun nest suddenly diverts and sparks as it ricochets off a boulder some twenty-five meters inside the perimeter. Why there? Then Brown sees that Robin Hood has taken cover behind the boulder in a effort to get closer to the enemy command bunker.

The night is alive with assault and machine gun red and green tracer fire and explosions that send sickle edged shrapnel ever nearer. Brown's face twists into a grimace, every muscle in his body rigid. His hands, arms and shoulders wrestling to control the beastly M-16 that he fires indiscriminately at anything that might even think of moving.

Robin Hood rolls back his arm and with the strength and accuracy of a big league baseball player, launches a grenade that flies directly into the enemy bunker. The explosion that follows making the interior of the bunker glows with white death.

Seeing a chance, Brown jumps from the trench to land on his knees. Lifting the rifle as high as possible, he fires. An accurate stream of death again pours into the machine gun nest.

"*Shit! Shit! Shit!*" Brown's rifle jams again. He jumps back into the trench, pulls the bolt back and grabs at the double-fed bullets. NVA soldiers still manning the machine gun, probably now wounded, start to direct their fire to sledgehammer the trench wall, walking ever closer to Brown.

"Won't they ever die?" Brown jumps back out of the trench with the rifle slipping from his sweaty hands just as bullets *whizz* down its length. Grabbing the last grenade from his ammo pouch, he pulls the pin and lets it fly toward the machine gun nest. The grenade detonates with a bone shattering blast, enveloping the machine-gun position inside a brilliant inferno of shrapnel. Back inside the hole, he grabs his disabled assault rifle.

Brown kicks out the magazine, takes his cleaning rod and rams it down the barrel to eject the jammed round. He slams in a fresh magazine and pulls back the bolt to send a round slaming into the chamber. In the next moment, the mysterious black-capped figure that has been flying through his peripheral vision jumps from where his grenade exploded and again flies in line with his red tracer fire.

"My God."

As the cryptic figure bounds, twists and rolls through the area, it tosses black silhouettes skyward. Then like an evil black bird, it too soars to gather its flock. Hovering, it suddenly throws open its cape to expose a parched skull. Two red coals burning inside sunken eye pits, stare straight into Brown's soul, then *Swoooooop!* With its razor-edged sickle the Reaper slices apart two disorientated NVA soldiers in unison with Brown's M-16 rifle burst. The Grim Reaper swirls its cape and collects the lost souls that rise from the doomed.

"Damn!" Brown's rifle jams again. He looks to find the Grim Reaper's bone finger sticking into the rifle's bolt.

With a flying leap, General Morgan piles headlong into the Grim Reaper's side, breaking Its grip on Brown's rifle. Brown tumbles backwards as something slams into his chest knocking the wind out of him.

Brown ejects the magazine, draws out his cleaning rod and rams it down the barrel to knock out the jammed round. He locks and loads as the NVA regroup and sneak toward him along the trench. In an evasive move, he slithers back into the trench. Guardedly, he rises from the trench till he barely sees the first soldier's head. Points and fires.

Raising even higher, he swings his rifle to fire into NVA maneuvering along the hilltop. With a single long burst he's able to disorientate the group that retreats or drops immediately to the ground. His rifle jams once more.

"Robin Hood!" Brown screams over his platoon sergeant, who has returned to the trench barely able to hold their right flank. "My rifle keeps jammin'!"

With a swoop of his arm, Robin Hood javelin throws an M-16 rifle. Brown's hand wraps around the blood-covered hand guard of his dead friend Klick's rifle. Robin Hood begins firing away

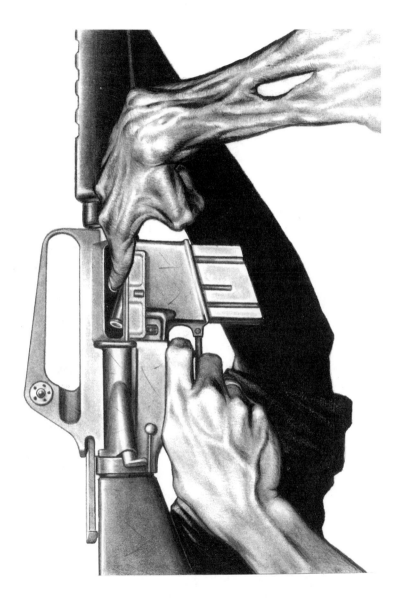

Plate 62   Grim Reaper's finger *(Illustration by Curt Chiarelli)*

with an enemy AK-47 rifle. A brilliant idea, Brown thinks, using the enemy weapon will confuse the NVA about their actual position.

Brown throws in a magazine, switches the new rifle to rock 'n' roll, knees and fire three entire magazine without a malfunction.

Again, the voracious Grim Reaper follows Brown's bullets to slice out more lost souls. Then the Reaper whirls and with a hand gesture sends a paralyzing icy spike through Brown's heart. Brown swoons as he watches the Grim Reaper whip the cape tightly around its body. Paralyzed, he watches the black draped figure transforms itself into human form. A short, bespectacled man sporting an ill-fitted brown toupee emerges, puffing on a cigar and wearing brown colored pants with a mismatched sports coat. With an air of confidence, the man walks toward Brown.

"Dad?"

His father smiles wryly giving a nod of recognition.

"What are you doing here?"

"I came because you need me," his father said sounding like the good parent.

"What? Mean you care?" Tears come to Brown's eyes.

A disarming smile sweeps across his father's round face and with open arms he says, "You've always been such a unique person and well, I'd like to let bye-gones-be-bye-gones."

Completely taken-in, Brown lowers his M-16 and begins to stand.

Seeing the trap, General Morgan levels his Spencer repeater and squeezes the trigger. A black-powder cartridge explodes, its heavy 52-caliber lead ball smacks with a deadening thud into the human skull. The face shatters sending the ill-fitting toupee flying. The bald-headed abomination shakes violently, splitting open from head to toe, an eerie light coming forth. Out of the cocoon shell steps forth the unharmed Grim Reaper.

"Gedown!" Morgan yells.

The spell broke. Brown drops to the ground and rolls into the trench as bullets riddle the now vacant air. Then just as he lifts his head a rocket-propelled grenade (RPG) explodes, sending sharp-edged steel *whizzing* through the cool night air. Collecting his senses, Brown again raises his rifle overhead and begins firing down the length of the trench. Re-loading, he stands and fires magazine after magazine after magazine at a frenzied pace into anything remotely similar to an enemy.

"Brown!" Sergeant "Jelly Belly" Grauer yells, dropping to the ground outside the trench. "What the fuck?" The Second squad's leader fires his rifle. "This is a goddamn NVA perimeter!"

"I know," Brown shouts, his mind clearing. He ejects a magazine, reloads and both he and Jelly Belly lay down a blanket of fire along the length of the trench and up to the top of the knoll.

"We can't hold it," Brown shouts. "Gimme a flare."

Without question, Jelly Belly rummages through his rucksack, takes the illumination tube, and thrust it into Brown's outstretched hand.

Brown twists off the firing pin cap, slides it over the back of the cylinder and smacks it with the heel of his hand to send a flare streaking through the night. The parachute pops open and hangs like a cynical jack-o'-lantern, illuminating the entire mountaintop.

All small arms fire and explosions cease. Friend and foe seem to take a deep contemplative breath as the area becomes eerily quiet. The flare reveals a mountain strewn with dead or wounded and crawling NVA, six crouching American soldiers and a second enemy perimeter on an adjacent knoll to the left.

"Jelly Belly, get me some ammunition. Then you and the rest dee-dee outta here!" Brown orders.

Within minutes Jelly Belly is back with nearly twenty magazines of ammunition. Quickly, he fills Brown's ammo pouches, stuffs his cargo pockets and stacks the remaining five magazines next to him.

"Got any extra hand grenades?"

"No. Not really."

"Then *goooooo!* Damn it. *Go, go, go!* I'll cover."

The illumination flare fizzles and goes out. Robin Hood and Jelly Belly let grenades fly at the NVA positions, turn and with the other, bound down the hill headed for the safety of the tree line.

Brown opens up with suppressing fire and keeps up the frenzied pace across the NVA perimeter for the next five magazines. The second knoll spots him and opens fire. Regardless, he continues to blanket the area with his rifle fire. Over his shoulder, he watches as Jelly Belly and the rest disappear from view.

"They made it." He looks back up the hill. "So this is it."

At the sound of crashing steel, he turns to see Morgan's Spencer rifle barrel spark, turn red hot and bend under the impact of the Grim Reaper's sickle. The force hurls General Morgan backward, who hits the ground hard among some jutting rock, knocking the senses out of him. The Grim Reaper looks over at Brown, moves his jaw ever so slightly, then lunges for Morgan who draws his cavalry saber. The Reaper grabs the blade at mid swing and bends it back toward Morgan's throat.

Morgan resists with all his might, but can't stop the steel blade from inching downward till it creased his throat and blood begin to stain his neck. With one last almighty thrust of his knee, Morgan shoves off the Grim Reaper and rolls free.

"Morgan! There's no way out." Brown screeches over the deafening noise of the battle. The escape route is under repeated strafing and rocket fire. "We ain't gonna make it."

"Talk like that only gives the Reaper more strength. Shake out of it, Gunfighter," General Morgan cries out, wiping blood from his face and leveling his Colt revolver. "Don't give up! A doubt is what he wants." He fires point-blank into the Grim Reaper's face, who bucks backwards only to recoil. He fires again and again and again with the Reaper only momentarily recoiling.

Then fearlessly General Morgan jumps in close to deliver a crashing left fist to the Grim Reaper's bone face, and follows it with a shattering haymaker-right punch that cracks the jaw and shatters teeth. The Grim Reaper barely moves while Morgan continues the good fight, repeatedly punching the Grim Reaper with no more effect than to move It back a few paces.

"Don't roll over and just die!" Morgan yells between punches. He delivers another series of punches which crack his fingers making them bleed profusely. "You've gotta live!"

The sickle-arm swoops to catch General Morgan in the side. He goes down coughing up blood. The Grim Reaper levitates and dangles against a background of lightning streaked sky. Its restructured jaw opens to create an ever-increasing vacuum that sucks in streams of weak, cooling souls.

Brown swoons at the sound of soft melancholy music, the smells of flowers in bloom, and the caring words of his father. Succumbing, he's gets drawn further into the very jaws of death with delicious hell's fire licking his face.

"Look out!" Morgan yells, holding his bleeding chest with one hand while working himself into a standing position.

The impact of an explosion throws Brown to the ground. Morgan lunges to grab the cape of the airborne Grim Reaper. They both tumble to the ground with General Morgan's head smashing into a boulder, his Colt revolver flying from his grasp.

"Run, Gunfighter. *Runnnnnnnnn!*" Morgan shouts with waning strength. "For the love of God, *run!*"

The Grim Reaper raises its sickle in a slow rolling arch. At the last possible second, General Morgan raises his bent saber and runs it's full-hooked length through the Reaper, causing the doomsday sickle to narrowly miss its mark.

"*Runnnnnnnnnnnnnnnnnnnnnnnnnnn!*" General Morgan shrieks as the sickle plunges through his body making him winch in pain. An enemy grenade explodes. Shrapnel pings off a rock and more punch his fragmentation jacket and steel pot.

Brown ejects the empty magazine and reached for another, but finds both ammo pouches empty. "Shit!" He dives for the trench and collides with an NVA soldier. Rolling free, he grabs a magazine from his side pocket and, while keeping an eye of the enemy soldier who gathers himself together, frantically re-loads. Brown's fingers wrap around the trigger.

Plate 63   Grim Reaper *(Illustration by Curt Chiarelli)*

The NVA soldier looks over and quickly releases his AK-47 which drops to the ground. Raising both hands, he motions toward the tree line.

Keeping his rifle trained on the enemy, Brown turns and finds himself staring into the Grim Reaper's face.

"*Gunfighterrrrrrrrrrrrrr!*" General Morgan shrieks and, with his strength waning , fires the last bullet from his Colt revolver into the head of the Grim Reaper.

With a heel stomp, the Grim Reaper crashes down General Morgan's chest. Then it grinds its boney foot till it literally disappears inside General Morgan's chest with steam hissing from the cavity.

"*Aaaaaaaaaaah!*" General Morgan screams with his hands set firmly around the Grim Reaper's leg bone that continues to grind deeper.

Brown, for the moment forgetting the NVA, swings his rifle and lets loose with a burst of lead that shatters the Grim Reaper's skull. One magazine after another, he pours into the hilltop. The Reaper momentarily disappears on a mission to collect more lost souls.

Reloading, he checks to find only three magazines left. It's now of never. He takes a deep breath.

"Go!" he yells. Both he and the NVA soldier jump from the trench and run like mad, zigzagging across the open field. Brown trips and rolls furiously down the hill. Then with a single swift motion, he bounces back into the air and onto both feet.

Miraculously, he finds himself in the safety of the tree line. The NVA soldier, the one from the trench, stands a mere ten feet away. And though bent over with hand on his knees and breathing hard, the soldier stares at him.

Brown slowly raises his rifle thinking he might just go for another kill. "Enough," a voice commands from inside his head.

His hand acquiesced into a salute. The enemy soldier straightens and returns the military courtesy.

"Go." He waves the soldier away with a sweep of his rifle.

DEAL WITH IT

It's   having
nothing   t o
h o l d, that
hollow   n ess
in his chest, and
he can't tell what's
going down. But he deals
with it. He searches through
unraveling sanity, stuffs down
fat-caked C-rations unfit for a dog,
and does his best to ignore leeches and
mosquitoes that feast on his blood, leaving
welted flesh behind. That's what he's trying
to deal w i t h.   Spilling blood, sacrificing
blood, a loss of a limb, an organ, or buddy.
Now that's just asking too damn much. It's
gotten outta control, outta hand! It's all
gone to shit.   He can't deal with it no
fuckin' more! Didn't figure it a skate,
didn't figure on getting creamed
either.   But he's s t i l l a
believer and believes the
Man up above is still
saving a place,
just for him.

POWELL, JOHNNIE EARL	30 MAY 68	63W 019
ANELLO, BRUCE FRANCIS	31 MAY 68	62W 004
COWELL, JAMES EDWARD	31 MAY 68	62W 007

Rocket Pocket

Lz Bayonet, on Highway One, Chu Lai District, Vietnam
—September 1, 1968

A-choooo!" he sneezes for the third consecutive time with his neck muscles nearly cramping. While still bent over waiting for yet another nose-tickle, Brown wipes the dribbles from his nose. "Man."

When the urge passes, he straightens to find himself sitting on a folding cot in the open air next to field army barracks. Next to him on the bunk lay a ration meal of:

MEAL, COMBAT, INDIVIDUAL
TURKEY LOAF   B-3 UNIT

He goes through the four cans: crackers, peaches, cheese spread and turkey loaf. Armed with a P-38 can opener, he moves it around the edge of a C-ration can with the speed and precision of an electric can opener. By habit, he leaves a quarter-inch of uncut metal that will serve as a hinge. He pulls the lid back transforming it into a handy little handle and take a whiff of the turkey slices.

"Ummmmmm, ummm. Come to mama."

Opening the other cans, he spreads the entire mix out on the bunk. Looking around guardedly, he slides a can from his pocket. "Pound cake," he says and kisses the can "Peaches and pound cake well ain't that somethin'. It's time to party." Earlier, when no one was watching, he had scavenged through an entire case of ration until he found the most coveted can in the C-ration case—pound cake.

Placing the cellophane wrapped spoon, that came with the ration meal, into his shirt pocket, he pulls a dirty one from the same pocket. Sticking it into his mouth, he washes it clean with his tongue, then spits out the dirty saliva. Sliding the edge of the spoon into the fat-caked food, he takes a bit and follows it immediately with a cracker.

"Desert before the main course?" He dumps out the pound cake. "Yeah. Why not." With edge dipped into the can of peaches, he lets it soak up a generous amount of sugar juice. While continuing to savor every morsel of food, he casually surveys the rucksack, fragmentation jacket, steel helmet and the rest of his combat equipment lying on the ground with his assault rifle propped against it. With can raised, he sucks out a peach slice along with heavy syrup. Before swallowing, he takes another bit of pound cake.

Hearing the subtle sound of an approaching Huey helicopter, he turns and shields his eyes from the morning sun. Looking across the expansive windswept military installation where dust chases itself, he spots the chopper approaching from the mountainous west.

So absorbed in the moment, Brown doesn't notice when General Morgan appears sitting on the next bunk over. "Familiar?" General Morgan asks.

Still not registering the circumstances, Brown finishes desert and grabs the can of turkey loaf. Then with wide eyes, he focuses on the general who's chest, head and both hands are wrapped in bandages.

"Damn, man. You look like shit."

General Morgan smiles and grimaces as the tender facial skin stretches.

"Thought we were both dead meat up *there* on that hill."

"You never gave up."

Brown's eyes radiate with concern as he looks at the pitiable General Morgan. "Only because of you, am I still alive."

"You fearlessly went against an entire company of NVA and lived to write home about it. God must have a purpose for you," Morgan said thoughtfully.

"I'd like to think so."

"You should receive the Congressional Medal of Honor for what you did."

"There was talk, but. . . ."

"But?"

"The two officers with me put themselves in for Silver Stars for valor. Robin Hood got a Bronze Star for valor and the guys killed, well, they deserve everything they get." Sadness slackens Brown's face. "Medals of valor for me? Just ain't gonna happen." He pauses. "I ain't a suck ass."

"The officers in your war are self servers aren't they. Tell ya what Gunfighter, I'll vouch for your bravery."

"You mean that?"

"Yes, I do." Suddenly, Morgan is standing holding his re-shaped cavalry saber ready to slash. Then striking a comical Grim Reaper face, he stares with calculating cold eyes. "Now you shall die."

"Hold that pose, I wanna take a picture."

"You look rested," Morgan said cheerfully as he sheathed his warped sword and sits back down.

"I oughta," he nods eating a cracker. "Just got back from seven days of R&R in Australia." Brown rubs his hand vigorously along his arm to show General Morgan that no more dead skin would roll off. "It took me a week to get myself clean."

With teeth glistening from the turkey loaf, he adds, "I've got a couple hours to get ready to go back into the bush." He motions to the combat equipment. "You comin' with?"

"If you don't do nothin' foolish." They laugh and Morgan again wrenches in pain which makes them laugh even harder.

He takes a bit of turkey. "Wanna some?" he offers. "Oh sorry, you don't exist." His eyes alert realizing he's been talking out loud. Quickly, he looks around at the rows of canvas and galvanized roof hooches, burlap sandbag bunkers, outhouses with nearby barrels of burning feces and drainage pipes pushed into the ground for urinating. And is relieved to find only a few slow moving sweat soaked soldiers walking through the area.

"This another unforgettable day?" Brown asks. General Morgan nods. "Okay, lemme think." Looking around, he points at the signature dust rolling up from a gravel road bed. "Well, that's Highway One. So that makes this, ah . . . LZ Gator?," he said trying to piece it together. "No, not Gator," he decides. "While in the bush my infantry unit moved their basecamp to Hill 69. But this isn't Hill 69 because it's too flat. Wait, don't tell me, this is LZ Bayonet just east of Chu Lai.

"And that. . . ?" He contemplates the approaching chopper flying through the early morning blue sky trying to jog his memory. The Huey rolls into a bank heading for the landing zone just to his front. There appears to be a soldier lying on the platform, though slightly off the edge with wind ruffing his short black hair. The head bobs up and down, back and forth with the Huey's washing machine motion.

"Why is he laying down like that?" Although knowing he should wait for the Huey to land because of the dangerous blade flop, Brown begins to walk over feeling the unexplainable urge to get closer. While still munching on a cracker, he covers his face to protect it from the obscuring cloud of stinging dust. The helicopter lands and its engine slows to idle.

Plate 64 LZ Bayonet (*Illustration by Art Rydell*)

Everything seems to move into a frame-by-frame mode. The dust clears more with each foot-drop. The scene starts to unwrap as Brown uses his sleeve to keep dust from his eyes. Soon he stands a mere twenty feet away from the helicopter.

"Oh my, God. No," he whispers. A shirtless GI runs to hand off some official looking papers to the helicopter pilot. The strangely familiar bobbing head is Angel's and next to him under the pile of other KIAs, lay Elvis.

The helicopter engine begins to rev and the dust builds till the scene is again engulfed in dust and flying debris.

Brown recalls the hot dusty day when the NFG, Pimentel, jumped off the resupply chopper to join the platoon. He stood tall, lean and youthful, quite a contrast to the rest of the platoon's bedraggled shoulder-warped grunts.

Pimentel carried with him a cassette recorder—the first ever to make it into the field. The battery operated player, Brown remembers, was an immediate sensation. He had tapes of the Mamas and Papas - Jefferson Airplanes - Doors - Jimmy Hendrix and of course Elvis Presley.

One day Brown overheard a heated debate coming from under a poncho tent.

"Elvis is still the King!" Pimentel shouted defiantly.

"Say, Elvis," Brown joked. "Need anything on resupply?" The nickname stuck.

The pilot revs its engines and the Huey lifts, banks and disappears.

"Do you remember?"

"You mean how Angel took the five day R&R and I took the seven day R&R. That with a little twist of fate, me not him, would have been a KIA on that chopper?"

"The rest."

"Yeah, I remember. I join the platoon later in the day," Brown said walking over to his gear to grab a canteen of water. "I'll find them on their mountaintop position which is part of a network of connecting ridges. A piece of real estate collectively called the Rocket Pocket, situated just west of *Chu Lai*. So named because the dinks are always hiding out in the area shooting mortars and rockets into Chu Lai.

"Anyway when I get there, the guys are all sitting around the perimeter stone faced and only Robin Hood will brief me on what had happened. Apparently, Charlie Company had walked into an ambush just south of their night logar. My second platoon was ordered into a flanking maneuver to cut off the NVA's retreat. Elvis took point and Angel followed a few meters behind."

As Brown talks he remembered how frequently Elvis was made to took point. Then again, "field initiation" meant the NFGs took point more often.

"Elvis gets hit at first contact," Brown remembers. "Angel tries his best to get to him, but is hit in the neck by an AK-47 bullet. And another one gets past his Marine fragmentation jacket to finish him off."

Brown looks to Morgan. "That was just like Angel, wasn't it. Always caring more about the other guys than himself. A man with a heart of an angel."

ELVIS AND ANGEL

Didn't know much about
Elvis's or Angel's families.
About their dream cars, how
many brothers and sisters
they each had. Wasn't
even sure where
they came
from.
But lately, I've had a recurring vision, about this girl running
with outstretched arms. Who stops to cry over an empty crib.
War's all about random choice, or rather, there being no clear
choice. How it's not right to complain, and
that we're all really part of it.
Anyway, Elvis lay out there
on point, blood pouring
from a bullet wound
to the chest.
Angel knew what
he had to do, and a round
went through his neck. They
died moments apart, trying to reach
each other. It's comforting to know their
names are etched only inches apart on The
Wall. And those Vietnamese children, the ones you
guys used to love horsing around with, they didn't know
what to say when I told them you both had gone to heaven.

BUSSE, DANIEL DEAN	01 SEP 68	45W 018
GOMEZ-MESA, LUIS G	01 SEP 68	45W 019
LAWS, LONNIE CHARLES	01 SEP 68	45W 020
OHARA, STEVE MASAO	01 SEP 68	45W 021
PIMENTEL, RONNIE CARDOZA	01 SEP 68	45W 021
REYES, ANGEL LUIS, JR.	01 SEP 68	45W 022
SHREWSBERRY, ROGER LYNN	01 SEP 68	45W 022

LZ Moore

A single rifle shot rings out shattering the predawn tranquility. Alerted, Brown peers through the front rifle slit of the mountain side command bunker, and into the haze of South China Sea fog. More shots ring out and echo down to the valley floor. Knowing only M-16s have fired, Brown holds his breath while waiting for an enemy response.

"Brownie," Okie, the third squad leader, said awakening next to him, "What?"

"I think the west LP made contact."

After listen to a short radio communication from the LP, Brown confirms, "Yeah, it's your listening post, Okie."

Without another word, Okie straps on his pistol belt, dons his helmet and grabs his rifle. Then with two others in tow, jogs

Plate 65   LZ Moore *(Illustration by Art Rydell)*

straight down the jungle trail and into the jaws of shadowy danger.

Three days later, Okie nails a painted commemorative sign to a shrapnel-scarred tree.

MOORE, WALTER LEE JR.   **29 SEP 68 42W 042**

Old Grunt

"Saddle up! Come on, *dammit*. Get ready to move out." The angry shout startles Brown who turns to face the speaker, an officer with a three-day beard and stern eyes. "I'm talking to you, too."

"Well, well. If it isn't our fearless platoon leader," Brown said not caring to hide his disdain.

"You're nothin' but an old grunt that can't keep his eyes open on guard duty," his newest platoon leader snaps.

"With all due respect, *fuck you*, sir. And I didn't fall asleep on guard. I never fall asleep on guard. Never."

"Tough guy, who thinks he knows it all."

"You ain't no John Wayne, yourself?" Brown snaps.

"Watch it," the lieutenant warns sneering at his platoon RTO.

Plate 66   **Platoon leader** *(Illustration by Art Rydell)*

"Oh*hhh*, I'm scared shitless now. Please don't send me to Vietnam, and make me take point, sir. Look," Brown nods toward his boots, "I'm shakin' in my boots."

Despise would be an understatement of what Brown felt toward his platoon leader—the sixth in last eleven months. All of them having left the field after a few weeks with medals of valor pinned on their clean and starched uniforms.

"You're just another asshole trying to make a name for himself."

"Youuu-u." The lieutenant's face flushes with uncontrolled rage. "We'll talk later." He turns and shouts to the rest of the platoon, "Saddle up, damn-it! Quit draggin' ass. Third squad you have point. Follow the trail leading north." He turns with a satisfied grin and glowers at his renegade RTO. Earlier they had a heated argument where Brown warned him about staying away from the trails because of the high incidence of booby-traps.

When he turns, Brown lightly touches a hand grenade attached to his ammo pouch, preparing for the *right* moment.

"Gunfighter!" The shout brings him up rigid. General Morgan appears standing next to him. "This will only provide the rope for your own lynching."

"Fancy that coming from you," Brown said sarcastically. "Lead by example. Show you care. Take the fight to the enemy. That's what you taught me." He glances at the platoon leader.

"These shit-for-brains officers are out here for one reason," Brown said, "and one reason only. They wanna play GI Joe for a few days. Get a few no-account grunt killed . . . like me." Brown points to his chest. "And grab a filthy medal of valor from the Candyman on the way out."

"Then they *dee dee* to the comforts of the Steak 'n' Lobster Officer's Country Club where they come up with stories that make them look like heroes. Where they stay in shape by playing tennis and swimming in the ocean while cooking up schemes to get rich off of us old grunts. They take our rightful food, pilfer our footlockers, sell us drugs, take our gear, and pimp round-eye prostitutes."

"You're not thinking straight."

"No?" Brown shouts in defiance. "Am I wrong?"

"Well not exactly, but this is insane. You can't. . . ."

"Can't what? I'm the one dealing with reality here," Brown claims. "Do you know who the real enemy is? Well, it ain't the VC. And it ain't the NVA. The real enemy is the World. The enemy within. Our own people for chrissakes."

Brown steps around a depression and in the dusk that quickly fades to dark, scans the foliage around the field they just crossed. He quickens his pace to close the distance between him and the officer.

"I've heard, the battalion has already lost seven men because of this prick. And you know what? This sorry ass excuse for a officer doesn't give a damn how many wounded or dead he piles up."

"You're going mad."

"Going mad is the least of my worries. Look at me! I'm a fuckin' wreck. My whole body hurts all the time. I'm only nineteen-years old and I'm an old man. What the fuck do *I* got to look forward to! Huh? What do I got left?"

Brown glances over his shoulder to see General Morgan has faded from view.

"And now even you think I've gone crazy. Well, you were just baggage, anyway. I don't need you. I don't need anyone. The only thing I need is an M-16 and a full magazine."

Humping along in the darkest mood possible, a voice inside his head begins to say, "So what if he's gone. Fuck it. Just fuck it. Don't mean nothin'."

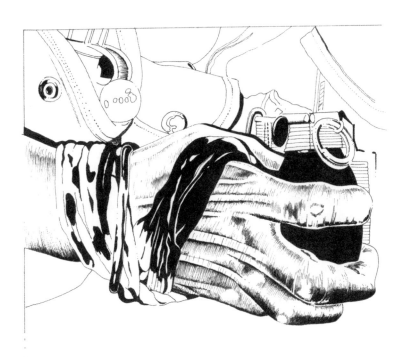

Plate 67

Handgrenade *(Illustration by Frank Schaffer)*

Gold Star

A soft luxurious breeze brushes against Brown's face. He hears the chirp of playful birds and a buzz of a busy bumblebee. Still kneeling, he pries his finger from **45E 046**, Benji Yamane's name and rises exhausted. Grabbing the brim of his U.S. Marine soft cap, he smiles inwardly because he half expected to find a steel pot. With cap off, he runs fingers repeatedly through his hair while searching for the M-16 rifle, pistol belt and the rest of the combat equipment but finds it gone as well.

With the blood receding from his eyes, he finds in place of a free-fire-zone's gunmetal gray mountains, again stands Chicago's granite, steel and glass skyline silhouetted against a darkening charcoal sky.

The backflashes had ended leaving in their wake a veteran both depressed and excited, spent and refreshed, old but new and growing. A middle ground where he felt—in a word—*calm*. A peaceful feeling comparable to the first warm, sun-shiny spring day after an especially snowy, wet and miserable winter. Yeah, he felt calm, real calm. Pleased that he had survived the tug and pull of war and made it to the *other* side.

Stepping away, he turns to face the wreckage of a soldier smoking a cigarette. But he isn't just smoking, no, he is sucking fretfully on the cigarette as if it was a reed leading to oxygen at the surface of the water. Standing there sucking, shaking like a leaf and stretching his neck, he wears a stained, thread bare olive-drab T-shirt stretched tight as banjo strings over a protruding belly. A stomach bloated by far too many troubles, problems and inner conflicts.

"What does that cross," he points, "next to a name mean? They MIA or somethin'?" the rather short balding ex-soldier asks with sweat beading down his forehead.

"I think." Brown quickly checks his brochure. "Yeah, here it is." He reads, "The cross symbol signifies 'Missing in Action.'"

"I was on R&R in Australia when they got it," the bald-headed veteran said with the cigarette bobbing between his lips. "One of my buddies was copilot and the other a passenger. They went down in the Mekong Delta."

They stare into each other's eyes with the vision of a plane catching fire and screeching downward headed for the muddy delta.

"I'm sorry."

"They found one of 'em, but the other was blown to bits." The veteran looks back at The Wall. "I think that's why I can only find one name." He looks questioningly at Brown. "But they should be together right here. Right? I mean they were killed at the same time."

"Yeah, from what I've seen. Their names should almost touch if they died on the same day."

"But look," the veteran points to a name, "it's just Crazy Harold." His shaky left hand opens to reveal a mangled, flame scared *Zippo* lighter. "This is all I got left of either of 'em."

"What kind of mission were they on?"

"They were on the way to see the Bob Hope Show." He smiles. Fingers close around the stainless steel lighter as he draws his hand to cover a small cough that leads to raspy hack. With shoulders slumped and hand over mouth, his face contorts as he holds back a flood of tears. He begins to study the cigarette butt deciding it worthy of one last draw. With a deep inhalation, he draws the tar and nicotine into his expanding lungs. Calloused fingertips roll off the amber tip and he begins to shred the butt into small pieces letting it sprinkle to the ground.

"Still field-stripe your cigarettes, huh."

"Yeah. Guess I do at that." A smile sweeps across his face. "Ain't that funny—never really thought about it. A lot of things stuck since the 'Nam, man." Staring into the mirror surface of The Wall he said, "Why did they leave *me* behind? Huh?" He looks at Brown through pained eyes. "Why?" He turns to continues to search for the missing name.

The name-patch sewn next to a Gold Star pin on the camouflaged, jungle fatigues of a gray-haired woman reads: HANSON.

Was that his name? Brown wonders. The name of the replacement who died in Dragon Valley? Probably not, but Brown did recall a time in the field when a replacement asked him what the 'Nam was like.

"I think the word free-fire-zone kinda says it all," he had explained. The NFG nods. Then Brown decides to put a little drama into the explanation. "Actually, now that I think of it, it's like the Old West where the law of the land is written in lead," he says in a crusty cowboy voice. "Where you feel like you're walking down the streets of Tombstone Arizona along side Doc Holliday and Wyatt Earp and the way to the gunfight at the Ok Corral."

"Really?"

"Yeah, really."

TOO LATE, SERGEANT

Tell me, Sergeant, do we get all the beer you can drink?
Are the girls really that
wild?
Soldier,
the only thing you'll likely
find over here is lots of sweat and desire.

Sergeant, it's high time I should know. Is the jungle breeze
sweet and refreshing? The ground
soft and green?
Soldier, you got it all
wrong. In the boonies the wind has the stench
of decaying flesh, the ground is pitted and charred.

Sarge, give it to me straight, the assault is beginning. Is the
enemy a believer in God and heaven? Is he merciful
and forgiving?
No, not at all. He
worships the devil and hell. He'll attack when
he knows you're at your weakest. The same as we do.

Sarge, tell me . . . tell me now! While the battle rages
and I'm bleeding. Is my mother home resting?
Is she content and worry free?
I'm sorry, soldier. But your
mother, she's been crying herself sick since you left,
'cause she already knows you have gone . . . gone
forever.

The Hanson woman strode on, head high, shoulders square until she finds the black slab that carries the spirit of her child. She slumps over, arranges her glasses, and begins to scan back and forth, reading line after line. Then she turns sheet-white, eyes wide, head rocking back as though buffeted by a stiff breeze. With hand poised, she reaches but all the fingers curl back except for the brave index, which stays its course. At first the finger only lightly touches the outline of a single letter. Ever so slowly it dares to run across the first name and finally to caress the entire inscription. The other fingers now bravely straighten and they too stroke the name while she sinks to her knees with tearing eyes.

God, how long has it been? Bet she tells everyone how she stopped counting a long time ago. "Who me?" she'd act surprised at the posed question. "Oh, no," she waves away the notion with pursed lips. "Never think about it, the war, much—that's all behind me now." A valiant smile radiates from her face.

But isn't it a bit curious the way she avoids using his name? "Now, I relish the present and anticipate the future," she continues to sound upbeat. "Have to get on with my life, you know. Move onward," she says casting her hand toward the horizon.

"Oh, you're so courageous," a female acquaintance responds. "It must have been a horrible, though. So unimaginable. I don't know if I could've been as strong as you." She pulls her young son close to plant a kiss on top of his little head.

"I'll tell you this," the gold star mother says after ripping her eyes from the handsome youth. "Count your blessings. All of them. And even when they're not at home, call them and tell them how much they mean to you. Never feel embarrassed. Tell them you love them more than life itself. Becau-*se*," the word breaks up in her throat. "*Couugh*,"she pretends to dislodge something from her throat, careful not to show a break in the facade.

"A little tickle in my throat," she said giving her signature smile with glowing white teeth. "Now where were we. Oh yes.

Love them as much as you can because it will all be over sooner than you think."

How *unbelievably* brave and without even a hint of mist in her eyes. Amazing. Absolutely amazing. But it's only a grand facade, isn't it? Put there for the benefit of the public, acquaintance and friend. Because in reality, she still recounts her son's every laugh, every word and last good-bye. She still tries to piece together where she was and what he was doing and thinking when he took his last gasp. Still counts the minutes, hours, days and years since his violent passing. And often times catches herself staring longingly at a strong, successful young man thinking her son might have been "just like him." That the grandchildren would have been so beautiful and she would have spoiled them rotten.

Betcha she walks past Ronni's room, pleased that she doesn't break down and cry anymore—God forbid—at least not in front of anyone. And at those moment when she's feeling extra strong, she'll stop at the doorway daring to embrace the memory.

"Honey, it's time to get up for church." She'll softly knock on the door. "What would you like for breakfast? Maybe I'll fix you those *Aunt Jemina* blueberry waffles you like so much. And I bought a new can of *Log Cabin* syrup."

She'll stand there dead pulse, her nose searching for the smells of dirty clothes, of a wet bath towel, or the over powering smell of cologne. She'll slowly push the door open and again see the woolen high school letter-jacket with the class of '67 sewn on the sleeve slung over the back of the desk chair. On the dresser is a half empty bottle of Coke, a Snickers candy wrapper, a bottle of Old Spice aftershave, a cheap wind-up Timex watch with hands frozen, and a lot of those special occasion cards. Tucked into the mirror frame are dime store Polaroids of him and his buddies sticking their tongues out and making those weird, ugly, funny faces; a formal pose of him and his special prom date; a girl in a bright yellow cheerleading outfit; an autographed picture from his girlfriend inscribed, *"Love you forever, Karen."*

She smooths out the cowboy and Indian print covers, turns down the bed, and fluffs the pillow. Then she takes his childhood teddy bear off the chair, and after sitting on the edge of the bed, places it tenderly on the pillow.

"I think it's way past your beddy-bye time young man," she begins to talk to the teddy bear.

"Oh no. Don't you, 'Oh mom me!' Now get some rest because you have a big day ahead of you tomorrow." She leans over to breath the animal's aroma and gives it a hug and kiss.

There's a noise. She raises her head and almost shouts, "Did you wipe your feet before you came in?" but catches herself. She looks back at the teddy bear, and starts tickling it as it squirms and tries to wiggle free.

With nice warm blankets pulled around the teddy bear's shoulders, she begins singing the first verse of "Rock-a-bye Baby." But when she gets to the verse "the cradle will rock," grief floods her soul with the darkest misery imaginable.

Flooded with grief she looks toward the ceiling. "I know that somehow, from somewhere you're watching. That you can hear me." She looks back at the furry brown stuffed animal, "I love you and I miss you so much." Tears roll freely down her cheeks as she leans to give the teddy bear a tender kiss.

"Sleep tight and don't let the bed bugs bit." She tip-toes from the room, then turns before closing the door and smiles at the words she's just heard. "And, I love you too."

Most of the tears are gone—run out, spent. In place of them is a gaping, black hole that festers and forever aches.

Back at The Wall, the Hanson woman—Gold Star mother whose hopes were shattered on a distant battlefield—places a single rose at the base of slap 46 east. She turns, straightens her shoulders and gallantly takes on the rest of the day.

A women wearing baggy pants and shirt stands alone looking at The Wall. Taking one last look at a letter she'd placed against a slab, she exhales, turns and disappears among the other spectators.

Hi,

I was here to be with
you on this day of honor.
A day that all hoped would
happen. You did not die
in vain. You have remained
in my fondest memories
for all these years. I know
that you are with me.

Love you

(From letter found at Moving Wall, Chicago 1986-author unknown)

A widow accompanied by her teenage daughter, both dressed in black skirts, leans to stroke a hungry finger over the name of her deceased husband. After smiling sweetly at her daughter, she opens her purse and produces two dog-eared photographs. The first picture of the young couple shows him with long hair and big bodacious smile, arms wrapped lustfully around her thin waist, chin on her shoulder. The second is of him in uniform their lips locked forever in a passionate kiss. Photographs of herself with the one she loved—still loves.

The saddest kiss of all are those in a time of war, Brown sighs.

"I remember that day like it was just yesterday. It all comes back," the mother said with wayward eyes. "The way he'd hold me and push my hair back behind my ears and kiss my neck." As she talks she wraps her arms around herself. "He said I had the cutest little ears. See," she points at the picture, "my hair is pulled back. He pushed it there right before the picture. And lookie here," she moves the picture closer so her daughter gets a better look, "you have your daddy's little pug nose. He'd be so proud." The widow steps to the monument and gently leans the mementoes against the slab.

"Daddy," the daughter said stepping forward. Not much going on, same-old-same-old. Except that you're not here," she said swallowing hard. She produces a sealed envelope. "I wrote a letter to you last night. It's private. I wouldn't even let mom take a peek. It's for you." She places the letter next to her mother's mementoes. Then she looks squarely at his name and gently begins to stroke her index finger across the letters. She licks her dry lips and steps back.

"Guess what mom and I did?" Her mother gives her a reassuring smile and nod. "While mom made your favorite meat loaf and mashed potato dinner, I set up the table for all three of us. You know, the plate, napkin, knife, fork and spoon. A coffee cup. And with my own money I bought you a very special red rose with angel breath plus three pretty candles. A red, white and blue one. I placed the rose across your plate and lit all three candles. One for each of us." She coughed softly to clear her throat, the settled back on her heels.

"All three of us were there like a *real* family," she looks at her mother pleasantly. "A regular candle light dinner and we talked with you a whole lot. And when the homemade apple pie came out of the oven, we went into the living room for some pie alamode. That's when mom brought out the shoe box of your old letters." She turns to her mildly composed mother. "Didn't you mom."

"I felt so embarrassed, honey," the mother said speaking to her deceased lover and husband, "but after the first few it's wasn't so bad."

"It was great, mom. And it was so much fun. We both acted like giggling little school girls."

"I'm sorry, honey" she said again addressing the name on The Wall, "That was the first time I've ever shown anyone our private letters."

"Daddy wouldn't have minded, Mom. And touching the paper that he wrote on, it was like . . . well like magic." She almost burst into tears, but a few quick sniffles held them at bay.

Staring intently at his name, she continues, "Look, daddy." She straightens and wiggles her shoulders sweetly. "I'm all grown up now." She sighs. "I really wish you could have been here," her brave eyes were suddenly flooded with tears. "It would have been so nice having you at the *Father Daughter Dances*." Cascading tears cause her mascara to streak down her cheeks.

"Daddy, sometimes just thinking about you gives me strength. It's like when things get really, really bad you're right there at my side holding my hand. I love you so much, Daddy."

"And I know that he loves you too, honey."

Both women wrap their arms around each other to cry unabashed with broken hearts, their bodies wavering with grief.

Goose bumps pop on Brown's arms as he tears his eyes from the scene. He remembered all too well the life of an infantry soldier. A soldier who was doomed from the out set. That unbeknown, before he'd even set foot in Vietnam he was already marked.

There were so many ways to get killed, maimed or wounded besides from the enemy. There were the killer viruses, diseases with no names, and jungle sores that would rot your flesh and boil your blood. There was the venom of poisonous snakes. There were spiders, leaches, scorpion, flesh eating piranha and charging water buffalos. There were heat casualties, malaria, river drowning, drugs, food poisoning, friendly fire, PTSD, and Agent Orange that would kill you one molecule at a time. There were traffic accidents—accidents of all kinds. But one of the most heartless killers of all were the Dear John Letters.

INFANTRY SOLDIER He   has stumbled i n t o a land of grief, where barbed wire strangles the earth, where madness i s ablaze, and where a n infantryman can plod t o his destiny.   Darkness crawls over him and   brings with it lost dreams, memories, and appalling   r e a l i t y, w h i l e impassionate storms of war strip him o f youth and bring t h e prospect o f a future filled with emptiness. In the end, the land will sleep to await its rebirth. The   soldiers who fell will be just bones of the past.   The survivor's heart must not b e strained anymore, but somewhere in their grey

vault, all is

remembered.

Lonely Are the Brave

The Vietnam veteran shakes like a sapling in an autumn thunderstorm, emotions flying like leaves in a strong wind with tears raining from cloudy orbs. Every now and again, he lifts a feeble hand to take a draw on the grief moistened cigarette or to softly wipe a river of tears from red quivering cheeks.

The distraught veteran with bowed shoulders seems to be experiencing a mind projection—flashback—similar to Brown's. It serves as no comfort to know the syndrom is spawned by Posttraumatic Stress Disorder.

Would supportive words or a conversation help? Like, "Hang in there buddy. I think I know what you're goin' through." He turns to the veteran's friend and asks, "So, why's he crying like that?"

The veteran's partner slowly pivots around like a robot, then bores into Brown with a cold as steel stare. "I don't know about you . . . buddy," he growls, "but it hits everyone in different way." The veteran's friend grinds his teeth as anger flows from beady ferret eyes. "Now don't it?"

Caught totally off guard by the callous response, Brown's face slackens. A sideways glance at the distraught veteran, who remains oblivious to his immediate surroundings, made him realize a conversation is out of the question. The soulful Wall had a different effect on everyone, granted, but don't they want some empathy? Brown locks stares with the crazed veteran and realizes all he needs is his own disease.

As anger rolls his fingers into tight balls, he turns away. How he despises getting stonewalled by a brother-in-arms. Despises it like nothing else. Shaking with anger he quickly reminds himself, "Don't waste time on things you can't change or do nothin' about."

With a deep cleansing breath, he tries to shake off the twisted encounter. Continuing to breath deeply, his nose detects a whiff of Honey Blossom perfume. Searching for its source, he spots a beautiful woman, similar to the one who ran through an earlier flashback. This time she isn't part of an anti-war protest. There is no burning American flag or draft card. No poster that reads BABY KILLER. Though still in excellent physical condition, she is near his age. In place of love beads and cut-off jeans is a gold chain necklace and conservative flowered spring dress.

The woman, with streaks of gray running through her dusty blond hair, bends over to place a note next to a bouquet of wilting flowers, photographs and a miniature American flag. The note reads:

> To Allyn Troy Stevens,
> You were the best of the best!
> Love Laura

(From letter found at Moving Wall, Chicago 1986)

Plate 68   Laura *(Illustration by Jean Altepeter)*

His attention diverts to a semitrailer truck that moves slowly across the park lawn in a motion reminiscent of a funeral hearse. It parks behind the Vietnam Veterans Memorial Moving Wall. The bearded driver, along with a group of twenty helpful spectators, begin to unlatch and load the one hundred-twenty-three feet of black panels into the vehicle.

Keeping his distance, Brown remembers what a nurse at the Army Hospital in Texas once told him, "You'll get used to saying good-bye."

The beautiful nurse was just as wrong then as she is now. Brown swoons with a sense of loss as he watches the panels disappear one-by-one into the back of the trailer. If he'd had any tears left to shed, this would have been the time.

His dry eyes search out the sunset for solace, as he had often done during the twilight hours while serving in Vietnam. In the western sky, he is pleased to find the red ball of fire sun flaring around the elegant lines of the world's tallest building, the Sears Tower.

He begins to understand that, no matter what, he'd have to face up to the past every day of his life. No escape. No easy way out. Can't just up and walk away. No denial. No running because there is nowhere to hide. And also, it became painfully clear that the dead need the living to remember them and the living need the dead to teach them.

CROSS OVER
Left the 'Nam,
   his   brain
almost gone,
   his system
shot.   He
should have
been dead, he
wasn't. Looking
back, he wouldn't
have changed a thing,
but he thinks about it.
It's always there, even when
it's not: memories, a cold sweat,
and a load of tears. Long strings of
energy had oozed from his bones, the kind
everyone reads about in novels, and whenever
he marched, pieces of him kept peeling off. Now,
he's gotta get moving and learn to use his hands
as a mouth, never to turn for that thirsting glance.
Has to square his shoulders, hold his head high.
He's the one who crossed over with no way
back. But it's not so bad once you get
used to it, just lonely, that's
all—just a little fuckin' lonely.

Section Two

Unsung Hero

O NE WEEK LATER, NORTHSIDE OF CHICAGO, ILLINOIS
—JUNE 21, 1986

The first day of summer is off to a beautiful start, Brown thinks, watching the pale yellow fingers of dawn creep across the deep blue sky. Laura, the woman from The Wall, had noticed him and struck up a conversation. The ensuing dialogue culminated in them mounting their ten-speed bicycles to cruise leisurely on the bike route that skirted the shores of Lake Michigan.

A beautiful day indeed, he thinks, smiling as he eyes Laura's tan legs pumping—her dusty blond hair trailing behind.

Cresting a hill, they find themselves over looking a cove. The sunlight glistens off its softly rolling moss-green water and the multicolored sails of the boats anchored in the harbor. The mystic cove sends energy surging through Brown's body.

Pushing harder and harder on the crank, he makes his bike wheels sing with desire.

Plagued with rapidly declining health since the Vietnam War, Brown hasn't straddled his favorite metallic-blue-colored Italian Galmozi racing bike for an extended ride in over six years. However, today is special; even his weak body seems to understand and wants to fully cooperate.

Up and over a hill. They power down the incline to zoom past two slow moving cyclists, then roller-coaster to the top another hill, still holding a vigorous pace.

"Go! Go! Go!" Brown shouts encouraging Laura as he powers past, pretending they are competitors in a bicycle race. Pacing themselves, he now imagines the *chasing* riders close behind and slowly gaining.

Moments later, after zooming into the beautiful residential area of Evanston, Illinois, they slow to a more relaxing pace.

"Whewww!" Laura sighs, coasting while stretching her legs and lifting herself off the leather saddle. Steering with one hand she points to a majestic house with circular driveway. "That's Clement Stone's mansion. One time I rode inside the gates, just to see if I had the guts to do it."

Mesmerized by her moisture-covered athletic figure, Brown said, "You're sweating."

"No. Ladies, like me, perspire. Men sweat." Laura raises her eyebrows wryly. "Pothole!"

When he jerks from a reflex action, she smiles contentedly at having tricked him.

"Arrrrr," he growls. "Watch that little lady."

"Take a right, Freddie," Laura said. They bank their bikes to speed past steel gates leading into the Fort Sheridan, U.S. Army military base.

"You ride like a racer," she said.

"I'd like to think so," Brown said proudly. "I rode a bike across the country in 1976, sort of a tribute to the Vietnam veterans and the United States Bicentennial."

"Get out," she said thinking it some kind of a jokes. "No way."

"No. Really. I did," he said, barely holding in his escalating pride. "I rode 4,250 miles in 39 days averaging 115 miles a day. Made Chicago's *Channel 7 Eyewitness Evening News* and was on the national A.P. wire. Everything. Whole nine yards. It was great."

"Wow, you really did then. That's so cool."

"When I was in the Army, I had walked, ran, and crawled a distance equivalent to the whole United States, east to west," he said with a modest shrug. "I knew I could do it if I put my mind to it. And why not. I'd fought for this country—hell, why not see it."

"Up close and personal."

"A ride of a life time."

"I wish some of your *conviction* would rub off on me," Laura said. "I'm an overworked, underpaid state social worker. And I hate it," she groans. "I mean, I work well with people and all that, but I hate it when I don't feel like . . . like I'm accomplishing anything."

"Yeah, I know what you mean."

"Tell you the truth, I'd rather be playing my piano," Laura said.

"You play the piano?"

"A concert pianist in the flesh," she says proudly. "I've even played in Europe. Problem is, work wasn't steady and there wasn't enough money. So now, I play my *baby grand* with the windows wide open and listen to the applause of people on the street."

"Sounds like something right out of New York City's Greenwich Village."

"I'm running out of water," Laura said after taking a long drink. She looks both ways, crosses the street, and coasts her bike into the parking lot of the Fort Sheridan gas station and to a water fountain.

After standing their bicycles against the building, they take out their water bottles.

"Here," Laura said, walking over. She spread the fingers of her right hand into a fan. "Put your fingers between mine."

"How's that?" Brown questions thinking it some kind of a joke.

"Come on. Don't be a baby. It won't hurt you."

"Oka*yyy*." Still apprehensive, he slides his fingers in between, feeling her smooth warmth. When fully integrated, she begins squeezing her fingers laterally.

"O*www-w*," Brown cries as she adds pressure. Returning the pressure, he quickly finds he's no match. Instead, he tries to pull free.

"Had enough?" she asks smugly, showing little signs of effort.

"I give up. Ah*hhhh*," he cries with body contorting. After one last crushing squeeze, she released her hold. "I thought maybe you were gonna kiss me," he said wiggling his hand. "Not break my fingers."

"Oh*hh*, poor baby," she said through pursed lips.

"No, I think you really did," Brown continues complaining. "That was like a vise." He stops shaking his hand long enough to inspect the damage. "That really hurt."

"There's only one way to get that kind of strength, and that's by playing a piano," Laura explains.

When she heads for the fountain, Brown pulls out the stopper on his water bottle. "Say, Laura." When she turns, he squirts her square in the face.

Unprepared she freezes in place with arms wide letting the water dribble off her eyebrows, nose and chin. "Why, you little shit."

"Oh, I'm sorry. Did I squirt you?"

With poised water bottle, she darts after Brown who bobs and weaves across the parking lot. She squirts, but Brown easily dodges the stream. Out of water, she bares her teeth menacingly. "Gr*rrr*."

"How dare you. And after a nice apology." He lunges but finds he's out of water, too. Panting, they walk over to the water fountain and drink their fill.

While refreshing themselves, Brown notices the military personnel are giving him the once-over and seem to be talking quietly among themselves. He believes they are making fun of his ultra tight riding apparel.

"You know, it irks me when people stare at me like that," Brown gripes as they ride from the filling station. "I've done the most macho things they could ever imagine, but yet they look at me like I'm some kind of weirdo."

"Weirdo? You mean like in nuts. Wacko. Crazy." She smiles. "Listen Freddie, just by looking at you, no one could even imagine who you are or what you've done." Changing the subject, she nods toward a row of wooden buildings, "Those barracks look familiar?"

What am I doing with this woman? Brown suddenly finds himself asking. And why is Barbara, my wife, putting up with this craziness? Maybe because she knows that I'm searching for something. It isn't sex. Not even Laura herself. No, Barbara knows I'm trying to find out who I am. I'm trying to find myself.

"Yeah, they're familiar alright," he responds and smiles. Laura actually likes hearing about my experiences, he thinks to himself. How unusual. Normally after a few shallow question everyone would move on to self-centered topics and mundane subjects. But by the sound of her voice and eye contact, he knows it's for real. For the first time in his life someone actually cares to hear about his experiences.

"I stayed in barracks like those for seven months back at Fort Bliss Army Hospital recovering from wounds." Brown shifts his bike into an easier gear and moves to an upright sitting position. "Though I'm permanently disabled and receive a monthly pension, it took me four years and several letters to my congressman, Ed Derwinski, to finally get one of my three Purple Hearts."

The expression on his face turns dead serious. "After all I did." His nostrils flare. "The Army gave me no respect. They treated me like . . . like I didn't belong."

Laura focuses on the road while listening.

"Maybe it wasn't such a good idea telling off the battalion commander when he visited in the medivac hospital after my last wound."

"I'd say that might have had something to do with it," Laura said.

"Still, the Army broke its promise. Sergeants Walker, Grauer and Rogers witnessed my bravery up on this hill where I was left for dead. In my one-man firefight against a company of enemy soldiers, I fired off nearly eight-hundred rounds of ammunition and covered my platoon's retreat. I saved their asses. All of 'em. When I came running off the mountain they said it was the most heroic thing anyone had ever heard of or seen. They said I should receive the Congressional Medal of Honor."

"You were that brave?"

"I swear on a stack of bibles. And outside of that, they denied me my two Bronze Stars for valor, a Combat Assault Air medal, a Valorous Unit emblem, and two other Purple Hearts."

"And there's nothing you can do?"

"Like I said, I wrote my congressman and he said my file was empty."

"How could that be?"

"They can do anything they want. They can say part of my records were lost in a fire, in a flood. Got misplaced. Misfiled."

"I'd be mad as hell, too, if they did that to me," Laura sympathizes.

Tears sting Brown's eyes. Why did he feel like crying when she said she understands? If he'd dare talk about this before everyone would look at him like he was crazy. But why? All his life he'd heard about soldiers from other wars finally receiving their just reward. But not him. No the difference is, he is a Vietnam veteran, so no one is listening. In the past twenty years if he even mentioned the war he was labeled as sub-human, insane, abnormal or . . . ashamed? Ashamed? Ashamed of what? Ashamed of doing his duty as any patriotic Americans would? Ashamed of volunteering to be pointman? Ashamed of doing his job as a soldier to the best of his ability? Ashamed of his willingness to fight so other might have freedom, justice and liberty?

But getting back to the subject, why did they think him crazy just because he wanted to talk about the war? *Why?* What is so wrong with talking about a life experience? Everyone who went to college talks about their learning experiences. They talk about their professors, about their course study, about their reports. They talk about their wild drunken parties, sexual conquests, panty raids. And they don't get labeled.

"Fred, write about it. Tell your story."

"I swear to God, Laura, I'm not lying."

"I believe you. Tell the children. Go to the schools."

"I'd really like to do that."

"I found this letter at The Wall." She produces a letter from her bicycle pack. "Let me read it to you:

Dear Sisters and Brothers,

I am a veteran of the 'Nam. I am a combat veteran, 1971, Americal Division. You know what that means?

I now see this wall for the first time. It is hard, black and absolute. The Wall of your names. People see a wall and they see something which separates. They think it separates the dead from the living. They don't know. They don't know. They don't know that when we got on the plane for the 'Nam, we all died.

I see your names and I can't help but think that you're the lucky ones. You didn't have to come back from the 'Nam and be spat at. Called Killers. Baby killers. Friends left. Loners for the duration. We trade one chaos for another. In the new chaos, we were unarmed but labeled crazy. Suffering from a bloodless wound they call Posttraumatic Stress Disorder (PTSD). It's all in your head, they said.

Some reacted to the chaos by going inside of themselves. You can see them on the streets of every city. Some left. To where? The wilderness? Parts unknown? Who knows?

A life where the phrases "everyday life" "normal life" have no meaning. Many will never be helped. Thank God for my family, my brothers and sisters - Sonny, Larry, Loretta, Pat. Why even try to describe those years since?

Fifteen years later, we are still warriors, still fighting.

I see your names in black and I am back in the jungle. The heat, the sweltering, suffocating heat. From the sky came the spray. It felt so cool and refreshing. We danced in it. It went into our water and we bathed in it. Cooked with it. Drank it. No one knew what it was, the cool and refreshing spray. It had no name then. Now it does — Agent Orange

Many have died from unexplained sicknesses. Cancers. Degeneration of nerves and tissues and organs. Their names go alongside yours as they join you on the other side of this wall. How many?

500,000? Do we dare erect ten walls? How many others on this side are the walking dead?

Let's pretend it never happened. It never happened. There is no proof. It's all in your head.

Sisters and Brothers, they are forgetting you. They want to forget you, and they are. They are not teaching the children about the 'Nam. They teach World War I, World War II, and Korea. They do not teach about the 'Nam. How can future generations avoid repeating this tragedy, if they do not teach the 'Nam?

Sisters and Brothers. You are my commanding officers in my last tour of duty. I understand your orders clearly. I am charged with nothing less than making sure you are not forgotten. I am charged with making an entire nation remember the 'Nam. My time is short. I am filled with Agent Orange and it eats away at me. But while I breathe, I know my mission. Forward! Always Forward!

When I pass to your side of the wall, we will meet on top of that mountain. There will be a cool breeze, a gentle cool breeze. No heat. No spray. Just the cool breeze. We'll toast, for at that time, and only at that time, I will have peace.

Sincerely,
Gary Kruchten
Viet Nam 1971-72

"Amazing."

"Pretty good wasn't it." She folds the copy and places it back inside the pouch. "Fred, just like your bike trip. It started with one turn of the crank."

"I can see the headlines now: PIANIST TURNS PHILOSOPHER," he said sweeping his hand through the air.

"Freddie, from what I've heard, a lot of guys didn't receive their just and fair due."

"And to this day, they still deny the effects of Agent Orange. I got a friend who right now is dying from that defoliant and at one point the VA said they didn't even have a records of his unit even being in Vietnam."

"That's insane."

"The deck is stacked against us."

"Don't give up. If you do than all the unsung heros will lose, too. And I for one want to know the truth."

"People need to hear about what happened from the men who actually fought the battles."

"That right. You can do it."

"Thanks."

"No. Thank you. Thank you for giving me my freedom. Thank you for your sacrifice."

At the airfield, they playfully speed, side by side, down the runway. Faster and faster they ride, edging out the other's front wheel, pretending to be building up momentum for a takeoff.

"Squeeee-ch!" Laura makes the sounds of an aborted takeoff as she clenches her brakes. They both apply their brake coming to the end of the tarmac that overlooks Lake Michigan.

Brown careens his bike around her and sprints back up the length of the runway, feeling so young and alive. A vital teenager without a care in the world on a date with the girl of his dreams.

For the moment, he is free from the aching, aging veteran who looks back at him in the bathroom mirror. He's alive, full of inspiration and ready for an adventure. He rolls his face toward the sun, fills his lungs with pure lake air, then takes both hands off the handle bars and raises them into a **V** for victory.

"Wait up!" Laura shouts.

"Pooped already?" Brown calls back over his shoulder.

With beads of perspiration rolling down her beaming face, she catches up.

"Sweating yet?"

"*Nooooo.*" she said in protest.

"I feel really great today," he said when they slow the pace. "This must be one of those special days that only God can promise."

"I'm thinkin' the same thing," she said, beaming.

"You really have a pretty smile."

A rosiness comes to Laura's cheeks as she lowers her eyes. "It's been a long time since I've met someone. . . ." Laura's voice quivers. "I mean a lot of guys at The Wall *hit* on me. This one colonel was actually coming onto me right in front of his wife. Disgusting."

Laura looks up the road, then finally she looks back at Brown, a pensiveness in her face. "I have trouble with relationships. I really don't know why, they just never last." She exhales noisily. "Like my boyfriend. He's a Chicago cop and really hates guys like you from Vietnam."

"What?" Brown said shocked. "He hates me. Why? He's never even met me."

"Well, first off, he was too young to go to Vietnam, so that probably bothers him. But he thinks you guys are just a bunch of macho know-it-alls who play off all the hardship stuff to get sympathy and jobs."

"You're serious?"

She nods.

"I don't believe it."

"It's just a hang-up, he and a lot of other people have," she said. "But it sure set him off when you 'King Fish' veterans got all that publicity for the Welcome Home Parade. Matter of fact, it's been a nightmare living with him lately because of it." She let out a self-pitying huff. "I always fall for the wrong guy."

"'Nam vets get it from all sides," Brown said, only slightly aware that Laura is sniffling back tears. "I'm sorry, but I'm not gonna roll over and die just to please people like him." Noticing Laura's discomfort, he abruptly changes the topic. "How many times have you almost died, Laura?"

She sighs at the breadth of the question. "Oh, I don't know," she said thinking. "Only once, really. I was acting stupid and foolish, making believe I was so strong, tough, together and all that garbage. I do my best to eat right and workout, but I'm still a bubble-head. You know the Fox River?"

"Sure."

"My parents live in St. Charles along the river. Well, I was bragging about how I could swim across the river, and my niece asked if I'd carry her with me. . . ." She lowers her head at the memory. "My legs cramped in mid river. And. I'm just lucky that boat came along when it did." Tears rolls down her cheeks. "It was so horrible . . . *horrible*. I never felt so vulnerable . . . so *stupid.*"

"But you learned a lot about life and yourself in a short time, didn't you?"

"Yeah, I guess," she sniffles. "Like I should just admit to being me? Just dizzy old me."

"And?"

"I realized how *really* short life is. That at any moment you could do something stupid that could change or even end your life."

"Laura, you're a sweet lady. And you have a lot going for you. Just remember never beat on yourself. Learn to love yourself," he said making her smile. "In 'Nam I had this buddy of mine, Dig-it, who had engraved on his lighters:

**You've never lived
until you've
almost died."**

THE VICTOR   When his Vietnam War is over, who will
know how he fought? Who cares? Life will go on, as
though it never happened. But it was HIS blood
that spilled on that ground. The monsoon rains
will   still pour, the rice fields will still be
planted, and the jungle will cover the scars,
all except his. Things will continue like
they   always   have,   since before his
arrival in that foreign land.   He
didn't make a difference really.
Maybe it was planned that way
all along. But he'll tell himself
he did his job! He endured
the ultimate test. And
like all the   other
vets, he learned
how to survive.
N o w   he's
his own
M a n.

TAPS

An expansive eighteen-hole golf course looms into view. And off to the left, at a curve in the road, stands the granite block columns that hold the grim iron gates to Fort Sheridan Cemetery.

As Brown nears the gates of eternity, his limbs grow strangely heavy. His whole body slackens succumbing to the pull of gravity. He feels tired . . . so tired. This is a bad idea. I don't want to go through with this, he says beginning to doubt himself.

"Gunfighter!"

On hearing the voice of his second brain, Brown swallows hard. He pulls out the Pardon Crucifix tucked under his shirt and lets it hang pendulumlike from its gold necklace. His heart surges, sending electrified energy sizzling through his veins. He jumps on the crank, and his bicycle lurches forward.

As though a *force* were trying to stop him, Brown feels like he were pedaling up a steep incline on a windy day.

Unexplainable grief suddenly rips through his gut sapping even more of his resolution.

Don't give up, he said to himself. Don't give in. Forward always forward.

Like getting launched from a sling shot, once past the gate, he flies for another good hundred yards before braking to a skidding halt at the base of a crucifix-shaped monument.

With a trembling hand, he wipes sweat from his face. Needing time to regain his composure, he's relieved to see Laura still trailing behind. Swinging a shaky leg over the handlebars, he snatches a banana from his jersey pocket and, as calmly as possible, begins to munch.

"In a hurry?" Laura asks as she pulls near.

With a grin plastered on his face, he breaks off a piece of banana and offers it to her. Peeling more, he looks away in need of a few more moments to himself. Military graveyards are full of the kind of men he had served with and this particular one is haunted with the ghosts of more than six American wars.

"No, not in hurry," he said after a long silence. His mouth twitches. "Gardens of stone make me think about things. A lot of things." He looks around wide eyed. "Let's walk."

Laura motions across the road to the right. "Let's go this way." Together they read the headstone of a soldier who died during the American Civil War.

"There are German POWs buried over there by those trees."

"What're they doing here?" he asks looking to where she points. "I thought the bodies of POWs get returned at the end of a war."

"True enough but they're still here," she said as they continue to walk their bikes. "The caretaker is the one who told me about them. Do you wanna see for yourself?" Her head darts.

"Look!" She retrieves a piece of a purple linen flower that has been shredded by a lawn mower. "This is part of a bouquet I placed on Allyn's grave."

Brown stares at the piece of sun-bleached silk as it disappears inside of her closing fist.

"I ended up here by accident," she said, taking whimsical steps. "I felt drawn to this place." A shadow of uncertainty creases her lower lip.

"And?" Brown said stepping past a gravestone. Turning into the wind, he lets the soothing lake breeze brush his face.

"Well," she pivots to walk backwards, "when I got here, I started walking around in a circle just like this."

Strolling, he pauses to read the headstone of a former soldier who had died in 1876. "This guy died the same year as Custer's Last Stand," Brown states. "I grew up fascinated with the Battle of Little Big Horn."

"Then after a while," Laura continues with her story, "there it was, ALLYN TROY STEVENS with the same birth year as mine."

She places the linen flower into his hand. "My fear, Fred," she takes a deep breath, "is that there lies the man who should have been mine. My dearest love." Laura's blue eyes take on an odd glow. "I feel this connection."

"Connection?" Brown asks uncertain of her meaning.

"Yes. A connection with a dead man. A man I never knew." She faces Brown with purse lips and frowns. "This is crazy, isn't it?"

"Crazy, as in nuts," he jests trying to cover his shock. All this time he had thought she knew Allyn Troy Stevens. That he was a classmate. Met him at a party. Maybe a friend of a friend. At least a family acquaintance. A glance into her stormy blues told him she wasn't coping well with the present, and so, went to the past—a past that might give the present meaning. How ironic, he thinks, here they both stand trying to make sense of the past in order to make sense of the present. Using it as a sort of guiding light.

"Lemme tell ya a little about myself," he said calmly, as they continue to walk with their bikes through the cemetery. "In the middle of the night I'll suddenly start talking, and sometimes even hop out of bed to participate in my own dream. Actually, I dream in story form, and live my life the same way. There's times when

I can't even decide whether it happened for real or just in my mind."

She listens intently.

"See, I got these characters inside my head. And they all want to have a say-so in my life. So diplomatically, I give them all parts in my brain movies." He nearly mentions his second brain, General John Hunt Morgan of the Civil War, and his ego Mustang, but feels that would be pushing it.

Laura nods her understanding.

"Here's how it works," he resumes, "I'll be walking around, just anywhere and suddenly it's the summer of 1864—I'm a Union Civil War scout going into battle somewhere in Kentucky. Or just maybe–just maybe–it's the 1880's, I'm a no-count drifter cantering my horse through DEAD WOOD GULCH, DAKOTA TERRITORY. Or it's early 1968. I'm a Vietnam War Gunfighter who has survived Tet Offensive, the biggest battle of the entire war, and who is on point making his way through Que Son Valley, the Valley Of Living Death."

"Gunfighter?"

"Right. The honorary we gave the guys who walked Point."

"Oh, okay," she said, obviously not quite understanding all he was saying.

"What I'm trying to get at is, I think I know what you mean," he said measuring the words. "See, there are other people who think like you—and me. It's just we never met . . . until now."

"There's a name for guys like you," Laura said, laughing.

"Oh? And what's that?"

"Eccentric," she said, playfully.

"Yeah, I've been called that," Brown acknowledges. "That's probably one of the nicer names, but I haven't a clue why."

Laura rolls her sparkling blue eyes implying one part reticence but another intrigue—a recipe that adds to her charm.

"Seriously, cemeteries are special places," he continues. "Since before I can remember, I've gone through graveyards to read the headstones. To imagine, or even invent, how life was when the dead were alive—and the possibility of my

BROWN
✝
FRED LEO
RIP 1839
BORN
DiED 1886

Fred
this is not
art
D—

Plate 69　　　　　　　Second-grade art *(drawing by the author)*

reincarnation. I wonder if maybe that's the grave of someone I knew. A brother, a sister, acquaintance, maybe a friend . . . someone I shot down. Or maybe the man who betrayed or shot me."

He glances to assure himself of her interest. Her expression continues to urge him on. "My second-grade teacher told us, 'Now children, I want you to draw *anything* you like.' Well, that's just what I did. I drew a headstone over a grave with the inscription Fred Leo Brown born 1839 died 1886."

"You're somekinda deranged kook and you know it," Laura said playfully, almost laughing.

"Well, I may be certified but the Army still nominated me for West Point Military Academy."

"You went to West Point?" Laura asks shocked.

"Not hardly. I said nominated," Brown said, shaking his head. "School has never been my *thing*."

As they continue to traverse around the perimeter, Brown's ears perk. Could have sworn he heard the solemn notes of *Taps* being played on an old battlewise bugle. Nah, he thinks, shaking his head. Still the hallow mournful melody persists, ever so faintly, carried through the field of stone on the warm lake breeze.

Brown softly hums the song written by the Union soldier, Daniel Butterfield, during the Civil War:

> *Day is done, gone the sun*
> *From the lakes, from the hills,*
> *From the skies, all is well,*
> *Safely rest, God is nigh.*

The bugler's song always stirs strong sentiment and seems to reaffirm the reason he still lives: He lives so he can tell others about the common soldier who fights the ground war, who will always fight the ground wars. The ones who end up in foxholes sharing ammunition, food and water–and often, their last moments of life.

As at The Wall, he has the sensation that the dead are begging the living to take in their remembrances. That the deceased want to be seen as people who were willing to take that extra, unselfish step so others in the nation might follow more easily.

"There," Laura calls her voice urgent. "There it is." About twenty-feet away rests a granite headstone with a cross carved near the top. She reads aloud the inscription:

ALLYN TROY STEVENS
Illinois
Private HHC second battalion
third Cavalry first Cavalry Division
October 14th, 1947
June 21, 1969
Vietnam

They lay their bikes on the grass.

"You know," Laura said staring at the engravement, "before I saw this headstone, I never connected with the Vietnam War. It was as though it never happened," Laura said, as she slowly walks over to the tombstone. "But then at my foot," she motions to the ground that embraces the vault, "lay the bones of a flesh-and-blood American boy who gave his life in that war. Gave his life for his country—for me." Shame plays across her face as she sweeps her dusty blonde hair away from her face.

Brown makes no reply.

"What comes through so strong," Laura said, "is that I have a delayed reaction to the entire Vietnam War period. I didn't realize what the guys went through. The crying, the shame and the horror of it all. And too, the loyalty, heroics, and honesty that were also part of it."

She kneels reverently and with her palm sweeps grass clippings from the marker. "That was before Allyn reached out and called me to his grave."

Brown stands, transfixed. A shiver runs up then down his spine making his eyes bulge.

"I rode my bike straight home and went to the library and checked-out all the war books I could find. It didn't so much matter what war just as long as it was about war. I rented the classic Vietnam War movies, *Apocalypse Now* and *Platoon*. Read Audie Murphy's story, *To Hell and Back.*" Laura rises and brushes the grass from her knees.

Yielding no clue to his reaction, Brown thinks, Oh Laura, I had no idea how this was affecting you. Could a civilian suffer from a type of Vietnam War PTSD? Is she an indirect casualty of that war?

"When the Moving Vietnam Wall came to Chicago, I just had to do something, something that showed conviction, even a little bravery," she said, staring straight at Brown. "I wanted it to be *personal*, from me to Allyn." She lowers her eyes. "Well, I got this crazy idea."

She wiggles her shoulders and blushes. "I spent a whole day searching out the sexiest black panties I could find. It was fun," she said, giggling flirtatiously. "The whole time I kept daring myself to take them off right there at the monument." She pauses and looks thoughtfully at the tombstone.

Brown was going to say something like, I think you better slow down. I'm a happily married man with two beautiful daughters. You're unhappy because you can't find a decent partner—so you say, "That's why! He died before we had a chance to meet."

"I don't know what it all means," she said, admittedly puzzled. "But then you're here, and you're alive." Her pursed lips ooze with need and her hand starts to reach for Brown.

Side stepping, Brown starts thinking about how his wife, Barbara, always yells when he does something *presumably* bazaar. He didn't like the conflict, but she did manage to drag him back to a form-of reality. I wish I could do the same for you, Laura, he thinks. I wish I could help you, but the truth is, I can barely help myself.

"Laura, if I had died, would you be searching for me?" Brown asks as an interlude of comic relief. "Would you drop your panties for me?"

Their eyes meet and they chuckle.

"Freddie, look." She points in astonishment. "Today's the twenty-first of June. That means Allyn died thirteen years ago on *this* very day, the first day of summer."

"Wow. That is a coincidence," he confesses while noting the location number, 8A 156, inscribed on the back of the marker.

"Freddie, I want you to know that I was part of the 'drop-out' culture that locked you out," Laura begins to cleanse her conscience. "Maybe it was the media, but mostly there was no talk of ethics, pride—no focus on our fighting men as being good, noble." Noticing a dandelion, she plucks it from the stem and takes a whiff. "We just heard about the atrocities, the civilian body counts, the cutting off of ears. All that deranged kinda stuff. The atmosphere was pure hatred for all infantry soldiers—like you."

"Laura." He needed to stop her from saying anymore. Needed to control his rage, his anger, his temper. Needed to keep his defenses down. Need to think and talk rationally. "Liberty and justice for all comes at a price. People seem to forget that. Our freedom was bought by those loyal, gallant, brave patriots who came before us. Personally, I'm very proud to be listed among their ranks.

"And if you care to recall, the original intent of the Vietnam War was to give the Vietnamese back their freedom. This is what they told us: One weapon captured would save the life of an innocent mother and child. One enemy eliminated would save the lives of another twenty innocent civilians. To us that was the bottom line. We were simply soldiers following orders. Doing our job the best we knew how.

"But it wasn't us who screwed it up. When public outrage over the war began to gain momentum, the politicians–in their infinite wisdom–realized they needed a way out. I mean, why not blame people with no power or no political clout for the war's failure. Right? I mean think about it. Why not blame a nineteen-year-old pointman for the loss. Say he's a thug out of control. What can he do?" Brown rolls both arms. "And if he yells about it just call him crazy.

"Laura, they made us bend over, grab our ankles, and squeal like a pig." Though his anger and voice were rising, he still felt in control. So he continues. "And just like a women who walks into the police station to file a report of rape, no one believed us. They laughed at us. They degraded us. They said all these vulgar things to us. They destroyed our humanity. Took away our self esteem, our self worth. Stripped us naked," he said with voice booming. His stomach is shaking uncontrollably but he needed to finish.

"We became the anti-heroes. The bad guys with no dialogue in a Western movie," he said now almost shouting. "But Laura, our hats were not black. And I know I keep harping on it, but we *really* were just following orders."

To slow the tempo, they step apart and break eye contact. He takes several deep cleansing breaths and she does too.

"I'm ashamed to say this but, well, I was one of those protester at the 1968 Democratic National Convention here in Chicago," she admits. "And I still have a vivid picture of when the police and National Guard stormed the line. It's still in here." She lightly taps her temple.

Though she realizes Brown's discomfort with the subject, she continues. "My sister did her doctoral dissertation on the Vietnam veteran. She studied their values, morals, attitudes, drug problems and general behavior or misbehavior. She came to the conclusion that Vietnam veterans were one-dimensional burnouts who went around pissed off at everyone and everything all the time. My sister said they were . . . ."

"Bad company . . . dangerous," he said with voice rising again. "Anything could set off a trained killer, a murdering vet. Someone you wouldn't want to surprise your mother with, right?" Brown said, infuriated by the stereotype. "Laura I've heard it all. We've been called chilling, psychotic, reptilian, sinister, ruthless, spooky, surreal, haunted, dangerous, cold hearted and the creepiest men in America."

"Yes, exactly," she said apologetically. "Someone you wouldn't want buying you a drink." Laura giggles. "But I'd let you buy me a Margarita anytime."

You're drooling, a voice inside his head says. He drags his eyes away from her beautiful body and thinks, God, help me.

"Remember that old Civil War song, *When Johnny Comes Marching Home* again, hurray hurray. We'll give him a hardy welcome and?" Laura sings.

"Yeah, I know. It's actually an old Irish song. I remember hearing the *Kingston Trio* sing the original version."

"Yeah, I do too. Pretty graphic stuff but not any more gruesome than what I saw at the Welcome Home Parade." Her voice cracks. "I stood on the overpass to watch the amputees, the ones confined to wheelchair, and all those aching men and women march past. And the whole time I wanted to shout at the top of my lungs, 'I love all you guys. Thank you so much for everything you did."

Laura sighs, moves close to brush her hand against his furrowed brow and cheek, and looks into his eyes. "And all along you were just Johnny, the boy next door, who fought because his country called."

"Thanks," Brown said, feeling a lump form in his throat. "Shit, Laura. That's the first time anyone has ever said such nice things to me." He took a deep breath to compose himself. "We were sent there to fight for an honorable cause. But never to be betrayed."

Laura continues to stroke his face, her eyes warming with compassion and desire.

"I only wish more people would understand. I mean even my own father," Brown said in a voice edged with bitterness. He knew that he shouldn't talk about this, but it flooded his senses and he's unable to hold back.

"I was on my way to 'Nam and," he steps away from her, "I had just shoved my duffle bag into the trunk of the car. 'Okay, Ma, I guess that about does it,'" he said with a reminiscent tone in his voice. "That's when I realized my father."

"Oh nooooo," Laura said expecting the worse.

"My father just walks past, gets into his car and drives away. No, good-bye. No, good luck. No, keep your head down. Not a wave. Nothin.' Up to that point I'd always been hopeful. Like in the movies, everyone would pull together right before . . . ." Brown let the words trail off.

"Like a dumb little kid, I still thought it would have a happy ending. Here I was headed for Vietnam—probably to die—and my father just didn't . . . didn't give a damn." Brown's cry echoed through the garden of stone and he looks toward the blue sky.

Laura sees an opening and interjects, "Fred, sometimes people just don't understand what others are going through." She feels confident about what she saying. "Now, I'm not defending your father but maybe . . . just maybe he didn't think going to Vietnam was any big deal. Maybe, he thought the war would be over before you even got there. Did you ever think of that?"

"Sure," he said controlling his defenses. "For a while, I tried to believe he cared, but didn't know how to show it. In 'Nam, he would send these long philosophical letters telling me how proud he was of me, shit like that." Brown let out a loud gush of air. God, he'd never told anyone about these things before. He'd hardly admitted them to himself.

The past, after his return from Vietnam, flows. He remembered his father's 1968 company Christmas party. At the time his father was the bigwig president. After the main course but before dessert, Brown took the podium to talk about the fighting men in Vietnam. How everyone collectively should send them a nice *big* thank-you Christmas present. Though three-hundred filthy rich people were in attendance, he received only one twenty dollar donation.

Returning disabled from the war, Brown remembers listening to his father's paternal advice and expertise, and realizing the man didn't sound like he had a brain in his head. That although his father was forty years his senior, Brown felt far more insightful because of the combat experiences. To him, his father was a nothing more than a babbling, incompetent moron.

It shamed him that his *now* patriotic flag-waving, *show me the money* father had been hardly more than a draft dodger during the Second World War. That everything spilling from his father's mouth was based upon money. That to his father's way of thinking, your bank roll was a direct indicator of how much character you had and literally how right you were. That every conversation ended with, "Now what are you going to do for me?" His father had lawyers on retainer for the sole purpose of making sure he remained *always* in good character and always right. Asshole.

One evening, Brown had happened upon a letter his father was sending to a state politician. One of the many points discussed was: "disease, war and famine are all good things because they reduce the population." That war was basically an all around good idea because: "It cleans out the pipes and get rid of the trash in society." At the time, pictures of Adolf Hitler and the Jewish Holocaust had rushed through his mind.

Brown learned to hate his bigoted father. To hate everything he stood for. He wanted nothing more than to grab that lying, spineless, adulterous, cocksucking piece of shit by the throat and choke him to death.

"Penny for your thoughts," Laura said breaking the silence.

"Just reminiscing," he said attempting a smile.

"Didn't look like it."

"After I got wounded," Brown looks with blood shot eyes, "my father came to see me at the Fort Bliss Army Hospital in El Paso, Texas. After complaining about the long airplane ride, he said, 'thought you were a gonner.' Then he laughed. 'Thought you'd be dead by now.'"

"How cruel . . . how could anyone say that?"

"Probably thought it was funny seeing me with a bandaged head and paralyzed right arm in a sling. Did I ever mention that my father was a real jokester. Ha, ha. Mr. Comedian. Except no one's laughing," Brown said harshly. "He told me, he never wanted me born—that it was my mother's idea."

Brown found himself shaking with rage and simultaneously holding back a flood of tears. "I asked my mother why he talked to me like that. What did I ever do to him? Then she admitted that while pregnant with me, my father wanted her to have an abortion. That my mother almost died giving birth to me and he never even came to the hospital. Never even called. For all he knew me and my mother had died."

Brown avoids Laura's pressing stare. "I guess my father should have let me run down his leg when he had the chance—huh?"

"Oh, Freddie," she said. "I'm so sorry."

"Years later my brainless father lost all his blood money. But like they say, 'In a rat race the biggest rat wins.' So as all gutless wimps do, instead of facing up to it, he puts a gun to his head."

"He shot himself?"

"Never attended his funeral. Don't know where he's buried." To deal with his inner rage, Brown, like in Vietnam, visualizes himself thrusting a bayonet deep into his father's chest then twisting the blade and staring into the dying man's face. "I don't wanna know where he's buried because if I did, I'd spit on the grave."

As they gravitate toward the shade of a towering maple tree, Brown keeps picking dandelions and wild flowers till he holds a colorful bouquet. "For you."

"Well, thank you."

"When I came home from 'Nam, I was convinced that it would have been best if I had died over there. Suicide in a wake-

up. Now, I wouldn't give *him* or those like him the satisfaction."
There is a brief moment when Brown looks stricken—then
something deeper and darker than anguish crosses his face and he
said hatefully, "What kind of man would betrays his own son?"

Sweating, he pulls off his jersey to expose a battle-scared
chest. Shyly, she diverts her stare to the sunflower. "He love
me," she says pulling off a pebble to let it drift to the ground.
"He loves me not," she said pulling off a second petal. Dropping
the flower, she moves closer. Brown fruitlessly raises his hand to
stop her approach.

Regardless, the scene makes his pulse thunder. Whisked
back in time to days of crimson slaughter, he hears a blaring Civil
War bugle, booming guns and the rush of steel. A flag flaps and
soldiers with gleaming rifles run frantically into black gunpowder
clouds.

WE ARE COMING FATHER ABRAHAM,
Six hundred thousand more,
From Mississippi's winding stream
And from New England's shore.
We leave our ploughs and workshops,
Our wives and children dear,
With hearts too full for utterance,
With but a silent tear.
We will not look behind us,
But steadfastly before.
We are coming Father Abraham,
Six hundred thousand more!

(Civil War stationery dated 1863)

*. . . There, beneath the shade of maple tree stands a
beautiful woman, nervously folding the edges of her
plumed hat. She is dressed in a hoop skirt of delicate
whites and blues, her dusty blonde hair gently blowing in
the breeze.*

She is in the company of a stunning, bearded Federal cavalry officer with long, dark hair. He stands naked to the waist, wide leather suspenders stretched tautly over his broad, battle-scarred chest. His sky-blue pants are trimmed out with black leather cavalry boots that rise past his knees. His hand rests solidly on the walnut grip and brass strap of an army Colt revolver inside its holster. A long saber dangles from his U.S. Cavalry belt, and tucked behind the belt are buckskin gauntlets and a Bowie knife.

Esteem radiates from the woman's blue eyes as her hero speaks about the rolling thunder of a cannonade, the clash of steel, the gallantry of fallen comrades, and the neighs of sweating chargers that bore them into the battlefields.

Their eyes are filled with each other as she begins to smooth his tormented brow. His hand gently sweeps around the lady's slender waist and his strong forearm pulls her near, unable to resist the promised kiss.

She is all love, all surrender, as she melts into the firmness of the Yankee soldier.

THE GIRL I LEFT BEHIND ME

He turn'd and left the spot—O! do not deem him
weak—
For dauntless was the soldier's heart,
though tears were on his cheek.
Go, watch the foremost rank, in danger's dark career:
Before the hand, more daring then his,
wiped away a tear.

(Civil War envelope dated 1863)

WAR WIDOW

She grieves as
something in her womb
forces her to breathe the
black of The Wall, compels her to
step through gardens of stone,
dreading she might find what she
searches for. Disoriented by time
and space, a woman who mourns for
unfound love lays black lace panties
at the foot of The Wall, for Johnny,
the boy she never knew. But her
deepest fear is being right, truly
having a connection with a KIA. She
runs madly toward the vision with
outstretched arms only to crumble to
her knees. The War Widow shivers at
the coming of twilight. The one God
promised has been stolen, and she's
left to live it out . . . empty and alone.

Lessons of War

Laura and Brown straddle their bicycles, take a last farewell glimpse at Allyn's gravestone and pedal a short distance to the Fort Sheridan museum. After securing their bikes, they climb the worn stone steps and enter the stately brown-stone. Inside they are greeted by the stark aroma of an old building that houses old decaying artifacts. Turning right, they head down a musty cobwebbed corridor and enter a high-ceiling room, with flaking white paint, filled with rows of dusty glass display cases.

In the far corner, Brown spots a globe. Walking over, he spins it until he finds Southeast Asia.

"There," he said, pointing to Chiang Mai, Thailand. "That's where my sister Roxanna lives with her husband Joe and their son Jamie."

He places one finger on Chicago, then another on Chiang Mai. "Look," he turns to make sure Laura is watching. "She's literally on the other side of the world."

"How did she end up there?"

"Roxanna came to Vietnam in 1968 with the valiant idea of finding me. Then, figuring out a way to get me home safe and alive."

Brown moves to a display case with Laura close behind. "But by the time she got to 'Nam though, I was already wounded and in an evacuation hospital," he explains. "Regardless, she stayed long enough to find out what most of us already knew."

"And that was?"

"That war can be exhilarating. That it creates an inner excitement, a tenseness that you can't achieve in normal life. And she, like a lot of other people, liked the feeling of being at the heart of everything, of being part of it. Not an onlooker but a member of the team. Anyway, she stayed for seven years as a combat journalist until the fall of Saigon in April 1975."

"I didn't know anyone would stay in Vietnam if they didn't have to."

"There's a lot of things that happened *over-there* that people don't know about. 'Nam is a mystery to most and will probably stay that way."

They move to another case and stare at an Army Colt .45 pistol. "Vietnam is a very seductive country," Brown said staring at Laura's profile curious to whether she is still interested. "It has a way of getting into your blood without you ever knowing it."

"Like I do?" Laura said sweetly, looking at him full-faced and mischievously.

"Pretty much," Brown responds holding back a huge grin. "Roxanna found the Vietnamese to be a very kind and gentle people."

ROXANNA
THE ONE WHO STAYED

Her mix-blood child clings to her shattered body
as she struggles on wobbling canes
with hungry blue eyes that could cut through
a South China Sea fog.

She'd been sucked into 'Nam by a foolhardy brother,
but that only started the tears.
She screams over the tagged and bagged at Dau Tiang,
"If they were the RIGHT sixteen, this war'd be over!"

Seven years of d'Nam could eat through steel,
could twist, tear, distort—anything or anyone.
And after the baptism of fire, well
it would have taken a miracle to get her out.

Through a 35-mm shutter taking black and whites,
she saw her buddies forge careers,
get blown away, die,
or simply vanish.

Saigon, Hoi An, Da Nang, Hue,
the Mekong Delta, Highlands, Quang Tri province.
Exotic, haunting names that can reverberate, revitalize.
Now she can't rest anymore without their magic.

Plate 70   Roxanna M. Brown *(Photograph by Tim Page)*

"Look." They move to the next display to view a communist weapon. "That's an AK-47," he points. "I remember when we captured one of those that had this beautiful maroon-colored wooden stock. The guys wanted to keep it as a souvenir but couldn't."

"Couldn't? Why not?"

"Well, they might be able to keep it while in 'Nam, but they wouldn't let 'em take it home," Brown explains. "Like Roxanna's friends, Dana Stone and Sean Flynn. They had an entire apartment filled with captured weapons, but they never left the country."

"Dana and Sean?" Laura questions. They had shifted over to peer at a pair of leather Civil War gauntlets inside another case.

"You heard of 'em?"

"Maybe."

"They were both legendary Vietnam combat photographers. Dana Stone's work made the cover of *Time* magazine in 1967. And Sean, who they called 'Son of Captain Blood' was Errol Flynn's son."

"Okay," Laura said nodding her head slowly. "I think I know who you mean. They were captured, weren't they?" She brushed past Brown, wiping perspiration from her brow. "It's hot in here."

"A bit stuffy. Let's go."

Leaving the musty building, they let their eyes adjust to the sunlight before walking down the steps and over to their bicycles.

"A journalist's ultimate dream was to cover the war from the enemy side."

"You have to get captured to do that don't you?" Laura speculates.

"Pretty much."

"Sounds more like a nightmare not the ultimate dream."

"And their nightmare/capture took place on June 6th, 1970."

They straddled their bikes and start riding toward a shady tree lined street.

"At the time, a lot of people thought Sean would 'get the girl in the end,' but it never happened." Brown peddles his bike out front of Laura.

"That's it?" Laura calls, hurrying to catch up.

"My sister, Roxanna and Dana's wife, Louise, got word of their whereabouts but all the information reached a dead end."

"God, prisoners of war. That's the worst," Laura said. "And Louise?"

"When there was nothing more to be done, she left to go live in Spain. A few years later she came down with multiple sclerosis and right now she bedridden in her home town of Cynthiana, Kentucky," Brown said.

"What a bummer. That poor girl."

"Amen."

LOUISE   Chopper
blades splatter   the sound barrier.
It all ended with everyone's nerves shattered.
Yet the war lives on deep inside her chestnut
screaming eyes where she searches for one of the
missing. "There's a war going on over there!"   Dana
had yelled.   So they culminated their desires in
Aptos, California. Left their mountain dreams at
Sawyer's Bar and flew to Da Nang, husband and
wife. Dana quickly became addicted to the war,
until Louise felt married to a death wish.
But she had the circled-snake tatoo on
his ass, no mortgage and "That's where
it's at, man." Life now ebbs from her
limbs, as MS leaves her grappling.
And her mind? well it races
somewhere in twilight zone.
"Nam took , now nothing
else matters but 'Nam.
I watch as she
forms the word,
Saigon   on
her lips.
Dana smiles behind wire-rimmed glasses. Louise rises and is
once more in his love embrace. A beautiful cathedral sunset
streaks through clouds. God has called them home.

Plate 71   Sean Flynn at left with Dana Stone *(Photographer unknown)*

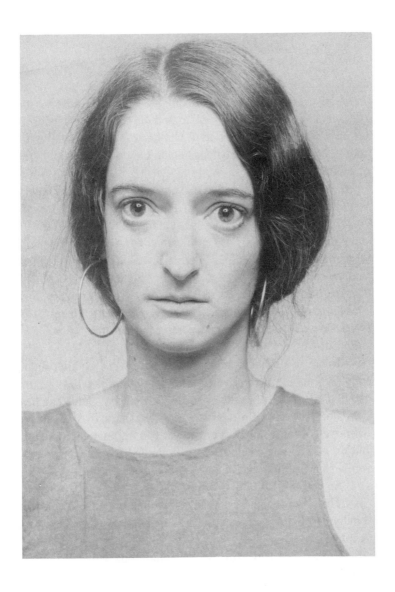

Plate 72   Louise Stone *(Photographer unknown)*

"Freddie," Laura said, retrieving his mind. "How is it you're not like the other vets? You don't seem to have all those typical problems."

"I put on a good show," Brown said, smiling.

"Seriously," said Laura, almost scolding. "You're different and you know it."

Brown watches as a glint of sunlight shines on Laura's eyes. He steers his bicycle clear of a pothole and swings back to Laura's side. "I view life as a challenge," he said. "But I'll admit The Wall showed me things I didn't know." His sigh is full of contemplation. "It showed me that it's just as important to learn from the past as it is to leave it behind. That, ultimately, you learn more from losing than from winning."

"Lose and move on," she said thoughtfully as they ride.

"You know, an hour of near death combat can increase your wisdom more than a lifetime of normal, everyday experiences," he said coasting his bike." He faces her. "I actually miss combat. Can you believe that. Because Laura," he said her name to draw eyes contact, "in the bush you knew who your enemy was. Everyone would bleed red, and we never left our buddies behind."

"But why did so many of the guys get *fried*?"

"Because probably that same hour of *real* combat didn't enlighten but ate them alive. Left them with a bloodless wound that drained decades from their soul. That said, wounds can heal if treated properly. So the real culprit was how they treated us when we got back home. I mean war is a traumatic experience, and we needed some help de-programming. It's like one minute you're in a firefight and the next you're back on the block."

"So you needed time to adjust?"

"That. But too, there was no one around to help. We needed someone to help us change the war template back to the peace template."

Laura's eyebrows furrow, seemingly puzzled. "So you're adjusted?"

"Ah*hhhh*?" He waves a flattens hand. "'Nam wrecked me, like everyone else," he begins talking slower, careful to create the right idea. "But when you're trying to make it back—back from anything traumatic, it's that first crucial step—in the right direction—that counts the most."

"And for you," she persists, "what was the turning point? That first step?"

"I was bumming around the little town of Mexia, Texas," he said, "and getting hotter and thirstier by the second. I pulls up to this little old Dairy Queen, got out of the car and bought a nice cool Doctor Pepper. That's when I spot these two pretty country girls cruising around. I said to myself, 'Ah, what the heck.' I walked over and tell 'em I'm doing an interview for a local newspaper. 'So what do you girls do for fun around here?'"

He pauses in his reminiscence. "Meeting Connie Cobb changed my life. The Cobb family, Clyde and Edna with daughters Connie, Karen—took me in. They liked me." He smiles. "You know what that meant to me?" Deep furrows crease his forehead as he concentrated.

"The entire family liked me for who I was. They let me roll out my sleeping bag on their living room floor. We went out grocery shopping together. I sat at their dinner table, washed the dishes, ironed the clothes. They trusted me. It was so normal—comforting. We just talked and laughed about regular stuff and I was okay. They helped me rebuild my self-esteem. Made me feel whole. Gave me a home."

Laura and Brown rode alongside the tree-lined parade ground, and watched the birds busily jumping and flying around, chasing after bugs. They slow their bikes to let past two servicemen with brown lunch bags, headed for a shade tree.

"Hungry?" Brown asks.

"Yeah, somewhat," Laura said. She drinks from her water bottle. But before putting it away, she takes aim and squirts at Brown.

"Hey, hey," he hollers. "Cut it out."

She speeds out of range as he half-heartedly reaches for his bottle.

"Come on, wait up," Brown calls after her. "Truce. I'm pooped." Replacing the water bottle, he rolls up next to her. "Will you let me finish for chrissakes?" he scolds. "I'm in the middle of a story."

Laura drops her head and scrunches her lips like a child. "Sorry."

"That's better. So after my discharge, I came back to Chicago where I met Barbara who became my wife. But there was still a long ways to go. And I didn't find the next step until I was in the delivery room the day my daughter Cara was born. They cut her umbilical cord and she started to cry. That's when I held my arms out, and they walked over and placed her in my arms. I pulled her to my breast and felt her breath. And I said, "Hi, Cara. I've been waiting a long time." As he thought about that precious moment he felt tears come to his eyes.

"And . . . what did Cara show you?" Laura asks, her interest peaking.

"She showed me the meaning of unconditional love," he said softly.

Laura looks at Brown with bittersweet eyes.

"Then Kathryn, my second child, began to sew what was left of my mind back together," he said. "Children can do things like that."

"Yes," she said sadly. "I can understand that."

By the sorrowful tone in her voice, Brown knew she didn't have any children of her own.

"Laura, do you want me to explain my lessons of war? How I continue to survive?"

"I'd like that.

"I'll make it simple: Give someone a reason to live and you give them a life. Simple enough?"

"A reason to live."

"Give life meaning. Search for the purpose of your existence. Learn to respect, cherish and embrace your own uniqueness. Fall in love with yourself. Stay away from casual sex, drugs, cigarettes and alcohol. They only mess everything up and complicate things."

"They do don't they."

"'Make it simple stupid,' that's how I like to say it. And when you simplify it you'll find yourself smiling and surrounded by loving caring friends."

Her eyes flicker and lips moves while she contemplates his meaning. "Oh, look," she said snapping back to her cheerful self. While coasting, she points to a historical brick house. "Lieutenant Colonel Harold A. Fritz lives there. He received the Congressional Medal of Honor from President Nixon. I have an interview set up with him."

"Really."

"But I think I've already met the biggest hero of the war."

"Keep it comin', Laura. Keep it comin'. Butter me up," Brown said and they laugh. "Seriously, why the interview?"

"History?" she said. "I don't know. I just want to." Then she faces him. "You know what?"

Brown listens.

"Well, I was just thinking that maybe . . . well just maybe next weekend, we could ride the bike paths in St. Charles along the Fox River. Then I could . . . could tell you all about the interview."

Brown's face slackens. Holy shit! She doesn't get it. I can't do this again. It's just like a battlefield. The war is fucking everyone up. You want to help your buddy, you don't want to see anyone get hurt or killed. But you can't save everyone's life. She can't expect me to rescue her troubled soul. Can she?

Brown and Laura dismount and lay their bikes inconspicuously in tall grass. Walking along a wooded path, they descend to the shores of Lake Michigan. The sun sparkles off the green lake as cool water rushes back and forth onto the driftwood and rocks. Speedboats playfully circle in the distance and sailboats sway to the rhythm of the winds.

Laura takes off her shoes and socks, then ventures into the cool water where her toes sank into the silky sand with waves lapping against her tan, shapely calves. Staring over the lake, she crosses her arms to console herself and whispers like a child, "I wish this didn't have to end." She attempts a smile as she looks over her shoulder at Brown, but sadness has cast a shadow across her face.

With shoes off, Brown steps into the refreshing water and moves behind to wrap his arms around her. He wants to comfort her, be her friend, but he knows it will never work. They stare across the lake to the horizon.

"Laura, I wish I could be *that* person you're looking for. But I'm not."

As they stare across the lake to a sailboat with billowed green and yellow sails, she squeezes his hand.

FOOT-
PRINTS
IN THE SAND

One night I had a dream.
I was walking along the beach
with the Lord, and across the skies
flashed scenes from my life. In each
scene I noticed two sets of footprints in
the sand. One was mine, and one was the
Lord's. When the last scene of my life appeared before me, I looked back at the footprints in the sand, and, to my surprise, I
noticed that many times along the path of
my life there was only one set of footprints.
And I noticed that it was at the lowest
and saddest times in my life. I asked
the Lord about it: Lord, you said
that once I decided to follow
you, you would walk with me
all the way. But I noticed
that during the most trouble-
some times in my life there
is only one set of foot-
prints. I don't under-
stand why you left my
side when I needed you
most. The Lord said:
"My precious child, I
never left you during
your time of trial.
Where you see only
one set of foot-
prints I was car-
rying you."

Author Unknown

Appendices

Appendix 1

Golden Rules of Combat

1. You are not superman.
2. Recoilless rifles - ain't.
3. Suppressive fire - won't.
4. If it's stupid, but works, it ain't stupid.
5. Don't look conspicuous - it draws fire.
6. Never draw fire - it irritates everyone around you.
7. When in doubt, empty the magazine.
8. Never share a foxhole with anyone braver than you are.
9. Your weapon was made by the lowest bidder.
10. If your attack is going really well, it's an ambush.
11. If you can't remember, the claymore is pointed toward you.
12. All five-second grenade fuses are three seconds.
13. Try to look unimportant. They may be low on ammo.
14. If you are forward of your position, the artillery will be short.
15. The enemy diversion you are ignoring is the main attack.
16. The easy way is always mined.
17. The important things are very simple.
18. The simple things are very hard.
19. If you are short everything except enemy, you are in combat.
20. No OPLAN (plan of operation) survives first contact intact.
21. When you have secured an area, don't forget to tell the enemy.
22. Incoming fire has right-of-way.
23. No combat-ready unit has ever passed inspection.
24. No inspection-ready unit has ever passed combat.
25. Teamwork is essential. It gives them other people something to shoot at.

26. If the enemy is in range, so are you.
27. Beer math is 2 beers x 37 men = 49 cases.
28. Body count math is 2 VC + 1 NVA + 1 water buffalo = 37 KIA.
29. Friendly fire - isn't.
30. Anything you do can get you shot - including doing nothing.
31. Make it too tough for the enemy to get in, and you can't get out.
32. Tracers work both ways.
33. The only thing more accurate than incoming enemy fire is incoming friendly.
34. Radios will fail as soon as you need fire support desperately.
35. If you take more than your fair share of objectives, you will have more than your fair share to lose.
36. Both sides are convinced they are about to lose -they're both right.
37. Professionals are predictable - but the world is full of amateurs.
38. Murphy was a grunt.

Appendix 2

Number One is:

1. You're socks are dry
2. Your boots are off
3. A Saigon bar hostess who doesn't like tea
4. A USO show with 20 dancing girls
5. Pre-filled sand bags
6. Being next in line
7. An incoming dud hand grenade
8. B-52s - gunships - Spooky Jolly Green Giant
9. R&R
10. Beer (any kind, hot or cold)
11. Your choice of C-rations
12. Can of mixed fruit
13. Plenty of heat tablets
14. Sleeping anywhere but on the ground.
15. Day in the village with the boy's sister
16. A letter from your girl (anybody for that matter)
17. Rolled marijuana joints
18. Being a short timer
19. Freedom bird
20. Huey

Number Ten is:

1. Monsoon
2. Hitting the dirt in a rice paddy
3. A USO show with no girls
4. A walk in the country
5. Un-sweetened Kool-Aid
6. A dud hand grenade
7. Incoming
8. Empty bottle of bug juice
9. Ham and Mothers Choke and Puck C-rations
10. Steak cooked in Nuoc Mam sauce
11. Combat Assault
12. Ambush
13. Mine sweep
14. Bunker guard
15. Tunnel rat
16. MOS-11B40
17. A Dear John letter saying your girl is engaged to your best friend who is 4-F
18. Your rifle is a Jammin' Jenny
19. You're an NFG
20. LP or Out Post
21. Pointman

Appendix 3

"A question RFK shouldn't forget: Who are the Americans?"

Boston Globe
April 15, 1968
written by syndicated columnist Joseph Alsop,
Staff Journalist with the *Washington Post*

Quang Tin Province, South Vietnam — By some standards, perhaps the scent was sadly banal. In a dusty clearing, on the flank of dusty Landing Zone Baldy, the formation was as smart as wartime ever permits.

The honor guard's uniform showed the scars of combat, though they had done the best refurbishing they could, and the guard commander's hand was messily bandaged, for he had lost most of his finger waving on his men in the Tet offensive near Da Nang. The men to receive decorations had been given a bit of help with their spit and polish, so they looked like peace-time soldiers—though the deeds for which they got their Silver Stars and Bronze Stars were high acts of warlike valor and sacrifice.

Here, one noticed all the strains of our America were gloriously represented—Irish and Yankee, Jewish and Puerto Rican, German and Central European and Negro, last listed, but by no means last in act and presence. The officer reading the citations was exceptionally impressive, very young Negro lieutenant, who is making the Army a career.

The Stars and Stripes drifted gently in the bright air in the iron grip on an even younger Negro draftee, who rather resembled Cassius Clay—powerful, ramrod, erect, proud of silken and symbolic burden. And at the head of the list of Silver Stars, along with Captain Francis X. Brennan ("Heroic Actions") and one or two others, was 1SG Hubert B. Ramier ("Heroic actions and personal example"), a giant veteran Negro who had led his platoon with such incomparable dash he and his men overran a whole hornet's nest of enemy-filled bunkers.

The unit being decorated was the 1st Battalion, 6th Infantry Regiment, which descends directly, albeit by the transformations, from the new-raised Regiment of the War of 1812 that the British Admiralty named "The Regulars." So, the unit colors, along with the Stars and Strips, were heavy with battle-honors from the old times.

Canada, Chippewa and Lundy's lane, The Bad Axe River, where they fought the Black Hawk Indian Wars, Vera Cruz, Churubusco and Chipultepec,

Manassas, Antietam, (Fredericksburg), Chancellorsville and Gettysburg, Santiago de Cuba and Panay in the Phillipines, Alsace-Lorrain, Sait Mihiel and Oruel Meuse-Argonne, from Algeria via bitter Anzio to the Po Valley where Wehrmacht broke at last in Italy—all were there except Korea which the Regiment somehow missed.

Now the 1st of the 6th was receiving yet another honor from its deeds in Vietnam. As the unit-citation was read in the standard, flat, military voice, the breeze grew strong, the old pennons fluttered out, and one could read the battle names embroidered on half a dozen of them. Thus vividly reminded of the long American past, thus simultaneously face to face with youthful patriotism and brave endurance and our country's strange accomplishment, and old men's eyes perhaps ludicrously misted.

That was over soon, however, with the concluding address by the Americal Division Commander, Major General Samuel Koster, a tough and able leader in the field, but not exactly a Churchillian orator. Or was it really over, after all? For as the helicopter lifted off again, one found oneself almost desperately asking, for the 100th time, the question that Vietnam always raises: Who are the Americans?

In this war, the question presents itself in novel guise that may have some importance for Senator Robert F. Kennedy. For the contest, this time is not the usual one, between the fat, forgetful comfort of home front and the hardiness and bravery of the field. That customary contrast is there, too, of course, but now there is another.

On the one hand are the large group senator's supporters whom someone flatteringly (or was it unflatteringly?) described as "chicly or leftish," who greet reports that their country has been successful on the battlefield with happy derision and almost eager for an American defeat in war. On the other hand are the people of every American strain, who stood proudly beneath the colors at LZ Baldy, serving their nation in war in the old American way.

In this way Senator Kennedy has his own credentials as, God knows, both his elder brothers did. Yet, there in Vietnam among the men of General Westmoreland's much vaster academy—so different in many ways from Berkely—the conclusion is unavoidable that Senator Kennedy cannot afford to forget the question: Who are the Americans?

Appendix 4

DEPARTMENT OF THE ARMY
Headquarters Americal Division
APO San Francisco 96374

AVDF-CG   27 May 1968
All Personnel of the Americal Division

It is with pride that I accept this opportunity to address you, the men of the Americal Division, on the occasion of the initial publication of our division's newspaper — The Southern Cross.

You have compiled a most enviable record since the division came to I Corps Tactical Zone as Task Force Oregon last April. You have consistently met and defeated the enemy on the battlefield. Your aggressiveness and zeal have been proven time and again, and have added laurels to the heritage of the Americal Division.

The Southern Cross is intended to recognize and publicize your exploits and achievements. Read it with pride -- pride in yourselves and in your Division's accomplishments.

I extend to you a hearty and sincere "Well Done," and the future Godspeed.

S. W. Koster
Major General, US Army
Commanding

Appendix 5

DA, HQ, 1st Bn 6th Inf, 198th Inf Bde (Lt), APO SF 96219

TO: Officers and Men

I take this opportunity to express my heartfelt admiration and appreciation to each and every "Regular" for the commendable manner in which you have accomplished the challenging missions assigned. The attached letter of commendation related but one of many impressive victories you have achieved in the past ten months. You prevented a major attack on the city of Danang by killing 268 enemy from the 60th Main Force Battalion during the Battle of Lo Giang (receiving the Valorous unit emblem). You killed 118 enemy from the 70th Main Force Battalion during the Battle of Op Bahn I, which resulted in the routing of the entire enemy force. During your 39 days on Operation Burlington Trail, you were credited with 145 enemy kills and 144 captured weapons, which turned back the 1st VC Regiment and allowed the road west to Tien Phouc to be opened for the first time since 1964. During the Second TET Offensive, while operating in the area around LZ Center, you killed 145 enemy and captured 50 weapons in 22 days of extremely heavy fighting against the entire 3rd NVA Regiment, 2nd NVA Division. The 31st Anti-aircraft Battalion and the 2nd NVA Division Reconnaissance Company were also encountered. Intelligence later revealed that you decimated one battalion and stopped the entire Regiment from accomplishing its mission. In your latest venture you have proved the night does not belong to "Charlie" and have successfully prevented his maneuver in the critical Chu Lai Area of Operation. You can be justifiably proud of your accomplishments and as the member of this elite unit I wish you continued successes in all future combat.

William D Kelley
LTC, Infantry

Appendix 6

DEPARTMENT OF THE ARMY
Headquarters, 198TH Infantry Brigade, AMERICAL
DIVISION
APO San Francisco 96219

AVDG-BC   8 August 1968
SUBJECT: Letter of Commendation

Officers and Men
1st Battalion, 6th Infantry
198th Infantry Brigade (Lt)
APO SF 96219

I wish to commend you on the fact that it has been exactly two months since rockets were fired at Chu Lai. It is significant that the last rocket attack took place the night previous to the day the "Regulars" were assigned the responsibility for the "Rocket Valley" (Rocket Pocket) area.

Your aggressive spirit, determination, and tireless efforts have been the primary factors in deterring the enemy from attacking with rockets the important Chu Lai Base Complex.

I congratulate you on the successful accomplishment of your primary mission. I wish you continued success in all of your endeavors.

/S/Charles B. Thomas
Colonel, Infantry
Commanding

Appendix 7

DEPARTMENT OF THE ARMY
Headquarters, 1st Battalion, 6th Infantry
198th Infantry Brigade, Americal Division
Apo San Francisco 96219

AVDF-CH   20 October 1968

Subject: First Anniversary Memorial Message

To the Officers and Men
1st Battalion, 6th Infantry, 198th Infantry Brigade
APO San Francisco 96219

In the short six months I have served as this battalion's chaplain over half of its casualties have occurred and I have often been asked, "Why?" Why did these good and brave men have to suffer and even die?

Each man had his own private set of reasons I am sure but this I know: the men who "poured out their rich wine of youth, and their years yet to be" did so for a dream too good to be true. Theirs was a dream of the earth without war, without the taking of lives in battle, a dream of a world in which every human being would be able to live in peace, honor and justice, in true brotherhood as happy, healthy, mature persons. Did they dream the impossible dream or reach for the unreachable star? I hope not, for I dream that dream too!

Since the "Regulars" have been in the Republic of South Vietnam one hundred and four men have given their last full measure of devotion for their country, but why you ask. Perhaps the War Memorial in Glasglow, Scotland, gives a hint:

These died in war, that we at peace might live,
These gave their best, so we our best would give.

They died for you! So keep them in kindly memory now, but do not stop there. Hear the ancient prophet Jeremiah speak:

You, that have escaped the sword, go, stand
not still. Jeremiah 51:50

Please do not stand still—do something: be concerned, informed and poised for creative action, America needs your help.

What can we do to rightly honor our war dead? Resolve that they shall not have died in vain; but that this nation, under God, shall have a new birth of freedom and justice for all, both where you are and where we are right now. Remember the "Regulars" and the part your loved one had in bringing us to where we are. We pledge to you and yours that we shall do our part, the best way we know how, so as never to bring shame or embarrassment to any of its members, both past and present, but rather to bring honor and peace. And help me, their chaplin, to help them through your prayers and concern for us.

Glenn Paul Hargis
Chaplain (CPT), USA

Appendix 8

DEPARTMENT OF THE ARMY
Headquarters, 1st Battalion, 6th Infantry
198the Infantry Brigade, Americal Division
Apo San Francisco 96219

AVDF-BCNV   22 October 1968

Subject: First Anniversary Memorial Message

The men of the "Regulars"

On 22 October 1967, the "Regulars" came ashore and remained in the Republic of South Vietnam little cognizant of what the future would bring. Many men have come and gone, but their individual and combined efforts are still gratefully remembered today. On this first anniversary in Vietnam I want to take this opportunity to express my heartfelt thanks and appreciation to each and every "Regular" for the excellent manner in which you accomplished your many diverse missions. Because of your hard work and splendid effort "The Regulars March On" with their heads held high, their chests sticking out proudly, their guidons waving bravely for all to see. No matter the length of your service, you did your part to help the battalion to do its challenging work in the highest tradition of the military service.

I take this opportunity to express my thanks to you and to wish the battalion the very best of luck. I assumed command of the unit on 1 April 1968 and will be departing soon to my next assignment. As I think back upon my tour with the "Regulars" I am deeply impressed by the high caliber of performance in all elements of the command. Thanks to you we opened the road west to Tien Phuoc which had been closed since 1964 and denied the enemy vast quantities of rice and weapons. We blunted and then shattered the NVA in their Second Tet Offensive. We destroyed a NVA battalion-size unit and stopped the entire 3rd NVA Regiment around LZ Center. We faithfully guarded the Division's northern perimeter against VC rocket attacks on Chu Lai. Thanks to you, we have done a commendable job in every respect.

I am honored to be your commander and you can be justifiably proud of your many achievements. I also am mindful of the terrible cost in wounded and dead we had to suffer. I have asked our chaplain to prepare a memorial listing of the officers and men who gave their all. Please take a moment to read this list and offer a prayer or two for the men and officers of the "Regulars" as we carry on what they started. And pray for peace, a just, honorable, lasting peace. Remember the "Regulars!" I will, as I bid farewell to the most courageous men with whom I have ever served. Good luck and God bless you all.

1 Incl   William D. Kelly
                                               LTC, Infantry
                                               Commanding

Appendix 9

DEPARTMENT OF THE ARMY
HEADQUARTERS AMERICAL DIVISION
APO San Francisco 96374
GENERAL ORDERS   19 April 1968
NUMBER 2065

AWARD OF THE SILVER STAR

1. TC 320. The following AWARD is announced posthumously.

YAMANE, BENJI   US 56823799 (SSAN 563-62-6876);
SERGEANT E5, United States Army,
Company D, 1st Battalion, 6th Infantry,
198th Infantry Brigade APO 96219

Awarded: Silver Star
Date action: 16 March 1968
Theater: Republic of Vietnam
Reason: For gallantry in action against a hostile force in the Republic of Vietnam. Sergeant Yamane distinguished himself by intrepid actions on 16 March 1968 while serving as a squad leader with Company D, 1st Battalion, 6th Infantry. On that date, Sergeant Yamane's squad was the lead element in a search and clear operation conducted by his company in an area southwest of Hoi An. Sergeant Yamane had positioned himself directly behind the point man where he felt that he could best observe and control the members of his squad. As he led the company toward their objective, he spotted a booby trap directly in the path of the point man. Immediately,

Sergeant Yamane shouted a warning to his men, then turned and shoved a nearby squad member to the ground, using his body to protect his fellow soldier. In spite of his warning, the mine was tripped and the explosion mortally wounded Sergeant Yamane. His actions, taken with utter disregard for his own life, saved the life of the soldier he had shielded from the blast and allowed the other members of the squad to get down and escape injury. Sergeant Yamane's courageous actions, unselfish concern for the lives of his comrades, and devotion to duty were in keeping with the highest traditions of the military service and reflected great credit upon himself, the Americal Division, and the United States Army.

Authority: By direction of the President under the provisions of the Act of Congress, approved 9 July 1918.

FOR THE COMMANDER

NELS A. PARSON, JR.
Colonel, GS
Chief of Staff

OFFICIAL:

DONALD Y. B. CHUNG
LTC, AGC
Adjutant General

Appendix 10

By direction of the Secretary of the Army
The Army Commendation Medal

is awarded to

Specialist Four Fred L. Brown, RA16903597
United States Army

Who distinguished himself by exceptionally meritorious service in connection with military operations against a hostile force in the Republic of Vietnam.   During the period

February 1968 to November 1968

he astutely surmounted extremely adverse conditions to obtain consistently superior results.   Through diligence and determination he invariably accomplished every task with dispatch and efficiency.   His unrelenting loyalty, initiative and perseverance brought him wide acclaim and inspired others to strive for maximum achievement. Selflessly working long and arduous hours, he has contributed significantly to the success of the allied effort. His commendable performance was in keeping with the highest traditions of the military service and reflects great credit upon himself, the Americal Division, and the United States Army

Appendix 11

AWARD OF THE ARMY COMMENDATION MEDAL

1. TC 320. The following AWARD is announced.

BROWN, FRED L. RA 16903597,
Company D, 1st Battalion, 6th Infantry, 198th Infantry Brigade.

Awarded: Army Commendation Medal with "V" Device (1st Oak Leaf Cluster)
Date action: 27 October 1968
Theater: Republic of Vietnam
Reason: For heroism in connection with military operations against a hostile force in the Republic of Vietnam. Sergeant Brown distinguished himself by valorous actions on 27 October 1968 while serving as radio and telephone operator. On that night, the platoon leader, Sergeant Brown, and seven enlisted men from the second platoon were moving to an ambush site, one kilometer west of Hill 69. While crossing a trenchline, a booby trapped grenade detonated, seriously wounding the platoon leader and Sergeant Brown. Refusing aid and ignoring his painful wounds, Sergeant Brown remained in an exposed position with his radio, directing two other squads to their location. He then called in a medical evacuation helicopter while also directing the other squads to pull security for the dustoff. Only when the medevac helicopter landed and the wounded platoon leader (who died fifteen minutes later) was on it, did he board the aircraft and submit to medical attention. Sergeant Brown's personal heroism and devotion to duty are in keeping with the highest traditions of the military service and reflect great credit upon himself, the Americal Division, and the United States Army.

Authority: By direction of the Secretary of the Army under the provisions of AR 672-5-1

For the Commander:
Official:

R.S. Temple, JR.
1LT, AGC
Asst AG

Jack L. Treadwell

Colonel, GS
Chief of Staff

Appendix 12

DEPARTMENT OF THE ARMY
Headquarters Americal Division
APO San Francisco 96374

General Orders   7 August 1968
Number 5261

AWARD OF THE BRONZE STAR MEDAL

Walker, Howard W. S/SGT Company D 1/6 198th LIB
Awarded: Bronze Star Medal with "V" Device
Date Action: 31 May 1968
Theater: Republic of Vietnam
Reason: For heroism in connection with military operations against a hostile force in the Republic of Vietnam. S/SGT Walker distinguished himself by extremely valorous actions on 31 May 1968 while serving as an acting platoon leader with Company D 1/6 Infantry. That night, the company had just broken contact with a NVA force with which they had engaged and were enroute to their night defensive position in Tam Ky district. Because of the thick terrain, consisting of elephant grass, it was necessary for the company to move in single file. As they neared the top of the hill, the lead element came under an intense volume of machine-gun, small arms, and rocket fire from a platoon size NVA force. S/SGT Walker immediately deployed his men and began to lead the assault on the enemy positions, one of which he single-handedly destroyed. As he led his men further up the hill, they came under machine-gun fire from both flanks. With complete disregard for his own personal safety he exposed himself to the fire as he re-grouped his men and moved them to cover in a treeline just below the hill. S/SGT Walker's valorous actions are in keeping with the highest traditions of the Military service and reflect great credit upon himself, the Americal Division, and the United States Army.

John K. Samet   Nels A. Parson Jr.
1Lt, AGC   Colonels, GS

Appendix 13

DEPARTMENT OF THE ARMY
Headquarters Americal Division
APO San Francisco 96374

General Orders   26 May 1968
Number 2785

Award of the Bronze Star Medal

1. TC 320. The following Award is announced.

Denning, Charles W., Staff Sergeant E6,
United States Army, Company d, 1st Battalion, 6th Infantry, 198th
Infantry Brigade APO 96219
Awarded: Bronze Star Medal with "V" Device
Date action: 8 February 1968
Theater: Republic of Vietnam

Reason: For heroism in connection with military operations against a
hostile force.   Staff Sergeant Denning distinguished himself by
exceptionally valorous actions on 8 February 1968 in the Republic of
Vietnam. On that date, elements of the 1st Battalion 6th Infantry made
contact with a reinforced battalion of North Vietnamese Army regulars
near the village of Lo Giang (1). As night fell, the friendly forces
established a defensive position along the edge of the battlefield.
When an enemy patrol probed the perimeter during the night, two
members of Sergeant Denning's platoon were injured in the exchange
of fire. Without regard for his own safety, Sergeant Denning left his
covered position and exposed himself to hostile fire as he raced across
open terrain to aid his men. Seeing that the wounded were being
assisted by medics, he set about making poncho stretchers and
directing the medevac helicopters to his position. Upon the arrival of
the evacuation aircraft, Sergeant Denning assisted in carrying the
wounded men across 50 meters of bullet-swept terrain to the waiting
aircraft. Staff Sergeant Denning's personal bravery, aggressiveness
and unselfish concern for the lives of his fellow soldiers are in keeping
with the highest traditions of the military service and reflect great credit
upon himself, the Americal Division, and the United States Army.

Authority: By direction of the President under the provisions of
Executive order 11046, 24 August 1962.

Appendix 14

Historic note: Both Generals Colin Powell and Schwarzkopf were in the Americal Division. The commander of all ground forces in the Persian Gulf War, General H. (Stormin') Norman Schwarzkopf was also the commander of the 1st of the 6th Infantry in 1969-70.

Americal Newsletter   May - June 1991
General, then an Ltc, won his third Silver Star while commanding the 1st Battalion of the 6th Infantry in South Vietnam's Batangan Peninsula. A portion of his battalion's Bravo Company became trapped in a mine field. Bravo's company commander and a lieutenant had both been badly wounded and a medevac helicopter had been called for. Schwarzkopf, airborne in his Huey helicopter with Captain Bob Trabbert, his artillery liaison officer, reached the stranded unit first and turned over his Huey to get the wounded out. Schwarzkopf and Trabbert then stayed behind.

The remainder of the patrol was still frozen in the mine field. Their commanders had been evacuated; they felt leaderless, abandoned. Schwarzkopf told them calmly that they were going to be alright, to walk out the way they came in and to watch where they put their feet and to keep to their old tracks, stay calm and keep their distance.

As they began to move again one young soldier, a dozen yards away from Schwarzkopf, stepped on another mine. The soldier's leg was mangled and Schwarzkopf and Trabbert were injured slightly. Schwarzkopf proceeded into the mine field and personally attended the soldiers wounds and got him out of the mine field. While assisting with the wounded soldier, Trabbert was seriously wounded and three other soldiers were killed.

In a recent Washington Post interview Schwarzkopf said, "Every waking and sleeping moment, my nightmare is the fact that I will give an order that will cause countless numbers of human beings to lose their lives. I don't want my troops to die. I don't want my troops to be maimed. It's an intensely personal, emotional thing for me. Any decision you have to make that involves the loss of human life is nothing you do lightly. I agonize over it."

Schwarzkopf and the 1/6th Infantry were the subject of the book, *Friendly Fire* by C.D.B. Bryan, and a TV movie of the same name.

Appendix 15

A list of some landing zones, places and base camps the "Death Battalion" (1st of the 6th) passed over and fought from. From 4 Oct 67 thru 10 July 70.

Chu Lai . Duc Pho . LZ Carentan . LZ Bronco . LZ Gator . Nuoc Mau . Binh Son Bridge . Camp Bravo . LZ Colt . Da Nang . Lo Giang . LZ Baldy . LZ Cacti . Que Son Valley . Hiep Duc Valley . LZ West . LZ East (Hill 488) . LZ Center . Tam Ky . Hill 218 . Hill 270 . Hill 488 . LZ Bowman . Hill 352 . Hill 350 . Hill 353 . Tien Phouc . Quang Tri . Burlington Trails . Dragon Valley . Rice Bowl . Hill 69 . Hill 76 . Hill 50 . Hill 54 . Fat City . LZ Ross . Rocket Ridge . Rocket Pocket . Rocket Belt . Hill 707 . Hill 661 . Hill 720 . LZ Angle . LZ Moore . Larson Field . LZ Chippewa . Pine Tree Island . Paradise Island . Ky sang . Ky Phu . Son Tra Bong (River South) . An Ton Bridge (River North) . Om Bau Bridge . Ly Tin . Ky Tra . Bong Song . Sa Huhyn . Batangan Peninsula

Field Infantry Troops

4 infantrymen = 1 Fire Team

3 Fire teams = 1 Squad + 1 Radio telephone operator (RTO)
  (12 infantrymen)

3 Squads = 1 Platoon + 5 RTOs
  (36 infantrymen)

3 Platoons = 1 Company + 17 RTOs
  (125+ infantrymen)

5 Companies = 1 Battalion
  (500 infantrymen) The Companyies' names were
Alpha, Bravo, Charlie, Delta, and Reconnaissance.

Infantry Battalion:
Consisted of anywhere between 250 and 400 hundred men.
The battalion usually comprised of five companies:
Alpha, Bravo, Charlie, Delta, and Reconnaissance Company.

Note: The above numbers are approximate, varied according to reinforcements, and are derived from my personal observation. They are not necessarily consistent with US Army specification.

Appendix 16

"You've never lived 'till you've almost died.
For those who fight for it,
Life has a flavor
The protected will never know!"

Read the sign at Ha Thanh SF Camp Americal Division
AO-1969.

In 1968 it was common to find:

You've never lived
'till you've almost died

engraved on a cigarette lighter.

Appendix 17

POEM	CONFIGURATION
Vietnam Veteran:	Dog Tag
Battlefield Of Da Nang:	Americal Division Patch
Wall Of Blood:	Vietnam Veterans Memorial Wall
Pointman:	Grim Reaper
Line Bunker:	Sandbag bunker
Rebel Raider:	Old version of a coffee pot
Eerie, Exotic, Erotic:	Map of South Vietnam
Bull:	Stairway to heaven
Yamane:	Military issue canteen
The Moment:	Setting sun
Winter Kill:	Smoke hand grenade
Peace Wants To Die:	Cross
Deal With It:	Hand grenade
Elvis And Angel:	Angel
Infantry Soldier:	M-16 ammunition magazine
Cross Over:	Genie's bottle
Victor:	V for victory
War Widow:	Head stone
Louise Stone:	Blooding heart
Foot Prints In The Sand:	Foot prints in the sand

Appendix 18

The following is a list of infantry soldiers who died in my combat unit. The other heroic men and women listed also inspired me by their supreme sacrifices. Their names are among the more than 58,000 Americans who gave their lives for freedom, justice and liberty, and the red white and blue.

Visit them at the **Vietnam Veterans Memorial,** in Washington, D.C. for what they represent should not be diminished or forgotten.

KAHLER, CHARLES EDWARD	01 NOV 67	29E	004
GREEN, WESLEY	03 DEC 67	31E	029
RUDLONG, THELMER ARTHUR	05 DEC 67	31E	041
LAMPLEY, JAMES JR.	09 DEC 67	31E	069
RICHARD, DONALD WAYNE	25 DEC 67	32E	059
KINSEY, JOE EDWARD	29 DEC 67	32E	096
LARSON, JEFFRY ARTHUR	02 JAN 68	33E	019
SHEETS, WINFRIED ALBERT	17 JAN 68	34E	064
WHITE, JOHN OLIVER	22 JAN 68	35E	012
PRIEN, DON	31 JAN 68	36E	023
O'CONNOR, RICHARD EDWARD	31 JAN 68	36E	029
MANGIOLARDO, MICHAEL A.	31 JAN 68	36E	031
WIERZBA, EDWIN RUDOLPH	05 FEB 68	37E	046
BOUTWELL, AMOS HAYES	08 FEB 68	38E	021
BOWMAN, JOSEPH B.	08 FEB 68	38E	021
CARRASQUILLO-DENTON, ALBERTO	08 FEB 68	38E	022
CERIONE, JAMES STANLEY III	08 FEB 68	38E	023
CLOVIS, FRANKLIN	08 FEB 68	38E	023

DAHM, RALPH ALBERT	08 FEB 68	38E	024
DENSLOW, GEORGE ROBERT	08 FEB 68	38E	025
DURR, BRIAN FRANCIS	08 FEB 68	38E	026
DYKES, ROBERT LEE JR.	08 FEB 68	38E	026
HALE, LANNY EARL	08 FEB 68	38E	029
HASELBAUER, JOHN IRVINE	08 FEB 68	38E	029
JERVIS, JOHN LEROY III	08 FEB 68	38E	030
LOPP, JAMES LEONARD	08 FEB 68	38E	032
McKINNEY, DAVID LEE	08 FEB 68	38E	035
PARKER, JAMES EARL	08 FEB 68	38E	036
POSO, JOHN RICHARD	08 FEB 68	38E	037
PRATT, WALTER RAYMOND	08 FEB 68	38E	037
TROYER, RODNEY PHILIP	08 FEB 68	38E	041
WILCOX, JOHN ARTUR JR.	08 FEB 68	38E	041
PUMILLO, MICHAEL	09 FEB 68	38E	059
GONZALEZ, RAMON HERNANDEZ	13 FEB 68	39E	025
CLAVERIE, RICHARD LEE	04 MAR 68	42E	062
HODGE, CHARLES EDWARD	08 MAR 68	43E	055
ARTHUR, RICHARD THORNTON	09 MAR 68	43E	064
CRAWFORD, WILLIAM DON	13 MAR 68	44E	033
HICKS, GARY DALE	16 MAR 68	45E	004
OWENS, DEWEY RAY	16 MAR 68	45E	004
YAMANE, BENJI	16 MAR 68	45E	006
HURTADO, JOHN BERNARD	06 APR 68	48E	028
REID, DANIEL FRANCIS	06 APR 68	48E	032
MAJER, CHARLES ANTHONY	10 APR 68	49E	013
MADSON, ROBERT WARREN	10 APR 68	49E	017
WILLOUGHBY, JESSE LAVERN	10 APR 68	49E	017
GAINES, PHILIP FALCONA	12 APR 68	49E	031
HARRIS, ROBERT GEORGE	12 APR 68	49E	032

PAVLOCAK, MICHAEL PETER JR.	15 APR 68	50E	007
ANGE, CARMELLO JR.	25 APR 68	52E	002
STADING, GARY ALAN	25 APR 68	52E	011
EGGERT, RUSSELL WILLIAM	05 MAY 68	55E	010
FREEMAN, JAMES PAUL	05 MAY 68	55E	011
NORMANDIN, DUANE MICHAEL	05 MAY 68	55E	025
QUICK, ROBERT EUGENE	05 MAY 68	55E	027
REINHARDT, BARRY THOMAS	05 MAY 68	55E	028
WEDDENDORF, ROBERT GEORGE	05 MAY 68	55E	035
FERGUSON, LEROY	09 MAY 68	57E	020
HARRIS, ROBERT EARL	09 MAY 68	57E	023
DUCE, ROGER	10 MAY 68	58E	015
MENCONI, WILLIAM LEE	11 MAY 68	58E	023
POHL, WILLIAM ANTHONY	13 MAY 68	59E	029
GILBERT, RICHARD LEE	14 MAY 68	60E	010
JOHNSON, DANIEL GENE	14 MAY 68	60E	012
MAURER, JAMES ROBERT	14 MAY 68	60E	014
HAYES, FRANCIS JOSEPH Jr.	15 MAY 68	60E	023
PICARELLI, JOSEPH HENRY	15 MAY 68	61E	001
PHELPS, LARRY DELTON	16 MAY 68	61E	017
SEGAL, JEFFREY BERNARD	21 MAY 68	65E	001
O'NEIL, TERRENCE EDWARD *	23 MAY 68	66E	012
TAYLOR, CLIFTON THOMAS	23 MAY 68	67E	003
CHITWOOD, JERRY MICHAEL	24 MAY 68	67E	007
HAYDEN, ROBERT ALLEN	24 MAY 68	68E	002
MICHALKE, RUSSELL ARTHUR	24 MAY 68	68E	005
TURNER, PHILIP GERALD	24 MAY 68	69E	003
MOODY, HERBERT WAYNE	25 MAY 68	67W	001

BASTARACHE, FIDELE JOSEPH	27 MAY 68	65W	005
McGUIRE, TIMOTHY PATRICK	27 MAY 68	65W	012
POWELL, JOHNNIE EARL	30 MAY 68	63W	019
ANELLO, BRUCE FRANCIS	31 MAY 68	62W	004
COWELL, JAMES EDWARD	31 MAY 68	62W	007
MUSZYNSKI, MICHAEL JOHN	01 JUN 68	61W	004
WOLFE, JOHN THOMAS	01 JUN 68	61W	004
YORK, LARRY LEE	01 JUN 68	61W	009
BLADES, THOMAS NELSON	03 JUN 68	61W	020
PROVOST, DAVID ARMAND	03 JUN 68	60W	004
THOMAS, ANDREW JACKSON	03 JUN 68	60W	006
WILSON, MICHAEL LUND	03 JUN 68	60W	007
DUNITHAN, THOMAS LAWRENCE	06 JUN 68	59W	001
POWELL, GEORGE RALPH Jr.	21 JUN 68	55W	015
MANCUSO, ANTHONY JOHN	25 JUN 68	55W	036
MIHALAKIS, ELLAS LOUIS	09 JUN 68	52W	007
WENZEL, ROBERT LEE	25 JUL 68	50W	011
JACKSON, RAY LEE	25 AUG 68	46W	016
STROMBACK, GLENN CHARLES	25 AUG 68	46W	024
BUSSE, DANIEL DEAN	01 SEP 68	45W	018
GOMEZ-MESA, LUIS G.	01 SEP 68	45W	019
LAWS, LONNIE CHARLES	01 SEP 68	45W	020
PIMENTEL, RONNIE CARDOZA	01 SEP 68	45W	021
REYES, ANGEL LUIS Jr.	01 SEP 68	45W	022
SHREWSBERRY, ROGER LYNN	01 SEP 68	45W	022
OHARA, STEVE MASAO	01 SEP 68	45W	021
BELCHER, FRED ARTHUR	13 SEP 68	44W	045
MOORE, WALTER LEE Jr.	29 SEP 68	42W	042
JONES, GREGORY THOMAS	03 OCT 68	42W	069
ABRAHAM, JAMES JOSEPH	12 OCT 68	41W	050

BIDDULPH, THOMAS A.	27 OCT 68	40W	041
LANE, SHARON ANN	08 JUN 69	23W	112
BROWN, ERNIE (1/1 CAV C TROOP)	?		
HANSON (AIRBORNE 173RD)	?		
WiSEMAN (AIRBORNE 173RD)	?		

COMBAT PHOTOGRAPHERS

CAPA, ROBERT *(France)*	25 May 1954
REESE, EVERETTE DIXIE *(USA)*	29 April 1955
HUYNH, THANH MY *(Vietnam)*	10 Oct. 1965
CHAPELLE, DICKEY *(USA)*	4 Nov. 1965
CASTAN, SAM *(USA)*	21 May 1966
FALL, BERNARD B. *(France)*	21 Feb. 1967
MINE, HIROMICHI *(Japan)*	5 March 1968
ELLISON, ROBERT JACKSON *(USA)*	6 March 1968
EGGLESTON, CHARLES R. *(USA)*	6 May 1968
NOONAN, OLIVER E. *(USA)*	16 August 1969
CARON, GILLES *(France)*	4 April 1970
BELLENDORG, DIETER*(German)*MISSING	8 April 1970
STONE, DANA *(USA)* *MISSING	6 April 1970
FLYNN, SEAN *(USA)* *MISSING	6 April 1970
SAWADA, KYOICHI *(Japan)*	28 Oct. 1970
HUET, HENRI *(France)*	10 Feb. 1971
POTTER, KENT *(USA)*	10 Feb. 1971
BURROWS, LARRY *(Britain)*	10 Feb. 1971
SULLY, FRANCOIS *(France)*	24 Feb. 1971
KHOO, TERRY *(Singapore)*	20 July 1972
HERBERT, GERARD *(France)*	22 July 1972
LAURENT, MICHEL *(France)*	28 April 1975

* Unconfirmed burial site found March 1991 by a group headed by their close associate and friend, Tim Page. It appeared that after being captured by Cambodian rebels they were turned over to the Khmer Rouge. The Khmer Rouge executed them not long after their capture.

Dana Stone and Sean Flynn were often mentioned in Michael Herr's book Dispatches. They were also written about in the book Two of the Missing by Perry Deane Young. Tim Page mentions them in his book Page after Page. Countless books on the Vietnam War use Dana Stone's photographs.

Tim Page heads the Indochina Media Memorial Foundation, London England dedicated to the journalists that died during the war. He with Horst Faas have produced the book *Requiem,* published by Random House Publishing, which shows the photos of the photographers who died in the war. Proceeds from the book go to the foundation.

I encourage everyone to visit the Lansing Veterans Memorial, Lansing Illinois. They have erected a a beautiful black forty-foot granite etched wall depicting *All Wars*. Benji Yamane's name is etched on the memorial wall as well. It is interesting to note that the Yamane family, while living in California during the Second World War, were put into an internment camp because they were Japanese. After the war Mr. Yamane became a barber in Oakland, California. Benji had one older brother, Lester. In 1993, I located his brother, mother, and old girlfriend. During the visit Lester with family and friends drove to Oakland and to a mausoleum where Yamane is laid to rest.

GLOSSARY

AFVN: Armed Forces Vietnam Network radio station.

Agent Orange: A defoliant chemical identifiable by the orange band of the shipping drums, principally used to defoliate dense protective jungle, thus denying the enemy his cover. The defoliant was dumped from C-123 flying boxcar tankers that used the motto "We Prevent Forests." Agent orange was first used during "Operation Ranch Hand" in 1962 and henceforth men working the chemicals referred to themselves as "ranch hands." Since the war it has been blamed for countless of birth deformities, diseases and disorders.

Air America: The airline that was technically civilian-owned, but worked extensively with the CIA.

Air Cav or air cavalry: 1st Cavalry Division. Instead of using horses these cavalry units used armored carriers and helicopters. The words *air cavalry* became a generic term attached to a number of units using armored vehicles.

AIT: Advanced Infantry Training.

AK-47: A Soviet Union produced assault rifle that was believed by most superior to the American made Colt M-16.

Americal Division: 23rd Infantry Division. *See*: Southern Cross

Armored Personnel Carrier or APC: The M-113 was a light armored aluminum vehicle.

ARVN: (pronounced: ar-vin) Army of the Republic of Vietnam.

Bao Chi: Vietnamese word for The Media.

Baptism of fire: Another way to say "Welcome to hell." In a war a person is baptized by fire, *fire* being the combat term for lethal projectile.

Beaucoup: (pronounced boo-coo) French for "much" or "plentiful." Many soldiers mistook it for a Vietnamese word.

Betel nut: A mixture of nut, lime, and tobacco the Vietnamese mixed and chewed which caused a slight "high."

Bewitching hour: Midnight or 2400 hours.

Bleeding heart: Derogatory term for a person who opposed the war. Also, one who did not fully support their fighting men.

Block: A stationary position with the purpose of intercepting enemy personnel swept in your direction. *See*: Sweep

Blow away: A slang phrase similar in meaning to "wasted." The essence of the words describes a person high on drugs or killed. "Let's get blown away tonight." "He got blown away."

Body bags: Zippered plastic bag dead soldiers were placed inside.

Boo-coo: *See: Beaucoup*

Boom boom: GI slang for intercourse. "Wanna boom boom? Why not? Numba one."

Boonies or boondocks: The field, bush, jungle. Any remote place that is away from a military base camp or city. *See:* Indian Country

Boonie hat: Olive drab or camouflage-patterned cloth hat with full brim with a nylon band with slots for bullets or camouflage materials, and a chin draw string. Used by LRRPs and others when authorized.

Bought the farm: Killed. "Johnnie bought the farm three days ago in Snipers Alley."

Buffalo Soldier: Slang for a black Vietnam War soldier. Derived from the 1870s when the Indians called black soldiers, Buffalo Soldiers.

Bug juice: Slang for mosquito repellant.

Candy Man: Derogatory name for an officer who gives out medals of valor for their own gain.

Choke and puck: Name for C-ration meal Ham and Scrambled Eggs.

Church key: Slang for a bottle-beer can opener.

CIB: Combat infantry badge. The badge was first established in 1943 and can only be awarded to a infantryman who was in a combat. Considered one of the most prestigious of the Army's combat awards. When the badge is awarded it is customary for the officer to say, "Soldier, you are bound to go to heaven because this CIB shows you've served your time in hell."

Claymore mine: Antipersonnel mine.

Cluster fuck: A cluster of men that makes a big, easy target.

Cold LZ: A landing zone that has no enemy activity.

Combat assault: To be brought into a battle by a helicopter.

Concertina wire: Coiled barbed wire.

Congressional Medal of Honor: The highest medal of valor an American soldier can receive.

Crispy critter: A person burned severely or to death by either white phosphorous or napalm. Derived from the name of a breakfast cereal.

Dear John: It became a catch phrase for a letter from a girlfriend or wife who had decided to end the relationship.

DEROS: Date of Expected Return from Overseas.

Di di: (dee-dee) Vietnamese for run or move quickly.

Dink: A derogatory term for the Vietnamese people. Perhaps derived from *dinky dao*, Vietnamese for "crazy." Other terms: Gook, slop head, spearchucker, yellow man, Charlie.

Dink lover: A soldier who would sympathizes too much with the Vietnamese.

Dink squat: A squat, with feet flat on the ground and the knees bent so sharply that the buttocks rest on one's calves.

Dispatch: A Vietnam-based news agency, cofounded by Michael Morrow. Dispatch printed the story on My Lai for the first time in 1969.

Dispatches: The term used for a magazine articles. Also the name of Michael Herr's best-selling book, *Dispatches*.

Doc: Nickname for a medic. However they were called "Medic!" when someone was hit. Also known as "Band Aid" and "Suzie."

DMZ: Demilitarized Zone. At the signing of the Geneva Agreement on July 21, 1954, a line was drawn at the 17th parallel dividing the country into North and South Vietnam. Also referred to as the McNamara line because then Secretary of Defense Robert McNamara pointed to the line daring the North Vietnamese to cross it—they did. GI slang for the line was the "Z."

Dragon: Southeast Asian dragon. The Asians, when considering matters of state, think of the dragon as a king. The Asians, when considering matters of religion, consider the dragon a god.

Dustoff: Another name for medical evacuation by helicopter. The term was derived from an incident where a man with the call sign "dustoff" was killed while on a Medevac. *See:* Medevac

Elephant grass: A grass possessing razor edges that grew to 15 feet. In areas it was so thick it could cut visibility down to a yard.

Fanny pack or butt pack: A pack only large enough for a few days of supplies that along with suspenders attached to the pistol belt.

Field cross: A cross built with the equipment of the soldiers who died in battle. Often it looked like a pile of equipment but specifically it is built with a boot pierced by a rifle-mounted bayonet with a steel pot placed over the butt of the rifle.

Field of fire: An effective area that a weapon or position is capable of covering.

Field strip: As in "Field strip your cigarette." Means to render the cigarette unrecognizable when discarded. Standard procedure in a combat zone.

Fire base: An artillery firing position, usually atop a hill or ridge, that would be secured by infantry and supplied by helicopter.

Firefight: Exchange of mortar and small arms' fire with the enemy.

Firefly: A Huey gunship, teamed with a Loach helicopter that flies in the lead position, trying to draw enemy fire.

Flak jacket or frag jacket: Vest filled with multiple layers of ballistic nylon material or kevlar plates. The vest was designed to stop low velocity missile fragments from mines, grenades, mortar shells, and artillery fire. It could also decrease the severity of a bullet wound.

Flare: An illumination projectile fired into the air.

Frag, or fragging: Short for fragmentation hand grenade. Also used in slang to mean killing an officer or a lifer.

Free fire zone: An area known as an enemy stronghold that was supposedly free of civilians and where the American military could, without specific permission, shoot to kill anything that moved.

Friendly fire: The term used for your own deadly projectiles. Killed by friendly fire means the soldier was mistakenly killed by his own men.

Fuck: The most used word in GI dialect

Fuck it. Just fuck it. Don't mean nothin': The phrase used when denial is needed to control the situation.

Gold star: As in "Gold Star Mother." A gold pin that is sent to the widow, parents, or other next of kin of a military person killed in action or serving presently in a military conflict.

Goofy Grape: Term used for a purple smoke grenade. Other colors were called Freckle Face Strawberry, Loud Mouth Lime, Choo-Choo Cherry, and OJ Orange. *See:* Smoke

GI: "Government Issue," slang for "American soldier."

Grunt: MOS 11b infantry. An infantry soldier. Other names: boonie-rat, eleven bush, ground pounder, or straight-leg.

Guerrilla warfare: Military resistance carried out by independent indigenous forces engage in sneak attacks and other harassing tactics.

Gunfighter: Name given to an infantry soldier who has taken the position of Pointman over twenty-one times. *See:* Pointman

Gung ho: Adjective describing an officer who is looking to make a name for himself. When used to describe a grunt it means devoted, zealous, or committed more. Derived from the Chinese, *keng ho*, meaning awe-inspiring or literally "more fiery."

Guns and butter: President Johnson's Great Society policy of spending to both provide for social welfare programs and keep up military strength to protect the world from Communism with guns.

Gunship: Armed helicopter. Most often a Huey with mini guns mounted underneath with rocket launcher, nose mounted M-5 40 mm grenade launcher and mounted 30mm cannons. But it also referred to a Huey with two Gunners, one on either side of the ship, that fired M-60 machine guns.

H & I: Harassing and Interdiction. Term for an artillery fire mission called into an area where the enemy is thought to be. *See:* Fire mission

Ham-and-Mothers: C-ration can of Ham and Lima Beans. P.S. Ham and eggs were even worse. *See:* Choke and Puck

Hearts and minds: President Johnson believed the war could be won if the Americans could win the hearts and minds of the Vietnamese people. It became a catch phrase for an American victory.

Heat tab: A flammable purple tablet used to heat C-rations in the field. Since they were in short supply, grunts often ate the fat-caked rations cold. However, they would soon learn to break open a claymore mine and use the explosive C-4 inside to heat the meals. *See:* C-4

Ho Chi Minh: The communist leader of North Vietnam. Born in a province of the central highlands. He died in 1969 before the war ended in 1975. Ho Chi Minh means "He who enlightens."

Ho Chi Minh's revenge: Slang for diarrhea. Also referred to as "The GIs."

Ho Chi Minh sandals: Sandals that had soles made from military vehicle tire tread and foot-securing straps made from inner tubes.

Ho Chi Minh Trail: The main North Vietnamese supply route that ran 300 linear miles along the borders of Laos and Cambodia. The trail itself was a tangled mess of camouflaged footpaths, dirt roads, paved surfaces and river crossing that covered 6,000 miles. Some of the heaviest fighting took place near the trail's arteries into South Vietnam. A North Vietnamese could carry 50 pounds of equipment on his back 15 miles a day. A bicycle could carry 150 pounds.

Hoi Chanh: The name for a Vietnamese who has joined the Chieu Hoi program.

Honcho: The boss.

Hook or Horn: Terms that referred to the hand-set receiver on a PRC-25 field radio. "You're wanted on the horn."

Hootch: A straw native hut. Also a temporary make-shift field enclosure built by the GIs.

Hootchgirl, hootchmaid: A Vietnamese maid.

Horse pill: Name for the big orange pill taken weekly to prevent malaria. *See*: Daily daily.

Hot: An area that is being fired upon or is likely to be fired upon. As in a "Hot LZ."

Huey: The UH-1 helicopter. This helicopter played such an important part in the war that it actually came to symbolize the conflict.

Incoming: Receiving enemy fire. Also "Incoming!" was what a man yelled when warning others of hostile fire.

In Country: In Vietnam . . . literally.

Indian Country: A name given to an area with known enemy activity. *See:* Free fire zone or Boonies.

Jacob's Ladder: The rope ladder dropped from helicopters when there was no place to land.

Jamming Jenny: Slang used in reference to the M-16 rifle that were prone to malfunction. Some reasons for the malfunction, which caused the death of many GIs, were the springs in the magazines, the recoil spring in the stock and dirty ammunition. These were all causes that were remedied; however, many times still, the M-16 would still jam. I know, mine did and I almost bought the farm.

Jarhead: The popular nickname for a marine.

Jesus nut: The mythical nut that holds the rotors onto a helicopter.

Jody: The name given to a guy who steals a soldier's girlfriend while he's away in the service.

Joint: A marijuana cigarette.

John Wayne: A popular movie star who's heroics on the big screen were legendary. However, soldier were sadly mistaken if they believed John Wayne movies gave a true depiction of war.

Jolly Green Giant: Sikorsky HH-53 helicopter, a large gunship that helped rescue downed pilots.

JUSPAO: Joint United States Public Affairs Office. The organization that covered information from both U.S. military and civil sources. It was where the media personnel had to go to get accredited. It ran the infamous "Five 0'clock Follies," which was slang for the information session that tried to explain, or justify the daily events of the war. It was held at the Rex in Saigon.

Ka-Bar: The common term used for a marine combat knife. However, the actual knife came into being during World War II and production ended in 1945. The only authentic Ka-Bars were made by Ka-Bar Knives of Olean, New York, and were fashioned after the Bowie knife of the 1830s. The "Ka-Bar" marking is short for the misspelled words, "Killed a Bear."

Khe Sanh: The name of the marine base in I Corps that came under siege for 77 days starting January 21, 1968. During the battle a lot of comparisons were made between Khe Sanh and the French stronghold of Dien Bien Phu. There was a public outcry when General Westmoreland ordered Khe Sanh abandoned just before he was relieved of his command.

Khmer Rouge: Cambodian communists.

KIA: Killed in Action.

Kit Carson scout: A VC or NVA defector working with an American infantry unit as an interpreter and scout. The name was taken from a famous American mountain man and Civil War scout.

Klick: A kilometer.

LBJ: Slang for the Long Binh Jail (stockade), derived from President Lyndon Baines Johnson's initials. This was Vietnam's main stockade for errant GIs.

Light observation helicopter, OH-6A. Smallest of the helicopters used in Vietnam.

Logar or Night logar: Termed used by the infantry to describe their nighttime defensive perimeter. "We'll night logar here."

LP: Listening post. A small group of men, usually two or three, who are sent beyond a perimeter to hide and listen for enemy movement.

LRRP: (Lurp) Long Range Reconnaissance Patrol. An elite team usually consisting of five to seven men. Their primary mission was to observe enemy activity without initiating contact. Sometimes referred to as "Night crawlers."

Lurp rations: Dehydrated lightweight meals named after the soldier to whom they were most often issued. Note: The military has gone exclusively to the dehydrated meals, replacing the C-ration meal.

LZ: Landing Zone. A clearing secured temporarily for landing of a helicopter. Common term for any place a helicopter could land.

M-16: The American assault rifle that weighed 8.3 pounds with a 20-round magazine. It was designed for close jungle warfare and, therefore, had an effective range of only 400 yards. Also called the Widow-maker, Black Magic, Jamming Jenny, Tonka Toy.

Marijuana: Cannabis (hemp), a narcotic. Often rolled in paper like a cigarette. Most commonly referred to as a joint, reefer, pot, weed or grass. The final quarter inch was called the roach.

Medevac: Medical evacuation that was associated with the helicopter. Because of the efficiency of the helicopter medevac, the survival rate of wounded soldiers on reaching the treatment center was 97 percent. Also referred to as "Meat wagon." *See:* Dustoff

MIA: Missing in Action. Also represents a person whose body was never retrieved, even if they were known for certain to be dead.

MIKE Force: Special Forces Mobile Strike Force Command. They were among the best trained and most reliable troops in South Vietnam and were often referred to as "The Best of the Best."

Million-dollar wound: A noncrippling wound serious enough to warrant leaving the field or returning to the United States.

Mine sweep: Roads from American installations were constantly checked for mines by a "sweep team." The infantry pulled security for the sweep team, therefore, walked in front and over the live mines.

Montagnard friendship bracelet: The bracelet was commonly considered by the GIs as a good luck bracelet. A solid brass bracelet made by the Montagnard people.

Montagnards: French for "hill tribes," the mountain or hill people were primitive tribes who occupied the Central Highlands of Vietnam.

Mortars: A mortar is a muzzle-loaded high angle fire weapon. Mortars were considered infantry field artillery.

MPC: Military Payment Certificates. Specially printed money to be used on American military bases in a war zone to discourage black marketeering.

My Lai Massacre: On March 16, 1968 Lt. William Calley was ordered to search-and-destroy mission on the My Lai Hamlet. After entering the village with little resistance, it is said that Lieutenant Calley ordered his men to systematically shot anything that moved. Body estimates range from 200-500 killed. Lt. Calley was eventually found guilty of murdering 122 villagers. With the taint of a War Crime, America could no longer rightfully claim her virtuous position as the head of other world powers.

Napalm: A jellied gasoline. *See:* Crispy critter

NFG: New fuckin' guy.

Number one: The best and prime.

Number ten: The worst.

NVA: North Vietnamese Army or North Vietnamese soldier.

OD: The army's term for the color olive drab.

Pardon Crucifix: With Ecclesiastical Sanction January 15, 1907. The Pardon Crucifix, the aim of which is to obtain pardon of God and to pardon one's neighbor.

Perforated steel planking: Used as a temporary landing surface for helicopters

Pigman: The M-60 machine gun was nicknamed the **Pig**. The infantryman who carried the Pig was call Pigman. "Pigman get that machine gun up here."

Platoon leader: A first or second lieutenant who is responsible for a platoon of men.

Pointman or Point: The lead man of a moving column of soldiers. Considered the most dangerous position during the Vietnam War and carried with it the life expectancy of less than 1/10th of a second at the moment of contact with an enemy force. *See*: Gunfighter

POW: Prisoner of war.

PRC-25: The standard infantry radio carried by the RTO, radio telephone operator. Nicknamed the "prick."

PTSD: Posttraumatic Stress Disorder. Often called the "bloodless wound." PTSD is a psychologically traumatic shock outside the range of usual human experiences could evoke this disorder. Persons with the disorder sometimes create illusions that are real but only to them. During the American Civil War they called the malady Nostalgia or Soldier's Heart. During WW I they called it Shell Shock. During WW II they called it Battle Fatigue. During the Korean War they called it Operational Exhaustion or Nerves.

Pucker factor: When the buttocks tighten from fear or stress. If you have a pucker factor of 10 you're in deep shit.

Puff the Magic Dragon: A fixed wing gunship that could put a bullet in every square inch of a football field in less than 60 seconds.

Punji pit: A Vietnamese booby trap intended to maim a GIs foot. A hole dug out, filled with punji sticks and then camouflaged.

Punji stick: Length of bamboo or wood with one end sharpened into a hook and often fire-hardened. Originally used by Vietnamese villagers in place of fences, to confine livestock and keep undesirable animals out. Later used in booby traps. Sometimes placed in hidden pits, sometimes on a swinging poles or swinging boards. Tip could puncture a GI boot and, if coated with animal feces, cause a deadly infection.

Purple Heart: The oldest U.S. honor, dating from the Revolutionary War, when it was an award for conspicuous military service.

Rifle poncho-stretcher: When two rifles are folded inside a poncho to form the poles of a stretcher.

Rock 'n'roll: Slang for firing weapons at their fullest level of fire power.

RPG: Rocket-propelled grenade.

R&R: Military term for Rest and Recreation, Rest and Recuperation, or Rest and Relaxation. GIs more commonly called it Rape & Rampage. In-country R&R was at China beach for the Marines near Da Nang; for the Army, at Vung Tau near Saigon. Out of country R&Rs could be spent in Bangkok, Manila, Tokyo, Hawaii, Sydney Australia, Taipei, Tokyo, Penang, Kuala Lumpur. The VC had their R&Rs at Ca Mau Peninsula and, rumors had it, Vung Tau.

RTO: Radio telephone operator. Considered the most second most deadly position in the Vietnam War. Life expectancy 2/10th of a second. *See:* Slow Poke.

Rucksack: Consisted of a nylon pack that was strapped to a metal frame. Commonly referred to as ruck, pack or gear.

Search and destroy mission: A strategy which meant that you would seek out the enemy and destroy all their base areas and personnel.

See the elephant: That the soldier has experienced the reality and weight of war.

Shrapnel: Pieces of metal from exploding shells, bombs or hand grenades.

SITRAP: Military term for Situation Report. "What's your SITRAP?"

Skate: A task or situation that requires very little effort to complete.

Slow Poke: Nickname for an infantry radio telephone operator. Because of the extra twenty-five pound radio, they were often the slowest moving.

Smoke: A smoke grenade that came in yellow, green, red or purple. *See:* Goofy Grape

Sweep: As in "sweep through the village." A group of soldiers who move through an area to clear or check it for any enemy personnel or war-related materials. Sometimes used in conjunction with a blocking force. *See:* Block

Talk the Talk but did you Walk the Walk: The point of this phrase, used by veteran, is that everyone can describe concepts and ideas with words but did they actual perform the deed in question. Only a true veteran can say they have "Walked the Walk."

Tet: The Vietnamese sacred Lunar New Year holiday celebrated from January 29th through the 31st. The 1968 Tet was considered by many to have been the turning point in the Vietnam conflict.

The Southern Cross: The name given a four-star constellation in the southern hemisphere that, when connected, represents the cross Jesus was nailed onto. The Americal Division, 23rd Infantry, used The Southern Cross as their insignia.

The Wall: The common name for the Vietnam Veterans Memorial in Washington, D.C.

Thousand-yard stare: Refers to the look in a man's eyes when he has experienced too much death in war time. In World War Two they called it the Two-thousand-yard stare.

Thumper: Slang for the M-79 grenade launcher. Also the name given to the man who carried the weapon.

Valorous Unit Emblem (award): Equivalent to the individual award of a Silver Star for gallantry.

VC: Vietcong, Vietnamese Communist or Victor Charlie.

Vietnam Veteran's Memorial: Project conceived by Jan C. Scruggs, a combat infantryman. Designed by Maya Ying Lin. It is a monument in Washington, D.C., made out of granite, and it has engraved on its surface the names of the men killed in Vietnam. Nicknamed "The Wall."

Vietnam Veteran's Memorial Moving Wall: Conceived by John Devitt. A half scale replica of the Vietnam Veteran's Memorial in Washington.

Walk in the sun: This was the phrase adopted by the grunts to denote a movement that was relatively free of a risk of contact with the ememy.

Westmoreland, General William: The commander of the American forces from 1965-1968. Troops called him "Westy."

WIA: Wounded In Action.

**Traveling play
that teaches**

FRED LEO BROWN

Resource For
Dedicated Educators

As the DIRECTOR OF EDUCATION for Vietnam Veterans Of American Chapter 796, Lansing Veterans Memorial of Illinois **Author/Poet Fred Leo Brown** has traveled extensively educating people about the meaning of peace.

Why so many personal appearances?
The power of touch heightens our awareness and makes a distant time more immediate. It creates the magic of a *real* moment.

Can one voice make a difference?
Like a child in a toy store at Christmas time, as the curtain draws down on the last act, the audience's eyes are filled with wondrous discovery. They find themselves grappling with the need to open their hearts and minds to the new message spilling forth from the Vietnam War experience.

What message?
To understand war we must look through the clairvoyant eyes of the soldiers who actually fought the battles. In so doing, we find the *message*. A message that focuses on country, duty, and honor. A message that speaks about working in harmony and crossing the bridges of race, creed and color.

Why a play?
By its very nature a play, in concert with a follow up discussion, speaks directly to the heart. A play can prepare the ground for the seeds of learning because it, like no other medium, incorporates all the facets of human communication: hearing, sight, sound, imagination, reading, writing and interactive discussion.

Example: School presentation of *Lessons of War*
The play is performed. However, this is no ordinary play. It is a combination of storytelling, poetry, acting and oral history. During the play the audience will experience a sweep of emotions. And to connect them even more, thirteen people from the audience are invited to work in and around the play.

Follow up workshop
After the visual poetry, Fred Leo Brown goes with instructor into the classrooms for the remainder of the day to lead the students in a meaningful discussion about the Vietnam War. This offers an opportunity to discuss the ramifications of the use of drugs, cigarettes and alcohol. A chance to discuss peer pressure, positive personal image, eating habits and caring for others.

Book: *Wall of Blood* by Fred Leo Brown
To complete the multi-media event, the audience has the opportunity to purchase a personally autographed copy of his nationally acclaimed book. This invaluable 'primary resource' book tells the powerful true story of an infantry soldier's quest for sanity; a journey which will inspire and enlighten readers for generations to come.

Price:
Play is offered *free* with honorarium to those schools who wisely use *Wall Of Blood* within their curriculum study. Quantity discounts and special study guide available.

To bring this ground breaking play to your school please write.

Author Fred Leo Brown
P.O. Box 39
Palos Heights, Il   60463

REVIEWS OF PLAY

"Mr. Brown dedicates himself to teaching and reminding the people that freedom comes with a price. I wish there were more veterans like Mr. Brown willing to enter the classrooms of the nation to teach 'Lessons Of War'."

— TOM LUBERDA, President
Lansing Veterans Memorial

"It takes people like Mr. Brown to come into a classroom and stand face to face with the students to get across the impact and significance of actual war."

— TOM CLARK, History Teacher

"I read your book in a single night. I was so intrigued by the way you wrote that I feel I have a much better understanding of what occurred. I was awestruck."

— KRISTINE R. LEE, High School student

"Your speech today was so great and it's nice to find someone on a common, human being level. I loved the way you went about explaining all of it. You opened up my mind very much to the topic of war."

— BECKY CALINSKI, High School student

"It made the war seem real, and students learned a lot about how it felt to be a soldier. My classes talked about it for days after the performance. I would be delighted if you would come back again next year."

— ANNA ZERVOS, History Teacher

"What you are doing is wonderful. It brings history alive to our students. You were terrific."

— STEVE WOODRUFF, Professor of History

"Please keep up the good work and continue to educate people with the knowledge you have. Thank you so much for sharing your stories with us."

— JENISE L. BRADY, High School student

"Keep up the job on letting America's young people know that war is life or death to all involved. I know most who have seen your play will not forget it or you."

— DONNA LEDD JEAN ADAMITZ, High School student

It was very meaningful not only to those of us who served during that (Vietnam) war but it was an excellent educational experience for our young cadets.

— DALE A. DAVIDSON, COL. USAF (Ret)
Aerospace Science Instructor–ROTC

Work such as yours is a great service to our young people and will impact their lives for years to come.

— JIM ROWLAND, History Teacher

I can definitely tell you that your presentation greatly benefitted our studies.

— PEG SEAMAN, Social Studies Teacher

The use of our students in your production gave them a sense of participation and added a chilling note and realism to an otherwise unfamiliar era.

— TODD KRISTENSEN, History Teacher

The information you presented sparked a great deal of debate and inquiry. We graciously thank you for the rewarding experience.

— DOUG WAINSCOTT, Social Studies Teacher

The actresses used in your production were completely in awe of the structure of the play. They seemed to have been deeply moved as a result of both content and participation.

— NATASHA COADY, Social Studies Teacher

"Author Fred Leo Brown brought the Vietnam experience to Marist High School like no other veteran or scholar possibly could. He taught me a number of valuable lessons on that memorable day as he addressed my three senior classes.

"Vietnam was undoubtedly the number one historical event that my students looked forward to learning about. They listened for weeks as I used a variety of different teaching techniques to try and have them get a better grasp of the Vietnam experience. Their knowledge of this tragic war increased during that time, but until I arranged to bring in a very special guest speaker, their education on Vietnam was incomplete. If any of my students were asked what they most remembered about senior history, a great majority would mention Mr. Fred Leo Brown.

"I do not feel that I exaggerated when I said that Mr. Brown brought the Vietnam experience to Marist High School. I feel that these young men wanted to know some things about this war that history books did not have time to cover. Mr. Brown brought to my classroom a combination of knowledge and energy that few people will ever see in a classroom setting. As the day went on there was talk of Mr. Brown throughout the halls of Marist. I will briefly explain what he did to get these young men so excited.

"The main goal of Mr. Brown is to teach students about the lessons of war. So many young people think war is "so cool," and Mr. Brown undoubtedly changed many of these people's views on war. Mr. Brown used three different techniques to bring Vietnam to my students. Dressed in full military gear, Mr. Brown started off the presentation with a theatrical performance. For about ten minutes he recited from poems he had written about the unforgettable experience in Vietnam. This is not a man who stood at a podium and quietly read these poems. I have never seen 17-year old boys sit on the edge of their seats like they did during this theatrical performance.

"Secondly, Mr. Brown told them what it was like to be a U.S. Soldier in the Nam. He tastefully found a way to truly tell these young men what American soldiers went through during this time. I appreciated how Mr. Brown told the kids not what they wanted to hear, but what they needed to hear. Finally, Mr. Brown answered a variety of different questions from my students. My students could have asked their guest speaker questions for hours if time would have allowed.

"Vietnam was an experience that changed the life of thousands of young Americans forever. Author Fred Leo Brown was a very successful businessman who has now decided he wants to focus his attention on telling his story to young people. His main goal is to teach these young people about the lessons of war. I guarantee that few young history students will forget the day that Mr. Brown addresses their class. I encourage any teacher who in the future may have the opportunity to have Mr. Brown speak in their classroom do just that. The students will never forget it."

— MICHAEL GALLAGHER, History Teacher